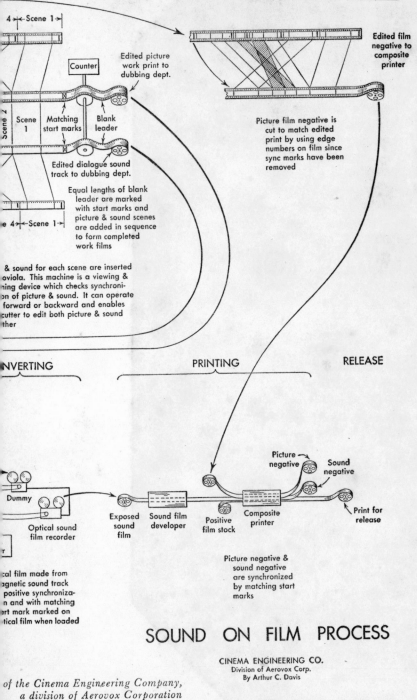

CUTTING

4 ⊦ Scene 1 ⊦

Edited picture work print to dubbing dept.

Counter

Edited film negative to composite printer

Scene 1 · Matching start marks · Blank leader

Picture film negative is cut to match edited print by using edge numbers on film since sync marks have been removed

Edited dialogue sound track to dubbing dept.

Equal lengths of blank leader are marked with start marks and picture & sound scenes are added in sequence to form completed work films

e 4 ⊦ Scene 1 ⊦

& sound for each scene are inserted oviola. This machine is a viewing & ning device which checks synchronion of picture & sound. It can operate forward or backward and enables cutter to edit both picture & sound ther

NVERTING

PRINTING

RELEASE

Dummy

Picture negative · Sound negative

Optical sound film recorder

Exposed sound film · Sound film developer · Positive film stock · Composite printer · Print for release

cal film made from agnetic sound track positive synchronizan and with matching rt mark marked on tical film when loaded

Picture negative & sound negative are synchronized by matching start marks

SOUND ON FILM PROCESS

CINEMA ENGINEERING CO.
Division of Aerovox Corp.
By Arthur C. Davis

of the Cinema Engineering Company,
a division of Aerovox Corporation

Techniques of
Magnetic Recording

THE MACMILLAN COMPANY
NEW YORK · CHICAGO
DALLAS · ATLANTA · SAN FRANCISCO
LONDON · MANILA

BRETT-MACMILLAN LTD.
TORONTO

To Emerson Stone

With the hope he will not
forget to point out my
errors of all kinds.

Joel Tall

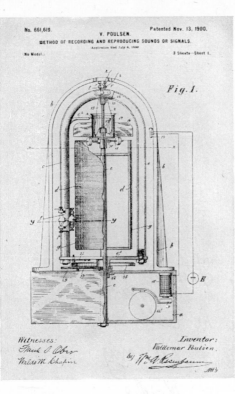

No. 661,619.

V. POULSEN.

Patented Nov. 13, 1900.

METHOD OF RECORDING AND REPRODUCING SOUNDS OR SIGNALS.

Application filed July 8, 1899.

(No Model.)

3 Sheets—Sheet 1.

Fig. 1.

Witnesses:

Inventor:
Valdemar Poulsen.

by Wm. A. Rosenbaum

661,619. METHOD OF RECORDING AND REPRODUCING SOUNDS OR SIGNALS. Valdemar Poulsen, Copenhagen, Denmark. Filed July 8, 1899. Serial No. 723,198. (No specimens.)

To all whom it may concern:

Be it known that I, VALDEMAR POULSEN, a subject of the King of Denmark, residing at Copenhagen, in the Kingdom of Denmark, have invented certain new and useful Improvements in Methods of and Apparatus for Effecting the Storing up of Speech or Signals by Magnetically Influencing Magnetizable Bodies, (for which I have applied for patents in England, No. 8,961, dated April 28, 1899; in Germany, dated December 9, 1898; in Austria, dated April 22, 1899; in Hungary, No. 6,494, dated May 1, 1899; in France, No. 276,184, dated April 26, 1899; in Belgium, No. 111,719, dated April 26, 1899; in Italy, dated May 2, 1899; in Spain, dated April 26, 1899; in Portugal, dated May 8, 1899; in Switzerland, No. 21,005, dated April 25, 1899; in Russia, dated April 26, 1899; in Norway, No. 11,076, dated April 26, 1899; in Sweden, dated March 20, 1899, and in Denmark, No. 1,260, dated December 1, 1898,) of which the following is a specification.

The first patent granted by the United States for recording magnetically. (Obtained by Valdemar Poulsen)

Techniques of Magnetic Recording

JOEL TALL

With chapter seven, Recording Sound in Nature,

by

PETER PAUL KELLOGG, Ph.D.
Professor of Ornithology and Biological Acoustics
Cornell University

New York
THE MACMILLAN COMPANY

Library of Congress Catalog Card Number: 56-7335

Foreword

Man has been called the two-legged, tool-using animal. The legs have not changed much. But the tools are always changing. The spear has been outmoded by atomic cannon, the caveman's ax by the power saw, and the goose quill by the ball-point pen. If diseases are being routed, our progress in dealing out death is also considerable.

Besides an inquiring mind, the reporter's basic tool has been the lead pencil. Matthew Brady added the camera, during the War Between the States. Now we have the magnetic recorder to preserve the promises of politicians (in their own voices), a bird's song, or the indecent noises of a nuclear blast. Tape recording earned its spurs as a reporting tool in the war in Korea. Some of us tried to catch the sounds of history with mobile recording toward the end of World War II.

Joel Tall describes the techniques of magnetic recording. Modern-day reporters and the legion of those who have taken to tape recording professionally and for pleasure will find it a most useful book.

Edward R. Murrow

Preface

Like Samuel Johnson, I believe that knowledge should be applied for the common good. It was with this hope that I brought together in one volume the fruits of my several years' research and experience in the relatively new field of magnetic recording. Since techniques employed in many totally different applications are described, workers in one field will be able to compare and adapt methods used in other fields to their own.

To make it easier for the reader to transfer techniques from one sphere to another, the greater part of the book has been written in nontechnical language. Mathematics has been practically excluded, since the primary concern has been the translation of theoretical concepts into practical, reproducible techniques.

In the case of procedures for which an understanding of the theory underlying a technique is essential, information about basic theory is given. For instance, a chapter on sound and another on the theory of magnetic recording appear, but neither chapter attempts a thorough exposition of its subject. Nevertheless, the reader who knows nothing of sound or of magnetic recording theory should be able to gain a working knowledge of both from study of this volume. While reading this book, the reader already familiar with theory may find leads for future investigation "suggesting themselves"; in fact, it is hoped that the book will suggest problems to those with theoretical background. On the other hand, the reader who is interested only in the practice of magnetic recording should find answers to the questions usually asked by the newcomer to recording, and for his *special* problems he may expect to find solutions in this volume—suggested by one or another of the techniques described.

Beginning with a description of the invention of magnetic recording by Valdemar Poulsen, the book presents next a condensed history of developments since, that is, after 1900. Extensive quotations from several workers who have contributed to our knowledge during this century have been included to illustrate the simple and logical advances in recording procedures and to afford the reader an insight into history in the making. (The laboratory notes of Dr. Hans Joachim von Braunmühl, one of the pioneers of magnetic recording, were included in the first chapter mainly for their historical value. These notes, which describe the Braunmühl-Weber discovery of ac bias, are valuable as a description of ac bias.)

The first eleven chapters contain information general enough in scope to be applicable to any kind of magnetic recording operation. The remaining chapters are devoted to techniques employed in (1) specific applications, such as radio broadcasting, motion-picture production, and recording of heart sounds and (2) varying milieus, such as the school, hospital, and courtroom.

The reader will note that some techniques have been more fully described than others. The techniques that are either more informative or adaptable than others were selected for fuller treatment, since it is not possible to cover adequately all methods in one volume. In the absence of a technique of particular interest, the reader is referred to the description of a technique that is similar. All present types of techniques are represented.

In a number of instances the explanation (in simple language) of a particular technique by its originator, if available, has been included, as in the part devoted to one useful psychiatric application, contributed by Dr. José Comas of the University of Buenos Aires. The chapter on recording sound in nature was written in its entirety by Dr. Peter Paul Kellogg of Cornell University. For the benefit of the reader, information from a few of the diverse sources has been somewhat simplified.

My own contributions are to be found mainly in the primary

fields of my experience: in the recording, editing, and re-recording of sound.

A glossary of terms used in magnetic recording has been appended for the convenience of readers unacquainted with the argot. The bibliography contains references that should prove useful to the researcher, the student, or the layman.

NEW YORK CITY   Joel Tall

Acknowledgments

This book could never have been written without the generous assistance of workers in many fields and without the cooperation of the many authors, editors, and publishers who allowed me to quote and/or to reproduce illustrations from their respective publications.

My thanks are gratefully extended to: Dr. Peter Paul Kellogg, who wrote Chapter 7, "Recording Sound in Nature"; Dr. Hans Joachim von Braunmühl, who so kindly lent me the original notes on the Braunmühl-Weber theory of ac bias recording; Dr. Grant Fairbanks, who supplied me with complete information regarding the Fairbanks-Everitt-Jaeger method of expansion and contraction of sound; Dr. George David Geckeler, for his unique contribution on the recording of heart sounds; Leon E. Dostert, for his exposition of teaching language and linguistics by means of tape recorders; and Dr. José Comas, for his description of his use of tape recording in psychiatric practice and teaching.

I am also grateful, for permission to publish various materials, to: S. Schmidt, of Reeves Soundcraft Corporation, for definitive information on the manufacture of coated media; B. Haynes, of Audio Devices, Incorporated, for photographs and text; R. L. Anderson, of the Minnesota Mining and Manufacturing Company, for photographs and information; the Department of Education of the State of Minnesota, for the excerpts from *Tapes for Teaching;* Engineering Research Associates (division of Sperry Rand), for excerpts from their description of the ERA Boundary-Displacement recording method; the International Standard Trading Corporation, for their description of the Intelex system; K. Sano and Photo

Products Gevaert, for quotations from K. Sano's work; Ipsophone Exploitations, Limited, for illustrations of the Ipsophone; Eastman Kodak Company, for illustrations of their film-splicing technique; Fairchild Recording Equipment Corporation, for quotations from descriptive texts; and the *Journal of the Society of Motion Picture and Television Engineers* and its editor, Victor H. Allen, for many favors and unstinting assistance.

I acknowledge with thanks the generous help of: A. A. Allen, R. Anton, E. Berlant, E. G. Bernard, K. B. Boothe, M. Camras, H. A. Chinn, A. C. Davis, C. C. Davis, A. B. deMandach, C. Ettinger, W. L. Everitt, W. D. Fling, E. Franck, J. G. Frayne, E. Gille, L. Goodfriend, S. Greene, J. T. Guthrie, D. G. C. Hare, C. Hittle, L. C. Holmes, M. Ibuka, R. P. Jaeger, S. W. Johnson, J. S. Kemp, G. W. Kisker, O. K. Kolb, P. V. Lauwers, J. P. Livadary, A. E. Luce, D. Mason, C. G. McProud, W. Meyer-Eppler, D. Morse, J. T. Mullin, W. A. Mueller, R. S. O'Brien, J. L. Pettus, J. L. Pike, R. K. Potter, A. Pulley, J. H. Quinn, R. H. Ranger, M. Rettinger, H. E. Roys, D. Ruthenberg, L. L. Ryder, M. Sbarbi, W. T. Selsted, S. N. Siegel, K. Singer, W. V. Stancil, W. E. Stewart, F. Telewski, E. W. Templin, M. Ulner, and W. W. Wetzel.

For their permissions, proffered information, and materials, I thank: the American National Red Cross, Ampex Corporation, Amplifier Corporation of America, Armour Research Foundation, Ateliers de Constructions Électrique de Charleroi, Audio and Video Products Corporation, Audio Instrument Company, Inc., *Audio* (formerly *Audio Engineering*), Bell & Howell Company, Bell Telephone Laboratories, Benn Brothers, Limited, Berlant Instruments, Inc., Bing Crosby Enterprises, Inc., the Board of Education of the City of New York, British Acoustic Films, Limited, the British Broadcasting Corporation, Brush Electronics Company, Cinema Engineering Company (division of Aerovox Corporation), the Columbia Broadcasting System, Educational Laboratories, Inc., Electric and Musical Industries, Établissements Emel, Gallant Engineering Company, General Electric Company, Indiana Steel Products Company, the Institute of Radio Engineers, the Instrument Society of America, International Business Machines Corporation, the *Journal of the Acoustical Society of America,* Kay Electric Company, Magnecord, Inc., Metro-Goldwyn-Mayer, Mohawk Business Machines Corporation, the National Association of Radio and Television Broadcasters, Paramount Pictures, Peirce Recorder Corporation, Radio Corporation of America, Revere Camera Company, Stancil-Hoffman Corporation, Tech Laboratories, Inc., The Calvin Company, *The Courier-Journal and The Louisville Times,* The Greystone Press, the U.S. National Bureau of Standards, Westrex Corporation, and Wirek Electronics, Limited.

I am appreciative of the encouragement and assistance offered me by Dr. S. J. Begun. For the description of intermodulation distortion measurement and his continued help I thank C. J. LeBel. And for their many gracious gestures I thank Lowell Thomas and Lowell Thomas, Jr.

I want to express my indebtedness to those who, either through their own desires or my inadvertence, shall here remain nameless.

I am immeasurably grateful, for helping me in the use of their libraries, to: Esther Reynolds, librarian of the Physics Research Library, Harvard University; Ruth McG. Lane, Vail Librarian, and Vernon D. Tate, Director of Libraries, both of the Massachusetts Institute of Technology.

My deepest gratitude goes to Agnes Law, former librarian of the Columbia Broadcasting System, who guided me throughout the writing of the manuscript.

For their unflagging encouragement, gentle prodding, and expert criticism—and long hours of typing—I inscribe the sweet kernel of my undying gratitude to my wife, Leona, my daughter, Benita, and my sister-in-law, Sally Wheeler.

J. T.

Contents

1

The Development of Magnetic Recording

There is no definite beginning to the history of the development of magnetic recording. Although we can be certain that credit for building the first magnetic recorder belongs to Valdemar Poulsen, there are indications that experimenters before him had thought about the possibility of recording sound magnetically. One of several references to the idea of recording sound magnetically may be found in *The Electrical World* of September 8, 1888. Oberlin Smith, a contributor to the publication, headed his article, "Some possible form of phonograph," and told about developing "a successful machine for spinning metallic dust into a cotton cord" on which sound might then be recorded. Like so many other experimenters, however, he "was obliged to lay aside the whole thing before arriving at any acoustic results" because of "press of other business." One of his sentences was prophetic. "The Lord's prayer could be written upon a few feet of thread or string while a young lady, receiving this small spool of cotton from her lover, would think herself abominably neglected if it was not warranted two hundred yards long."

EARLY DEVELOPMENTS

We have no way of determining whether the ideas of Oberlin Smith influenced the thinking of Valdemar Poulsen, the Danish inventor of magnetic recording. We do know, however, that the first patent of a workable magnetic recorder was applied for by Poulsen, first in Denmark on December 1, 1898 and shortly thereafter in almost every other civilized country in the world. (For U.S. patent see frontispiece.) Designated a "Method of Recording and Reproducing Sounds or Signals," his patent specified that it was a device "for Effecting the Storing up of Speech or Signals by Magnetically Influencing Magnetizable Bodies." Poulsen said that his machine would be used in three ways: as a substitute and improvement on the phonograph; for recording and imparting communications over telephone wires with no human assistance; and for telegraphic purposes, to record telegraphic code messages at high speeds (to save time in transmission) and play the recorded code back at much lower speeds so that the messages could be easily transcribed.

This basic patent of Poulsen's was granted by the U.S. Government in 1900; at the same time one of his early machines was being shown at the Paris Exposition, where it created a sensational interest in all who saw and heard it, especially in engineers who were concerned with the development of the telephone. One of these, J. Gavey, in 1900 described the Poulsen "microphonograph," as he, Gavey, termed it. It is interesting to note that Mr. Gavey associated the use of magnetic recording almost solely with the telephone:

Perhaps the invention of the greatest scientific interest is the Poulsen microphonograph, by which a telephone conversation can be permanently recorded on a steel wire and reproduced at any time. In this apparatus a steel wire, or a steel band, is moved by any suitable means with considerable velocity between the poles of a small electromagnet. On speaking into a telephone transmitter joined on the circuit, the undulatory currents set up in the transmitter react upon the electromagnet, and cause a continuous variation in the direction and in the degree of magnetism at the poles of the electromagnet. These variations are permanently recorded on the steel wire as it rushes by and when the message is complete the steel wire retains a definite record of what has taken place in the shape of a continuous series of transverse magnetized lines varying throughout in their polarity and in their strength. On connecting a telephone receiver to the electromagnet and again starting the wire on its course, this magnetized wire generates electric currents in the coils of the superimposed magnet as it passes between its poles, and these electric currents, which are the exact counterpart of those generated by the original voice, cause the telephone to repeat what was said in an almost absolutely perfect manner. In one variation of the instrument an endless steel band was caused to revolve at a high rate of speed around two wheels which stretched it out to its full extent. On one portion of the band was placed a magnet connected with a microphone; further on were half a dozen electromagnets connected with as many telephones; and finally an electromagnet through which circulated a permanent current. As the band rushed by in the course of its revolutions it picked up the magnetism from the speaking microphone circuit, next it reacted upon the electromagnets connected to the telephone and caused them to speak, and, finally, on passing under the electromagnet through which a steady current was flowing, the whole of the impressed magnetism was neutralized and the band wiped clean, so to speak, and rendered ready to receive a fresh impression.

At present this invention is in the early stage of scientific discovery. It may be used by a telephone subscriber to record an important communication, and it promises to afford means of obtaining a telephone repeater, a problem which has been before the electrical world for the last twelve years, and which so far has not been solved in a satisfactory manner. A telephone repeater would increase the range of telephonic speech and decrease the cost of long lines . . . *

The "telegraphone," as Poulsen himself named his invention, was extremely simple compared to present-day magnetic recorders, but it worked very well for the time and was acclaimed the electrical marvel of the age. Perhaps its operation can best be understood from the description written by Valdemar Poulsen and published in *The Electrician* of November 30, 1900.

THE TELEGRAPHONE: A MAGNETIC SPEECH-RECORDER
by VALDEMAR POULSEN

The following is a description of the principles and the arrangement of my invention, which I have called the telegraphone. A steel wire

* From *The Electrician,* Nov. 23, 1900.

(piano wire) about 1/5 m. long and 0.5 mm. in diameter is stretched on a board. Along it can slide the electromagnet which embraces it with one of the poles. The core of the electromagnet is a piece of soft iron wire about 8 mm. long and 0.75 mm. in diameter, and the electromagnet itself is in series with a battery and a microphone, or is connected to a transformer in the microphone circuit. At the beginning of an experiment the wire should be completely demagnetized.

If, while the electromagnet is sliding along the wire with a velocity of about 1 meter per second, the microphone is spoken into, the current fluctuations produced register themselves by means of the electromagnet on the steel wire. If now the electromagnet is connected up with a telephone and made to travel over the wire again, the telephone repeats what was spoken into the microphone. Thus, owing to the great coercive strength of steel, there has been impressed on the wire in undulations, so to speak, of magnetism, a kind of writing which is permanent, and faithfully records the articulations of the voice. When the electromagnet is put, now, in direct connection with a moderately strong battery and is made to pass once more over the wire the magnetic writing is obliterated under the influence of the constant magnetizing force, which is great compared with the intensity of the writing magnetic forces.

The wire is too short to contain many words. In order to obtain a larger capacity a very long piano wire is wound very firmly around a drum having a fine spiral groove on its surface, and the piano wire follows this spiral groove. Parallel with the axis of the drum there is a rod upon which a kind of sleeve can slide. The electromagnet is fastened to this sleeve. When the apparatus is in operation, the electromagnet embraces with one of its poles, or with both, the steel wire, and during the rotation this steel wire itself pushes the electromagnet and the sleeve along the rod. It is very easy to handle a drum of this kind, and the whole arrangement is very convenient for experiments. Of course, it must be borne in mind that in the various telephonic and telegraphic applications of the telegraphic principle there are certain conditions which must be fulfilled. The nature, dimensions, and cost of the writing basis, and the velocity, the construction of the electromagnet and the magnitude of the current must all be considered. Without going into details here I only beg to direct the attention upon some essential points concerning the three proceedings—viz., the inscription, the reproduction, and the obliteration.

Most frequently the inscription is effected by means of a polarized electromagnet; but the polarizing and the degree of the polarization must not be arbitrary. Let, for instance, the electromagnet, by means of which the writing is to be performed, obliterate a prior magnetic record and also simultaneously magnetize the writing basis. Then, during the inscription the electromagnet is given the polarization opposed to that which it had during the obliteration. In this way a lively movement of the molecular magnets seems to increase very much in that magnetic *status nascendi,* and every shade of the writing

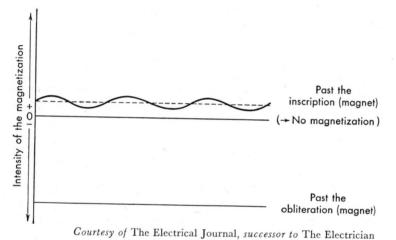

Courtesy of The Electrical Journal, *successor to* The Electrician

Fig. 1-1. ". . . the polarization of the writing magnet is only a very small fraction of that of the obliterating one." (From *The Electrician,* 1900)

becomes extremely perceptible. Ordinarily the polarization of the writing magnet is only a very small fraction of that of the obliterating one. (See Fig. 1-1.) The nearer its polarization approaches to the neutralization of that of the writing basis, however, the feebler may be, of course, the polarization of the obliterating magnet. The coercive force determines the degree of polarization which exactly neutralizes the magnetization of the writing basis. It is found that the writing is somewhat weak when the polarization of the electromagnet during the process of inscription is just equal to that used in the preceding obliteration. In order to polarize the electromagnet a constant current or a permanent magnet may be used.

If the positive and negative curves of an alternating current differ, their faculty of producing the writing may equally differ. This explains the peculiarity that the direction of the primary current with a certain polarization of the writing basis may sometimes influence the writing which, in the secondary circuit, is performed by an unpolarized electro-magnet. This is owing to the lack of uniformity in the manner in which the resistance of the microphone is increasing and diminishing. The inequality here spoken of is perhaps the more considerable the more the mobility of the carbon granules is considerable.

It seems that a speech (or a song) inscribed on the wire may be reproduced indefinitely without any perceptible diminution in clearness, the tone of the voice remaining perfectly distinct. Even when the apparatus is . . . primitive . . . , the produced voice is distinguished by the highest clearness and purity, and free from disturbing accompanying noises. The telegraphones of more recent date are able to reproduce with the greatest exactitude not only words spoken or sung into the microphone, but also whispers and even the feeble sounds of respiration.

The writing is completely obliterated by passage through a magnetic field of sufficient strength. Ordinarily it is sufficient to let the writing basis pass the writing magnet or another small electromagnet energized by a current from two or three cells. If a speech, however, be inscribed by means of an unpolarized magnet on a writing basis already written upon, there results, as a rule, not an obliteration, but an interference.

Besides common piano wires, steel ribbons and nickel wires have been used as writing bases. The dimensions of the steel ribbons were 3 mm. $\times$ 0.105 mm. The steel ribbon passes from a roll to a second receiving roll, where the layers of the ribbon may cover each other without the writing being destroyed. As to this last point, it has been proved by experience that the magnetism does traverse the ribbon, though, as a rule, there is sufficient air space between consecutive layers to afford nearly complete protection. With a speed of about 1 meter per second, 0.154 litre of steel is needed for a speech lasting an hour. Instead of ribbon, a fine piano wire unrolling from one place to another may be used. In some cases nickel may with perfectly good effect be used as a writing basis, which fact is in accordance with the known properties of this metal as regards permanence for weak magnetizations, and demonstrated by A. Abt. The great dependence on mechanical influences which is characteristic of the magnetic state of nickel demands, however, careful handling of the nickel wire. It is not likely that the common steel used hitherto is exactly the most suitable for telegraphonic purposes; most probably other and better kinds are to be found.

I have no intention of speaking of all the various specifically phonographic applications of the telegraphonic principle, nor of the constructive differences in connection with such applications. Nevertheless, I think that the following arrangement ought to be sketched: A long steel ribbon is stretched between two rolls which can rotate at a rather considerable speed. The ribbon passes a series of electromagnets at a speed regulated according to the circumstances. The electromagnet E inscribes words, music, &c., the other electromagnets—"the reading magnets"—reproduce the communications in the telephone of each hearer; and, finally, the obliterating magnet, V, equalizes the magnetic variations of the ribbon. As using does not weaken the writing, we are able to intercalate any number of reading magnets.

Again, it is possible to use the telegraphone to increase the telephonic current (telephonic relay). The engineer E. S. Hagemann has proposed an arrangement which, theoretically at least, is very simple; and which I here describe. A drum is provided with a series of circular steel rings having their centres in the axis of the drum, their planes perpendicular to the axis. As the drum rotates, whatever is spoken into the microphone is inscribed on the first ring by means of a writing magnet. By means of a series of reading magnets placed on the first ring, the words are transmitted to the other rings, which synchronically carry their equally formed writings past their reading magnets, duly connected together, and afterwards past obliterating magnets.

An elegant method of compensation has been invented by the engineer P. O. Pedersen and allows several speeches to be intermingled, so that they can afterwards be reproduced separately. As it is not feasible to describe this method satisfactorily in a few words, I shall not speak further of it here. Later, perhaps, Mr. Pedersen himself will make a communication about it.

In my endeavours to develop the telegraphone I have received the greatest assistance—first from Mr. P. O. Pedersen, and also from Mr. E. S. Hagemann. I owe them both my best thanks. I have, besides, to thank the Institution and experts abroad, as well as those of my own country, for the interest they have shown in the telegraphone.*

* From V. Poulsen, *The Electrician*, Nov. 30, 1900.

Note that Poulsen found that if the direction of the flow of battery current while recording (inscription) was exactly opposite to that of the erasing (obliterating) current, much better recording was obtained. As he puts it, the susceptibility "seems to increase very much in that magnetic *status nascendi* [state of being born], and every shade of the writing becomes extremely perceptible." It was this thought that in 1907 gave birth to the next improvement in magnetic recording, the use of direct-current (dc) bias by Poulsen. He found that by mixing the sound to be recorded on the wire with a precise amount of direct current of the correct polarity, he was able to reproduce the sound with much greater fidelity. (The term "bias" is derived from a similar method used to control the operation of radio tubes.)

Valdemar Poulsen and his chief engineer, P. O. Pedersen, investigated many of the possibilities of magnetic recording in the early 1900's. They, together or separately, patented methods of recording perpendicularly as well as longitudinally (the commonly used method today) and invented methods of electroplating magnetic materials, as well as new electromagnets or, as they are now called, magnetic heads. Pedersen, as a matter of fact, had thought of several different ways in which to use the telegraphone in telephone work. He thought of recording several different messages at the same time on the wire and then reproducing them separately. His partner and assistant, E. S. Hagemann, also suggested a specially built telegraphone that would, in effect, be a telephone amplifier or repeater. Although this use of the telegraphone as a telephone repeater seemed good at the time, it was never put into commercial operation, and the search for a telephone amplifier continued.

In the meantime Poulsen had searched all over Europe for a financial backer for his invention. But, although the telegraphone was loudly applauded on the Continent, no one there was willing to venture the money necessary to finance its exploitation commercially. Finally, in 1903, the American Telegraphone Company was formed and began the manufacture of telegraphones at Springfield, Massachusetts. The machine had been redesigned to incorporate many of the improvements devised by Poulsen and his engineers and was able to record half an hour of dictation or telephone messages. The wire traveled past the heads at a speed of 84 in. per sec., which meant that, since the wire diameter was 1/100 in., the wire spools had to be quite large compared to present standards. The American Telegraphone Company manufactured these machines for a number of years. Dr. Lee de Forest* utilized a telegraphone in San Francisco, about 1912, to record code at high speed and then to reproduce it at a much lower speed so that it could be decoded and typed by a wireless operator.

Still, as de Forest* noted, both the telephone and the telegraphone were plagued by the need for amplification. Long-distance telephony was impractical for the same reason that the telegraphone gradually lost public favor—the lack of a suitable amplifier. Perhaps the Telegraphone Company lost a great opportunity, for although de Forest demonstrated his amplifier connected to a telegraphone, the company did nothing toward acquiring the rights to use it for their own purposes. They did, however, lend him a telegraphone; with this he began in 1913 to experiment in synchronizing wire-recorded sound with moving pictures in the old Fourteenth Street Biograph Studios in New York City.

The reason for the demise of the American Telegraphone Company is not known now, but it eventually went into receivership and discontinued operations. Poulsen continued to work in telegraphy and in designing machines for telegraphic applications, but magnetic recording was practically forgotten by the scientific world. At that time Thomas Edison was occupied, among other things, in designing machinery for the production of his phonograph records; de Forest was busy with the Audion amplifier; the telephone companies were doing their best to create long-distance telephony by using the new audio amplifiers—no further thought was given to the development of magnetic recording. It is quite reasonable to suppose that the development of the acoustic phonograph—without electronic amplification—had gone forward so rapidly that the pub-

---

* See *Father of Radio, The Autobiography of Lee de Forest* (Chicago: Wilcox and Follett Co., 1950).

Patented Aug. 30, 1927.

1,640,881

UNITED STATES PATENT OFFICE.

WENDELL L. CARLSON AND GLENN W. CARPENTER, OF WASHINGTON, DISTRICT OF COLUMBIA.

RADIO TELEGRAPH SYSTEM.

Application filed March 26, 1921. Serial No. 456,020.

Our invention relates broadly to signaling systems and more particularly to a reception system for radio telegraphy.

The object of our invention is to provide an improved method for receiving signals by aid of a telegraphone.

A further object of the invention is to provide a method of agitating the recording element of a telegraphone simultaneously with the recording of signals.

Heretofore when employing the telegraphone in the reception of signals it has been customary to excite the recording element with a magnetic field created by a source of direct current simultaneously with the reception of signals. The purpose of this exciting field (sometimes called the polarizing field) being to set the molecules of the magnetic recording element in motion thus sensitizing said recording element to be actuated simultaneously by the incoming signal. This may be termed overcoming the hysteresis effect of the steel wire, i. e., the recording element. When using high amplification objectionable noises are heard in the reproduction process due to the direct current excited magnetic field. These disturbances are caused from the unevenly magnetized steel wire and the vibration of the wire as it passes the reproducing signal heads.

In our improved exciting system which forms the subject matter of the present invention the advantages of the exciting system above described are obtained to a greater degree and without the disadvantages encountered in the reproducing process, i. e., objectional noises. An alternating magnetic field of preferably high frequency is used in the exciting process.

It has been found when running a telegraphone at normal speed, that frequencies of 10,000 cycles per second and above are not recorded efficiently but that they have the effect of agitating the recording element so as to greatly increase the sensitiveness of said element to feeble signal impressions.

Our invention will be more clearly understood by reference to the following drawing wherein numeral 1 represents a tuned antenna circuit, 2, a tuned input circuit associated with the vacuum tube, 3, and coupled to the antenna circuit 1. The output circuit of the vacuum tube 3 actuates the input circuit of the vacuum tube, 6, by means of a radio frequency transformer 4. Vacuum tube 6 is adjusted to operate as a detector tube and has the usual grid leak and condenser 5 inserted in the grid circuit. Audio frequency transformer 7 couples the output of vacuum tube 6 to the input of vacuum tube 8. The output of vacuum tube 8 is connected to the winding 17 of the signal head 11 on the telegraphone 10, through the audio frequency transformer 9 and variable condenser 12. The usual filament and plate batteries are associated with the vacuum tube circuits. The recording wire 15 of the telegraphone 10 passes thru the signal head 11 from reel 13 to 14. The reels are operated by electric motor drive. High frequency generator 18 energizes the exciting winding 16 of signal head 11. This generator may be for example, of the vacuum tube or alternator type. Windings 16 and 17 are wound on the same iron core.

The operation of the system is as follows: The incoming signal is selectively received, amplified and detected. The audio frequency of the incoming signal is impressed on the circuit 9, 12 and 17 which is tuned to the frequency of said audio frequency signal. A high frequency energizing current preferably above 10,000 cycles per second derived from source 18 constantly excites the winding 16. The recording steel wire 15 as it passes the pole pieces of the signal head 11 is agitated by the high frequency magnetic field created in the pole pieces by the winding 16. Under this agitation the wire 15 is sensitive to audio frequency magnetic changes superimposed on the high frequency magnetic field by the signal energy in the winding 17. An intense magnetic stress is created on the steel wire conforming with the signal energy and without leaving any trace of the high frequency exciting magnetic field on the wire.

Having thus described our invention what we claim is:

1. A telegraphic receiving system comprising in combination a signal receiving circuit, a generator of high frequency current, a movable wire recording element, a pair of magnetic core members located on opposite sides of said movable wire recording element, sets of independent windings each set comprising a pair of sections with one section disposed on each of said core members, one set of said windings being con-

Fig. 1-2. Text of the Carlson-Carpenter patent. This was the first patent granted for recording by means of ac magnetization.

10

nected in said signal receiving circuit and the other set of said windings being connected with said high frequency generator.

2. A telegraphic receiving system comprising in combination a signal receiving circuit, a generator of high frequency current, a movable wire recording element, a pair of magnetic core members located on opposite sides of said movable wire recording element, a pair of windings carried by each of said core members and separately connected in series, one set of said series connected windings being arranged in circuit with said signal receiving circuit, and the other set of said series connected windings being connected in series with said generator of high frequency current whereby said core members are simultaneously saturated by radio frequency and audio frequency magnetic fields.

WENDELL L. CARLSON.
GLENN W. CARPENTER.

Fig. 1-2.   (*Concluded*)

Aug. 30, 1927.   W. L. CARLSON ET AL   1,640,881

RADIO TELEGRAPH SYSTEM

Filed March 26, 1921

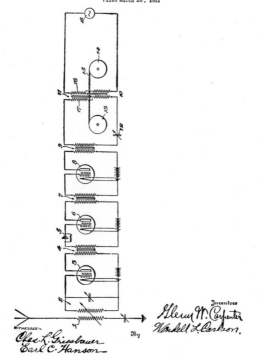

Fig. 1-3.   Diagram submitted with the Carlson-Carpenter patent application.

11

lic did not relish magnetic recording, which required listening with headphones.

Engineers and experimenters, however, continued to investigate the use of magnetic recording for various applications. Tube amplifiers were coming into general use, and it soon became possible to make the reproduction of sound from the steel wire or tape as loud as the listener wanted. It was also possible, unfortunately, to hear the large amount of noise that was reproduced with the recorded sound. In 1900, when the telegraphone was heard for the first time by an American engineer, Carl Hering, he wrote: "I had the pleasure of hearing it, and can vouch for the statement that it [the sound] is much clearer than from an ordinary phonograph as there is an entire absence of the objectionable scratching noise, there being no mechanical contact at all."* Mr. Hering could not hear the noise that was there, possibly because there was not, by present standards, sufficient amplification of either noise or sound. But when W. L. Carlson and G. W. Carpenter, two engineers working at the U.S. Naval Research Laboratory, applied in 1921 for a patent on alternating-current (ac) bias, they mentioned the reduction of noise as one of the basic improvements resulting from their new method of magnetization. They were working, as had de Forest and many others before them, on methods for using the telegraphone in high-speed telegraphic communication (see Figs. 1-2 and 1-3). They noted that although frequencies of 10,000 cy per sec† and over were not recorded efficiently, "they have the effect of agitating the recording element so as to greatly increase the sensitiveness of said element to feeble signal impressions." The Carlson-Carpenter patent, although its importance was not recognized at the time—indeed, the patent was not granted until 1927—showed the way to the practically noiseless, undistorted magnetic recording that we enjoy today.‡

* From *The Electrician,* Dec. 28, 1900.

† The phrase, cy per sec, denotes cycles per second throughout this book.

‡ It is interesting to note that in the case of Carlson and Carpenter and also in that of von Braunmühl and Weber about twenty years later, the discovery of ac bias was the result of a sound amplifier becoming defective during an experiment. In each case an audio amplifier connected to the recorder broke into oscillation and became, in effect, an ac-bias oscillator.

The theory of magnetic recording by means of ac biasing is entrancing, helping us to delve into the behavior of the microscopically tiny worlds of the molecule, the atom, the electron, and also the even smaller worlds within the electron. By means of ac bias and important improvements in magnetic mediums, we are able to record on the magnetic recording material a true picture of the signal that is impressed on it—a "picture" so faithful, in fact, that it is next to impossible, when a high-grade modern magnetic recorder is used, to discern any difference between the sound being recorded and its reproduction.

All work in magnetic recording until 1927 was done on solid or plated media, either on wire or steel tape of various dimensions. In that year J. A. O'Neil received the first patent in the United States for a tape with a coating that was applied in the fluid state to paper and then dried. The next year Fritz Pfleumer of Dresden received a German patent for a somewhat similar process.

RECENT DEVELOPMENTS

In spite of sporadic activity on the part of isolated experimenters, magnetic recording was, however, still unknown to the world at large. Its resurgence in the industrial world was chiefly due to the activities of Dr. Kurt Stille, in Germany and other countries in Europe. Dr. Stille, who has been called the press agent of magnetic recording, organized the "Telegraphie Patent Syndikat" during the 1920's with the object of licensing the use of magnetic recording patents that the syndicate had acquired. He sold the right to manufacture entertainment equipment to Louis Blattner, who formed a motion-picture company in England and employed magnetic recordings instead of the usual phonograph records for synchronized sound. The Blattner System was reported in *The Electrician* of October 18, 1929, as follows:

A system of making and reproducing sound records, which seems to be destined to supersede the old system employing discs or cylinders, was demonstrated last week to pressmen and others, by Mr. Louis Blattner, at the Blattner Colour and Sound Studios, at Elstree. The nucleus of the new system, which is now ready for commercial exploitation, was discovered some forty years ago; Dr. Kurt Stille began to work upon it 25 years ago, and the Ludwig Blattner Picture Corporation of London and the Telegraphie Patent Syndikat of Berlin have recently conducted laboratory and studio work which has resulted in bringing the system to a stage which indicates that the invention will probably revolutionise present-day practice. . . .

The items in the demonstration referred to included a reproduction of a monologue recited by Mr. Henry Ainley whose enunciation was faithfully reproduced and a "talkie" picture of Miss Ivy St. Helier, who sang, to her own piano accompaniment, and concluded her performance with an amusing talk. This picture was very realistic, and the sound record was distinct and well synchronised.

The most intriguing application of the invention demonstrated, however, was its use as a recorder of telephone conversations. A conversation through the Post Office exchange system was recorded, and afterwards heard, completely and clearly, through the hand-set attached to the instrument.

Records can be repeated in this manner immediately after the short interval necessitated by the running back of the wire.

Performances of instrumental music were also given in the studio, and the advantages afforded by the ability of the apparatus to give an accurate and immediate play-back were again realised.

Many uses of the recording telephone will readily suggest themselves, such as its utility as a dictating machine, a recorder of messages in the subscriber's absence, a "file" of conversations for use as evidence, and the teaching of languages and scientific and other lessons in schools.

It is stated that research work in progress at the Stille Laboratories, Berlin, includes the electro-magnetic fixing and reproducing of optical signs on steel tape as a substitute for television.

The Blattnerphone (afterwards bought by the Marconi Company) was used by The British Broadcasting Corporation, which, in collaboration with Dr. Heising of Stille Laboratories, Inc., incorporated frequency-correction circuits in order to improve the quality of reproduction. The machines have been used for repeat broadcasts—recorded broadcasts, such as that of King George V on New Year's Day, 1932 (see Fig. 1-4).

At this time (1920's) the Marconi engineers were occupied in developing for use in broadcasting an artificial reverberation machine which would eliminate the usual, costly echo chambers. The

Courtesy of The British Broadcasting Corporation

Fig. 1-4. Marconi-Stille tape machine. (Now in the Science Museum in South Kensington, London)

Dailygraph, an offspring of the German Stille organization, was designed as a dictating machine primarily. The model using wire was the first recorder with a removable magazine. The mechanism containing the two reels of wire could be quickly and easily removed, and another magazine could be installed. This feature obviated the long wait previously necessary during the time the reel was being rewound for removal.

Engineers on this side of the Atlantic were well aware of what their counterparts were accomplishing in Europe. C. N. Hickman, occupied in acoustical research at the Bell Telephone Laboratories in New York, made a novel contribution to the techniques of magnetic recording, using perpendicular magnetization in an adaptation of Poulsen's recording method.

Hickman continued to work on the development of magnetic recording, directing his energies toward finding an improved solid medium. His efforts resulted, in 1937, in the introduction of an alloy called Vicalloy, a material which performed so well that a solid tape traveling at a speed of 16 in. per sec reproduced sound far better than did Poulsen's telegraphone, whose wire speed was almost five times as great.

By the end of 1936 the Allgemeine Electricitäts Gesellschaft (AEG) and I. G. Farben, which had merged their magnetic recording interests in the new Magnetophon Company, were producing a recorder that used a film coated, according to the method patented by Dr. Pfleumer, with iron powder. Their machines, however, were surpassed in every respect but one by both the Textophone of the C. Lorenz Company (the redesigned Dailygraph of Stille) and the Stahltonmaschine of the same company. In that one respect the Magnetophon was outstanding—*it was cheap to operate;* steel tape cost about one dollar per minute of recording, but the coated tape cost only about 15 cents per minute. The chemists of I. G. Farben steadily continued to try to make a coated tape that would perform as well as solid steel. That they succeeded in doing so is evidenced by the fact that after World War II the Magnetophon, using coated tape, emerged head and shoulders above the rest.

Stimulated by war requirements of the early 1940's, the development of magnetic recording leaped forward. The Brush Development Company (now the Brush Electronics Company), whose research in magnetic recording has been headed by Dr. S. J. Begun, began a research program in 1939 that resulted in many improvements in machines, media, and methods. During World War II this company improved the coating, and methods of coating, of paperbacked magnetic tape, and also the designs of the machines on which the tape is used; it also developed a type of plated wire for recording that resulted in superior operation and sound quality. During the same period it manufactured several special types of magnetic recorders for the U.S. Armed Forces.

During the late 1930's many investigators of magnetic-recording phenomena, including a group of experimenters in Japan headed by Dr. K. Nagai, were looking into the possibilities of ac erasing and recording. Although Carlson and Carpenter had received the original patent in 1927, no one had made a commercial recorder that incorporated this improved technique. The first commercial use of ac bias is believed to have been in the Bell System's stereophonic recording machine displayed at the World's Fair in New York in 1939. A patent (U.S. Patent No. 2,235,132) was given to D. E. Wooldridge on March 18, 1941 for techniques in ac erase and bias systems; this was soon followed by patent No. 2,351,004, granted to Marvin Camras, who filed on December 22, 1941. Camras, working at the Armour Research Foundation* in Chicago, later perfected the wire recorder employing ac erasing and biasing that was used by the U.S. Armed Forces. Previously, in 1940, Drs. Braunmühl and Weber of the German Rundfunk (Radio Network) observed while experimenting with a Magnetophon that the use of ac bias resulted in considerably less noise and much better fidelity. (The Braunmühl-Weber patent was published in the United States in 1943 as a "Method of Magnetic Sound Recording," Serial No. 413,380, U.S. Alien Property Custodian. Their application was filed October 2, 1941.) Their improved Magnetophon, which employed ac bias and coated tape, became the prototype of some of the best of our present-day tape recorders.

So it was that development of wire recording was given an impetus in the United States during the same period in which the Magnetophon was being improved in Germany. After World War II, reports of its excellence and demonstrations of the magnetophon (several were imported into the United States) resulted in great efforts all over the world to duplicate or improve on its performance. In this country the production of wire recorders, which

* Of the Illinois Institute of Technology.

had boomed for a while during the war and for several years thereafter, began to drop. The fact was recognized that, although a wire recorder could be much more compact and lighter than a tape recorder of equivalent capacity, wire could not give comparable fidelity at equivalent speeds. Thus the division of uses took place: the coated tape or film for high-quality, almost perfectly timed recording and the wire for light weight, long playing time, and for special applications where tape or other media could not be used.

An interesting sidelight on the development of magnetic recording is contained in a letter to the author from Dr. Braunmühl; in it he tells how he and the late Dr. Weber discovered the superiority of ac bias. According to Dr. Braunmühl, who is at this writing deputy technical director of the German Southwest Radio Network, their discovery was a result of long and arduous efforts directed at improving the quality of magnetic tape recording. Finally, however, the solution was found by an experimental result of a somewhat accidental character. While they were working on a Magnetophon* its recording amplifier broke into high-frequency oscillations, and the two were agreeably surprised when the tape noise proved to be very much reduced. Subsequent investigation resulted in the Braunmühl-Weber ac-bias theory. A translation by Dr. Braunmühl of the first notes on this theory follows; the graphs referred to in the text have been omitted. Drs. Braunmühl and Weber kindly gave permission for its inclusion here.

TRANSLATION

Berlin, 14th September 1940

Internal Note for Office Use.

Re: Improved Recording Methods with Magnetophones.

Recent experiments have shown that an improvement of signal-to-noise ratio can be obtained by applying an HF-current simultaneously with the audio-frequency recording current.

In the following note we will give a tentative explanation of the physical process when using this recording method.

The previous method of magnetic recording made use of the straight-lined portion of the outer hysteresis loop of the magnetic carrier. The details are given in the graph of Fig. 1.

Before entering the recording head the carrier is magnetized up to saturation when passing the wiping head, say at point A in Fig. 1. After leaving the wiping head the magnetic induction drops along the line of the hysteresis loop

* "Magnetophon" originally, now customarily "magnetophone."

to point *B*. When passing the recording head the carrier is exposed to the combined magnetization of a DC-field superimposed by the AC-field of the speech current. The direction and the amplitude of the recording field are shown in the lower part of Fig. 1. The corresponding magnetization of the magnetic carrier is represented by the arrows added to the shape of the hysteresis loop.

After the recording process the remanent induction corresponding to the alternating field DEF remains upon the carrier.

In this recording process the background noise is mainly produced by the magnetic irregularities of the carrier. The consequences of the irregularities are changes in the magnetic conductivity of the carrier; and these irregularities produce a change of the magnetizing field, say by the amount of ΔH when the carrier is passing the recording head. Thus the carrier leaves the recording head with a corresponding irregularity ΔB of the remanent induction, and this irregularity induces a noise voltage in the playback head. Obviously the connection between ΔH and ΔB is given by the slope of the hysteresis curve at its working point. Since this working point has been chosen on the steepest part of the hysteresis loop in order to minimize the nonlinear distortions, the background noise has a maximum. This type of the background noise can be eliminated by superimposing an HF-current to the audio-current in the recording head.

We will explain the physical process of magnetic recording with a superimposed HF-current instead of a DC-current in connection with Figs. 2 and 3. Fig. 2 represents the process of magnetization in the case that only the HF-current is feeding the recording head. The field magnetizing the carrier is shown in the lower part of Fig. 2. The curve represents the distribution of the field in front of the recording gap along the path of the carrier. The recording head is ring-shaped and at the point of the gap there is the maximum of the field which drops at either side according to an exponential function. This form of the distribution of the field is a typical characteristic of ring-shaped heads. Before entering into the recording field the magnetic carrier has again a remanent induction *B* produced by the wiping head. The slowly growing field of the HF current produces a magnetization along the dashed line. In the maximum of the field, that is to say at the point of the gap, the magnetization follows the outer hysteresis loop. After that the decreasing field produces a magnetization along the dash-dotted line and finally point *C* will be reached in an asymptotic manner. In this state the carrier is absolutely unmagnetized as in the virgin condition. Consequently no background noise can be induced when such a tape passes along the reproducing head.

The reduction of background noise measured with a weighting network is shown in the curves of Fig. 5. The reduction of the background noise compared with the conditions of the normal recording process is given in db as a function of the HF voltage for different frequencies. In the practical case of the HF- and the audio-curves being superimposed in the recording head, the distribution of the field is represented by the curve in the lower part of Fig. 3. Regarding the difference in wave length of the HF current and the audio current, the amplitude of the latter can be considered as quasi-stationary, and this assumption simplifies the graph to a considerable extent. The amplitude of both currents has been chosen of equal amplitude so that the field is always extending from the 0-line into the positive range.

We suppose once more that the carrier is entering into the recording field with the remanent induction *B*. In order to simplify the graph the magnetization process under the influence of the increasing field is not shown. This simplification is justified as in the maximum of the field the magnetization will follow the outer hysteresis loop. Under the influence of the decreasing field however the magnetization follows the dotted line and approaches asymptotically point C. Now in spite of the presence of the HF current a remanent induction will be left which corresponds with the audio currents to be recorded.

With this recording process statistical changes of the field caused by the irregularities of the carrier have only a negligible influence, since the slope of the characteristic of magnetization at point C is much smaller than at the working point in Fig. 1 on account of the asymptotic approximation when using the HF method. The steepness here corresponds roughly to the condition of the virgin magnetization curve of Fig. 2. Therefore the background noise is a very low one, for the negative amplitude of the audio-frequency wave would lie in a similar way below the Zero-line. The remanent induction is therefore shifted into the positive and negative ranges symmetrically with the Zero-point of the ordinates. In the case of the audio-frequency amplitude varying, all intermediate values of the remanent induction from point O to point C are possible.

Furthermore Fig. 3 shows that the remanent induction left on the carrier is smaller compared with the condition of the DC-method due to the repeated change of magnetization. This loss however can easily be compensated by higher recording voltage. The main point is that the signal-to-noise ratio will be greatly increased.

It has been proved by experiments that there is another advantage of the HF recording method, namely a larger range of a linear relationship between recording voltage and the remanent induction.

Fig. 6 represents the measured values of the nonlinear distortion with reference to the reproducing voltage. The working characteristic has been derived from the differential curve and is shown in Fig. 4. It has considerable linear portion and a tendency to bend at the outer ends.

The derivations however are symmetrical in both directions and consequently only distortions of a symmetrical nature (3rd order) are to be expected.

A further increase of the signal-to-noise ratio can be obtained by utilizing the working characteristics into the nonlinear portions. The nonlinear distortions can be compensated in this case by using in the recording amplifier tubes of a characteristic which is mirrorlike to the working curve of the magnetization process. Such a combination can be obtained by a push-pull arrangement.

In Fig. 7 we still give the working characteristic derived from the measured differential curve.

As mentioned above, from this the curve of Fig. 4 has been drawn. The working characteristic when using DC magnetization is given in the same graph. The great difference of the linear portions is obvious.

Up to now we have always supposed that the carrier enters the recording field in a saturated state produced by the wiping head. This condition is not necessary for our new process; on the contrary the carrier can be recorded in its virgin state. The processes of magnetization represented in Figs. 2 and 3 hold valid as in the maximum of the field the outer hysteresis loop is used. Therefore the process in the decreasing field is identical to the curves in Figs. 2 and 3. The remanent induction is thus independent of any previous magnetization of the carrier. It has been shown in the explanation above that an essential feature for the noise reduction of the HF process is the shape of the distribution of the recording field at the recording gap and this mainly with respect to the decreasing part of the field, that is to say at the side where the carrier leaves the recording head. The necessary shape of the field can also be produced by the combination of two heads.

It is well known from experimental investigations and from technical publications that the previous recording process with DC magnetization shows an increase of nonlinear distortion for the high audio-frequencies and this to a higher extent than that to be expected from the magnetic characteristic.

Distortion of this sort does not exist in the new process. Precise measurements with an equipment of the type of intermodulation meters (2-frequency method) have the results represented in Fig. 8. In conformity with the expectations regarding the symmetrical form of the working characteristics the square-law distortions are very small even for high degrees of modulation.

Furthermore the characteristic distortions at high frequencies usually connected with a DC-process are not present.

Still another effect has to be mentioned. We have already said that the recorded amplitude in the HF process is smaller than that obtained with the DC process. In addition to that a special decrease of remanent induction occurs with increasing audio-frequency. This drop can be equalized either in the recording or in the reproducing network or both.

Even when eliminating the drop entirely by a boosting of the recording current the distortions are not higher than for the lower audio-frequencies.

The low amount of distortion at high audio-frequencies offers a further possibility to increase signal-to-noise ratio, namely by an extra boosting of the recording current at these frequencies in connection with an equalization in the reproducing network.

Since the most annoying components of the residual background noise lie in the higher range, a further drop of 4–6 db can be obtained.

The gain of the signal-to-noise ratio produced by the HF-process itself can be estimated as higher than 10 db, so that a total improvement of more than 18 db appears to be possible.

In addition an extension of the frequency curve can be effected without an undue increase of the background level.

Signed: H. J. von Braunmühl
W. Weber

2

Simplified Theory of Magnetic Recording

Anyone can record magnetically—and do a fair-to-middling job —without knowing anything of magnetism or magnetic recording theory. He would, however, do much better, even with poor equipment, if he knew some of the fundamental facts about magnetic recording.

Almost everyone has used ordinary magnets and compasses at one time or another. A compass is merely a magnetized needle that is free to rotate. When it comes to rest it will point approximately north and south. When this phenomenon was noted in the early days of experimentation with lodestone (a natural magnetic ore), the part of the lodestone or magnet pointing to the north was called the north pole and the other end the south pole. No matter how small a magnet is, it will always have north and south poles. Another fact to remember is this: In magnetism, opposite poles attract each other; similar poles repel each other. The force that does the "attracting" and "repelling" is called *magnetic induction* (it is measured in *dynes*), and wherever there is magnetic induction there is also what is called a *magnetic field*. It should be easy to recall the picture of a magnetic field, which appears commonly in school books (see Fig. 2-1). (A similar "picture" can be made by first laying a straight magnet on a nonmagnetic surface, then putting a piece of paper or glass or some other nonmagnetic material over it, and finally sprinkling iron filings or iron dust evenly on the paper or glass.) The lines in Fig. 2-1 represent *magnetic flux lines;* these show the direction, extent, and concentration of the magnetic field. Flux lines show that the magnetic field arises at one pole of a magnet and enters the magnet at the other pole.

One phenomenon of magnetism has helped to revolutionize our modern world—if magnetic flux lines are cut by an electrical conductor (a length of copper wire, for instance), a current of electricity will *flow* in the wire.

It was long ago noted that the lines of flux of a magnetic field

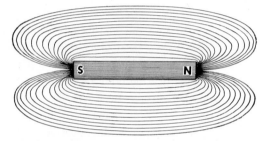

Fig. 2-1.   Magnetic field about a bar magnet.

have to *be cut* by a conductor if a current of electricity is to be induced in that conductor. One way of inducing a current is that of moving a wire physically through the magnetic field; another is causing the magnetic field to collapse and then to build up again. By the first method, electricity results from *physical* motion, by the second, from *magnetic-field* motion. The fact is that there must be motion, either physical or magnetic, if an electric current is to be induced.

The reverse of the above is also true; a magnetizable material— an iron bar, for instance—will be magnetized when it is placed within the electromagnetic field of a wire conducting a current of electricity. In the first place, a conductor cutting magnetic lines of force will have a current of electricity induced in it; in the second place, an electromagnetic field arising about a current-carrying coil of wire will *magnetize* any magnetically susceptible material within its orbit.

Although any material has magnetic susceptibilities, only iron and similar alloys and compounds have the ability to concentrate magnetism within themselves. These ferrous materials are termed "ferromagnetic," and they are the materials we are concerned with in magnetic recording. They have high *permeability;* permeability is the ratio of magnetic flux density* produced in a medium to the magnetic flux density that would be produced in air, or possibly in a vacuum, by the same magnetizing force.

If for some purpose or other we should want to determine the permeability of a sample of iron that had never before been magnetized (in magnetic language *virgin material*), we would find that the amount of magnetism induced in the iron by the magnetizing force would at first rise slowly, then more rapidly, and then again slowly, until at last the iron would absorb no more magnetism. This last state is known as the saturation point of the material. Thereafter, any increase in magnetizing force produces no more induction in that material (see Fig. 2-2). Note that the instantaneous values of induction do not relate exactly to the increase of magnetizing force all the way along the magnetization curve. If they did, magnetic recording would be a much simpler process, and the curve would not be a curve but a straight line. However, magnetization curves are not linear at all points; they are approximately linear only between the upper and lower bends, called the "knee" and the "instep," respectively (see Fig. 2-2).

If the magnetizing force, which may have been a coil carrying electric current (an electromagnet) or a permanent magnet, is removed from a piece of iron saturated with magnetism, the induction in the iron does not disappear entirely; but, following a path other than that of its original magnetization curve, induction decreases to a portion of its induction value (see Fig. 2-3). The induction remaining in the iron after the magnetizing force has been

---

* For a thorough explanation of magnetic flux density, see S. J. Begun, *Magnetic Recording* (New York: Murray Hill Books, 1949), pp. 32-47, 231.

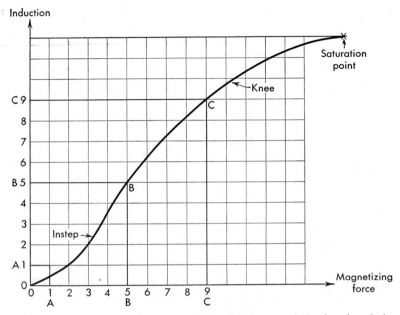

Fig. 2-2. Graph showing magnetizing force versus induction in virgin magnetic material. Note that induction varies linearly with magnetizing force only between points *B* and *C*.

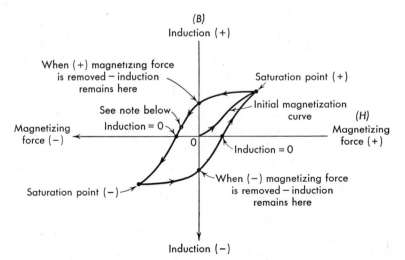

Fig. 2.3. Hysteresis curve. Note that at some point (such as the one indicated) within the straight portion of the magnetization curve, linear dc bias recording can take place.

removed is called the *retentivity* of the iron. Retentivity is the capacity of a magnetic material to retain magnetism after the magnetizing field (or the flux field) has been removed. If the remanent induction of this sample of iron is to be reduced still further, or if it is to be removed completely, a magnetizing force must be applied in the opposite direction to that of the force which magnetized it. If it has been magnetized by the north pole of a permanent magnet, it must be approached with a south pole. If it has been magnetized by an electromagnet, a reversal of magnetic direction will be necessary to demagnetize the iron. The ability of a magnetic material to resist demagnetization is called its *coercive force;* magnetic recording media are made with differing coercivities, which accord with the uses of the respective media.

If after this sample of iron has had an opposite or demagnetizing force applied to it, it is again subjected to the original magnetizing field, the induction pattern will not revert to the form of the original magnetization curve (its virgin curve) but will follow the lower curve in Fig. 2-3. Thus we have what is called a *hysteresis loop,* a graphic mechanism that is used occasionally by workers in magnetic recording to plot various magnetic values.

The normal magnetization curve of Fig. 2-2 shows why undistorted recording cannot be obtained merely by "magnetizing a magnetizable medium" in accordance with the modulations introduced within it by sound. Note that if the magnetizing force rises to point *A,* for instance, the induction in the medium does *not* rise as high.

The transfer of energy from the magnetizing force to the magnetic medium is not uniform, and faithful recording cannot take place. How then, if the foregoing is true, is it possible to record magnetically with such great fidelity? Valdemar Poulsen, the inventor, showed us how in 1900. His method (which he called "depolarizing" and which we call "biasing") was the dc bias method; little used in the art today, it did point the way to the development of ac (alternating-current) bias, now almost universally used. Poulsen found that if he first completely magnetized (saturated) his steel tape and then applied, while recording, a *definite* amount of magnetic force in the *opposite direction* (to that in which he had saturated the tape), the subsequent reproduction was much more faithful to the original sound than reproduction by earlier methods was. It was later found that the amount of oppositely polarized magnetization varied from one magnetic material to another, the desired effect being achieved when the remanent magnetization in the medium occurred within the straight part of the characteristic curve.

Alternating-current biasing was invented by Carpenter and Carlson in 1921, as related in Chapter 1. The first effect they noticed was the absence of the noise that dc bias normally leaves in the medium. They also noted that weak signals were recorded much more clearly by use of ac bias. The same observed effects, still true, are the main reasons ac bias is used in the overwhelming majority of magnetic recorders today.

Exactly how ac bias permits us to record with great fidelity is a story of too great length to reproduce here. The practical effects of the use of ac bias can, however, be described in a few sentences.

As noted in the description of the use of dc bias, linear recording takes place when the magnetization in the magnetic medium has been reduced, after magnetic saturation of the medium, to a level represented by a point on the straight portion of the transfer characteristic curve. After magnetization has been reduced to this level, the magnetic transfer from the recording-head field to the medium will be, when represented on the curve, approximately linear. The linear portion of the curve defines the limits of faithful recording; signals of too-low intensity (outside the linear portion) will be obscured by the dc noise "remanence," and signals of too-high intensity (also outside the linear portion) will be distorted because of "overloading." (Overload distortion occurs in magnetic recording when the signal intensity exceeds its proper ratio to the bias current; recording then takes place in a *curved portion* of the transfer curve.)

With ac bias, a completely demagnetized medium is used, and two linear portions of the transfer characteristic curve are employed, the positive and the negative. High-frequency alternating current, of an intensity several times that of an audio signal with which it is mixed, alternately advances from zero to the mid-point of the positive section of the transfer curve and retreats through zero to the mid-point of the negative part of the curve. Since the *peak values* of these positive and negative remanences have by far the greatest effect, the result is a fairly straight transfer characteristic, recorded at very high frequencies, for instance, 60,000 cy per sec. Sound waves or any other recordable waves, if mixed with this supersonic bias current, will displace the peak values. The resulting recorded remanence on the magnetic medium will vary in accordance with the signal, and, if the bias current has been correctly adjusted, very little distortion will be present in the recording.

Discussion of the interrelated effects of all the other elements that enter into magnetic recording has been purposely avoided in this chapter. They will be taken up in later chapters, in which the practical limitations of this method of recording will also be discussed.

3

Recording Media and Their Manufacture

Since the time when Valdemar Poulsen astonished the world of science with the telegraphone, many kinds of magnetic materials have been tried as recording media. Carbon steel wire, stainless steel wire, steel tape, paper tape, plastic tape, coated film, plated wire —almost every form of magnetizable material has been experimented with in one or another recorder. Forms in which materials have been tried include plated and coated drums, cylinders, sleeves, and disks. Of this variety of materials we shall examine in this chapter only those most commonly used; other media will be discussed in later chapters in which special uses of each will be considered.

At the present writing the most commonly used magnetic medium is coated tape, with film and wire following. The processes of manufacture of coated tape and film, quite similar, will be discussed after we first find out how recording wire, the first material used, is made and of what.

WIRE FOR RECORDING

The development of recording wire to its present state of excellence, a long and interesting story, need not be told here in its entirety. Experiments by Hickman, of the Bell Telephone Laboratories, and by others just before and during World War II, resulted

29

eventually in the general adoption of type "18-8" stainless steel wire. Better wire was experimentally used, but because of lower cost stainless steel wire is preferred today. Stainless steel wire is manufactured in 0.004-in. and 0.0036-in. diameters ($\pm$ 0.0002 in.) and is able to withstand, without breaking, a pull of over three pounds, and will stretch very little in normal use. As a matter of fact, because it stretches less than tape, wire is used in certain applications in preference to tape. The wire is produced with a smooth, bright finish, free from oil and dirt, and will not rust. Before stainless steel was adopted for wire recording, the rusting of wire was a major problem for the user, especially in the steaming humidity of the tropics. Very frequently the old type of wire rusted at a "kink" and promptly broke at that point. Even now, of course, wire will break when bent so sharply that it kinks, but there is not the ever-present danger of rusting which would make the whole spool of wire practically useless. Modern wire can be used indefinitely if it is not mishandled, and it is the most compact medium. At a speed of 24 in. per sec, an hour's recording will consume 7200 ft of wire.

In the manufacturing of stainless steel wire the ingot of alloy is first tested to make certain that it is free from impurities and exhibits the correct physical and chemical properties. It is then annealed (heat-treated), coated, drawn into coarse wire, and tested for magnetic properties. This process of annealing, coating, and drawing through dies is repeated several times, until the wire is drawn to the correct size. It is then cleaned to remove all foreign matter from the surface, lubricated,* checked again for magnetic properties, spooled, and packaged. Sample lengths of each lot are subjected to a final "listening test" in typical wire recording machines.

It has been pointed out many times that wire would be a perfect medium for magnetic recording were it not for three inherent faults. First, since it is round, it tends to twist; therefore, the parts in contact with the recording head may be twisted around when the wire is played back, enough to cause some deterioration in the quality

---

* A special lubricant eliminates vibration of the wire, which if present would cause "chattering." This lubricant does not cause any hardened grease to accumulate in the head gaps, an annoyance which tried the patience of the early users of wire recorders.

of the reproduced sound. Second, one recorded layer in intimate contact with another causes magnetic printing, which leads to echoes and a much higher background-noise level than that of tape. The third fault is that wire cannot be as easily edited as tape or film. Good knot-tying in thin wire requires more dexterity than many people possess.

Wire can be recorded and reproduced hundreds of thousands of times, without any noticeable deterioration. Of course, a magnetic head may wear out in the process, because of the comparative softness of its iron core, but the wire is practically indestructible so long as it does not jam in the groove worn in the head. If, through some ineptness on the part of the operator or because of some defect in the machine, the wire kinks and breaks, it can easily be mended by means of a knot tied with the two ends and pulled tight. (This operation will be treated at length in the chapter on editing methods.)

Because wire occupies so little space (the standard spool is 2 13/16 in. by 1/2 in.), is adaptable to magazine loading, and is usable at extremes of temperature and humidity where other media might fail, it is preferred for those types of military and scientific recording in which its dependability outweighs considerations of fidelity and editing ease.

PAPER-BACKED TAPE

Next on our list is paper-backed iron-oxide-coated tape. If one is willing to sacrifice some quality and to make use of a dual-track recorder at a low speed, he will find that paper tape is considerably less expensive to use than wire at normal speeds. Aside from cost, paper-backed tape is at present not preferred for quality uses because, although better than wire, it is slightly noisier than plastic-backed tape. Therefore it is used only occasionally—for reference and other types of recording where the utmost in freedom from noise is not required.

The unwanted sound, or noise, that any coated tape or film produces is caused mainly by two factors—1. the lack of uniformity in size and distribution of the tiny needle-shaped particles of ferric oxide in the coating and 2. the roughness of the surface of the base material. Since even high-grade Kraft paper has a noticeable "grain," the magnetic coating must, of necessity, have "hills" and "valleys" in its thickness; these irregularities produce noise in spite of the fact that the outer surface of the *coating* of the tape is smooth. H. A. Howell (of the Indiana Steel Products Company, Chicago, Illinois) suggested in 1946, when he produced the first paper-backed experimental tape coated with Hyflux powder, that the use of a composite paper-plastic tape might benefit from both the better dimensional stability of paper and the more uniform surface of plastic. Such tape, however, has never been marketed.

ADVANTAGES OF PAPER-BACKED TAPE

The advantages to be gained with the use of paper tape are these:

1. It does not stretch as much as acetate plastic (less than half as much at normal temperatures). It will stand more "pull" without becoming distorted in shape.
2. It does not curl when dry or become brittle as quickly as plastic and will not fracture as easily at extremely low temperatures.
3. It can be marked more easily on the uncoated side for various purposes, such as indexing or timing.

The disadvantages of paper-tape are these:

1. It is commonly noisier than plastic tape.
2. It ordinarily tears more easily when accidentally nicked.
3. It deteriorates more rapidly under adverse (very humid) storage conditions.

PLASTIC TAPES

HOMOGENEOUS PLASTIC TAPE

One of the two basic types of plastic tape is homogeneous plastic tape. As its name implies, in this tape the iron oxide is mixed with the plastic throughout its body. Homogeneous tape was never used to any extent in the United States, but it was favored until a few years ago in some parts of Europe and is still used occasionally there. It is subject to one major fault that disqualifies it for any high-quality recording: it "prints" excessively. (Spurious printing is the phenomenon that takes place when signals recorded on one round of tape are transferred to the adjacent round, or layer, on the reel.) A minor fault is that not enough oxide to permit good quality of recording can be mixed in the plastic without weakening the plastic excessively. Also, output of homogeneous tape at high frequencies is lower than that of coated tape because the oxide is dispersed and does not come in as intimate contact with the recording head.

COATED PLASTIC TAPE

Coated plastic tape is the medium used more than any other in all kinds of applications. Whether this will continue to be so cannot be prophesied at this time; there is some indication that for a few uses the limp cylindrical sleeve* may eventually eclipse tape in popularity.

Highlights of Its Development. It was mentioned earlier that Fritz Pfleumer of Germany was one of the first to suggest coated tape for magnetic recording, and that I. G. Farben undertook its development. The first kind of tape made commercially in Germany was the "C" type; this had a cellulose-acetate base and a coating composed of a ferric oxide. The tape used by the Germans during the 1940's was of the "L" type, in which the base, or backing, was formed of polyvinyl chloride (Luvitherm), and the active magnetic coating was again a ferric oxide. It gave excellent results in the Magnetophon, but was superseded by the "LG" tape, which resulted from extensive research by I. G. Farben and, like the "L" type, had a backing of polyvinyl chloride, an extremely pliant plastic. The "LG" tapes recorded and reproduced very well, but because of the incorrectly chosen magnetic properties of the iron oxide used, the frequency range was poor for the high tape speed (over 30 in. per sec) used.

* See pages 59, 304, and 305 (Fig. 14-2) for information about this medium.

In 1946, as already noted, H. A. Howell produced an experimental paper-backed tape which made use of a metallic coating that had permanent magnetic properties; this tape was known as Hyflux. The then Brush Development Company marketed a paper tape in the same year for use with the Brush BK 401 Tape Recorder. Shortly after the close of World War II the Armour Research Foundation* announced the development of an oxide (designated 140 A) of superior magnetic properties. Its manufacture was undertaken by the Minnesota Mining and Manufacturing Company.

In 1947 the Minnesota Mining and Manufacturing Company produced its first "Scotch" brand paper tape, a brand that is very popular today. The same company's development work in coating plastic and paper tape has been responsible for much of the technical progress in magnetic recording in the United States. It was early recognized by the Germans that the size and shape of the particles in the coating and the thickness of the coating have a great deal to do with the fidelity of recording. (Experimenters also found that a finely ground, dense but thin coating would record better at high frequencies. This made possible good recording at lower speeds, the objective of experimenters always.)

Although the Germans recognized the value of small oxide particles they were possibly not aware of the outstanding performance obtainable from oxide in the form of acicular (needlelike) particles. The laboratory of the Minnesota Mining and Manufacturing Company under the direction of Dr. W. W. Wetzel recognized the superiority of acicular red oxide, now almost universally used. Plastic tape with this kind of oxide was first produced by that company in 1948; it gave a signal output somewhat higher than that of any tape of German manufacture of the same period.

We cannot detail in this volume all the years of work that have gone into improving tape and film and making better oxides for coatings. That would take quite a large volume in itself. We shall, however, describe typical manufacture of modern coated tape and film. Knowing how and why tape is coated will be of considerable use to those who desire to record magnetically.

* Of the Illinois Institute of Technology.

MANUFACTURE OF PLASTIC-BASE
COATED MEDIA*

The Base. The base plastic of almost all kinds of plastic tape used is some form of cast cellulose acetate, a substance chemists call a "polymer." It is synthetically made by several large manufacturers, two of the largest being Celanese and DuPont. Cellulose acetate has no discernible grain (unlike paper), but is composed of continuous chains of particles too small to be measured. It is possible to view them through an electron microscope at a magnification of approximately 50,000 times, but for our purposes we consider cellulose-acetate tape to be comparatively smooth, with no observable grain structure.

The plastic is furnished to the tape coaters in large sheets or rolls and is generally processed in 6-in. to 24-in. widths. The material, except for some which is a few ten thousandths of an inch thinner, is 0.0014 in. to 0.00145 in. thick and maintains its thickness uniformly. It comes out of the casting operation almost completely free from scratches, ripples, or other defects and is therefore not polished before it is coated with the iron "pigment," as the coating is called in the trade.

COATING PIGMENT

The active "magnetizable substance" in present-day magnetic coatings is dry oxide powder composed of tiny, needle-shaped particles of extremely highly refined ferric oxide. These particles are uniform in size, rather less than one-half micron long (a micron equals 0.000039 in.), and they are approximately 1/20 micron in cross section. These ferric-oxide particles are made entirely by artificial means, and their magnetic properties are determined primarily by their size, shape, and purity. The smaller the size and the more uniform the magnetic properties, the better will the final recording properties be in every respect.

* The manufacturing process described is that used by the Reeves Soundcraft Corporation.

The dry oxide powder is normally combined with a binder, solvents, and a lubricant, none of which has any effect on the surface of the base to which it is then applied. True adhesion is obtained without depending upon a chemical bond between the oxide coating and the base, since such a bond might cause unevenness of the plas-

Courtesy of the Reeves Soundcraft Corp.

Fig. 3-1. Mixing vats, agitators, and filters used in the preparation of the coating mixture.

tic surface. An evanescently thin "undercoat" is generally used to fasten the oxide coating to the base. When tape is manufactured without a chemical bond, there is no "shredding-off" or stripping and flaking of the coating, a serious fault in the tape available some years ago.

The extremely small size of the oxide particles presents quite a problem in dispersing them throughout the mixture; in plain language, they are very difficult *to wet* with the solvents and the binder. (If you have ever tried to mix talcum powder and water, you know how difficult that can be.) The only commercially satisfactory method of accomplishing complete distribution of the ferric oxide throughout the solvents involves the use of steel ball-mills. In the ball-milling operation, steel balls slide, under heavy pressure, in the oxide mixture. The great forces generated by the sliding balls are high enough to overcome the resistance to amalgamation of the dry powder and produce a commercially satisfactory dispersion of the oxide powder in the coating mixture. For some highly specialized applications in tape recording this method of dispersion is still not satisfactory. Improvements in the milling process are continually making for better magnetic coatings. For certain applications in data recording extra precautions are taken to prevent individual particles from clumping together under the influence of the earth's magnetic field.

After it is milled, the mixture is allowed to stabilize in closed tanks in which it is kept in constant agitation for a given length of time (Fig. 3-1). Each mill load is filtered before the mixture is placed in the storage tanks, and the mixture is filtered again after removal from the tanks and before it is loaded into hoppers for the coating operation.

COATING METHOD

Whether it is full-width magnetic film, striped film, or magnetic tape that is being made, the coating method is basically the same. Fundamentally it is an extrusion method rather than a dip-coating method, such as that employed in the coating of photographic film and other materials. It was found early in the development of the magnetic coating process that dip-coating methods, which worked so well with soft, gelatinous substances, were not applicable in the coating of noncohesive materials.

The milled and filtered oxide mixture, which is highly viscous, is extruded under constant pressure through a hopper onto the wide tape or film (Fig. 3-2). In film coating or striping (such as that produced by the Reeves Soundcraft "Magnastripe" process), the hopper used is a rather small, lightweight device that rides on the surface of the base material, thereby not being affected in any way

Courtesy of the Reeves Soundcraft Corp.

Fig. 3-2. A film-coating machine.

by variations in the thickness of the base. Thus the surface coating of magnetic oxide is held strictly to its own specifications, which are more rigid than those of film base in which some variation in thickness is allowed. A vacuum is employed to hold the film base flat at the point where coating takes place. On the tape coaters (Fig. 3-3), the base, supplied in varying widths, is coated in any width up to 12 in. The tape-coating hoppers, which are much larger than the film hoppers, do not ride on the base material, but their clearance

Courtesy of Audio Devices, Inc.

Fig. 3-3. A tape-coating machine that permits precision coating. Vibration is minimized by means of support pillars at left, which are of solid concrete.

from the base is very carefully controlled in order to ensure uniform thickness of the coating.

CONTROL OF COATING'S THICKNESS

On these coaters, which deposit a layer of oxide whose thickness is approximately one quarter of the finished thickness of the tape, the following precision-control technique is employed during the coating process to make certain that the coating is *magnetically* uniform: An adjustable record-reproduce-erase magnetic head assembly is so mounted that it sweeps the under side of the base material as the other side is being coated. A low-frequency tone is recorded, reproduced, measured, and then erased; thus an exact indication of the coating's uniformity is instantaneously obtained and used to control the coating's thickness. This technique has not yet been applied to control coating on film because of the difficulty of recording properly through the thicker film base.

DRYING METHOD

After the tape leaves the coating hoppers, it is dried in more or less conventional drying cabinets. In these nothing contacts the magnetic coating until it is dry, when the coated tape widths are wound in rolls. Every effort is made to keep the air to the interior of the drying cabinets as clean as possible. The whole coating operation is performed in an air-conditioned, humidity-controlled room in which a positive, static air pressure is maintained so that dust cannot settle but tends to be blown out. The air supply in the drying cabinets is also maintained at an elevated pressure to ensure that no dust or foreign matter can penetrate the coating and cause dust "holes" in the coating.

BUFFING AND POLISHING OPERATION

Following the drying operation, the wide, coated widths of plastic are buffed by nylon brushes inserted in high-speed wheels. In the plants of some manufacturers a tiny amount of specially made lubricant (a form of wax) is buffed onto the coated surface during the buffing process.

Buffing eliminates any surface residue or roughness and ensures the best possible contact between the magnetic coating and the magnetic recorder heads. The manufacturer relies on lubricant, whether incorporated in the coating, applied to the surface, or both, to minimize any tendencies of the coating to become abrasive or of the tape or film to stick or vibrate. Use of tape and film of this kind reduces head and guide wear to a minimum.

SLITTING AND REELING

In the final process in the manufacture of coated tape—slitting— the wide widths are slit into quarter-inch tapes; these are wound on standard reels or hubs, as the case may be (Fig. 3-4). A quarter-inch width from each of the wide rolls is cut off and sent to the testing department, where its electrical and physical measurements are checked. These samples are kept as controls for rechecking when, and if, any complaints are received from users.

Although slitting may seem to be a comparatively simple operation, it must be accurately performed; control of tape tension in reeling is also an important process. From the manufacturers' standpoint, it would be desirable to spool the tape onto the reels under

Courtesy of the Reeves Soundcraft Corp.

Fig. 3-4. A machine that slits and reels tape is shown in operation.

reasonably high tension so that the tape would be held rigidly in place and present a good appearance. From the users' standpoint, however, a tight wind is not desirable. All plastic materials, even polyvinyl chloride, are subject to dimensional changes resulting from variations in temperature and humidity. Even though the tape is originally slit and reeled in regulated atmospheres under carefully controlled conditions, there is no assurance that conditions during shipment, use, and storage will be at all similar. If tape reaches the ultimate consumer at either extreme of temperature or of humidity, it may exhibit an extremely tight or loose wind. Both winds are objectionable. To ensure satisfactory recording, tape should first be allowed to stabilize under the conditions expected to be in effect during its use and then rewound before it is used for recording.

EFFECTS OF TEMPERATURE AND HUMIDITY

Cellulose acetate, which is the plastic base material of most of the magnetic tape and film made, is kept pliant both by the plasticizers contained in the material and by the presence of an optimum amount of moisture. An environment that contains from 40 to 60 per cent relative humidity and has a temperature of between 60 and 80° (Fahrenheit) best suits this material and keeps it in a stable, usable condition. If the relative humidity goes below 30 per cent, the base loses most of its pliancy and becomes brittle, in which condition the tape or film will perform very poorly. If the humidity is too high, the material will stretch excessively; poor performance will result.

The best condition for use and storage of tape or film is maintenance of steady temperature and humidity in proper ratio. Rapid changes in temperature cause degeneration of many kinds to occur. Chemical changes in the base are accelerated by higher temperatures; the least amount of change occurs at low temperatures, although at *extremely* low temperatures the plastic may fracture easily in use. If tape has been dried out (perhaps because of improper storage), it may be partially restored to its original pliancy by storage for a few days at proper humidity and temperature. (Mylar, a plastic little affected by heat and moisture, or lack of them, is coming into use as a base for coated tape.)

FILM AS A RECORDING MEDIUM

MAGNETICALLY COATED FILM

Film, which is coated in practically the same way as tape, has a triacetate safety base. It may be supplied to the magnetic coaters in widths of 24 in., 16 mm, or 35 mm or in 50-in. $\times$ 1000-ft rolls. The 16- and 35-mm sizes are previously slit and perforated. This film base has a thickness of 0.00550 in.; a tolerance of $\pm$ 0.0005 in. is permitted in casting. Comparatively free from surface defects, such as bubbles and ripples, film is coated, generally, in 24-in. widths or in the 35- or 16-mm sizes. We need say little more here about the coating procedure, since for full width it is the same in most processes as for tape, with the exception of the magnetic monitoring process.

FILM STRIPING

A process, developed by the Reeves Soundcraft Corporation for striping either new or salvaged film base with a magnetic stripe of any desired width, permits magnetic recording on the stripe (Magnastripe) laid down on the film; on the unstriped portion of the film there may or may not be an accompanying picture. The film so far has been striped in widths 0.050, 0.100, and 0.225 in.

Because the added thickness of the magnetic striping on one side of the film would cause the film to reel up crookedly, an additional narrow stripe is placed on the *same face* (normally the emulsion side) but on the *opposite edge* to allow even reeling. This additional stripe is not used for recording.

The Minnesota Mining and Manufacturing Company was the first to develop an "Edge Laminator," a machine that precision-laminates the edge of perforated film (between the sprocket holes and the picture area) with a magnetic sound track. The use of magnetically coated striped film has made it possible for the motion-picture and television industries to effect great savings in production costs and at the same time to provide sound of better quality.

4

Drive Mechanisms

Most practical magnetic recorders require that the medium (wire, tape, film) be carried past the magnetic heads at a constant speed during recording and playback. The mechanisms that provide transport differ widely—according to whether the medium is wire, coated tape, film, or some other material, but the principle of operation remains the same. That is, if recording and reproduction are to have the highest possible fidelity, the drive should move the medium at an unchanging speed under constant, even tension; there should be no motion of the medium except in the designated direction. The problem of obtaining constant speed is not peculiar to magnetic recording; it has plagued designers of all kinds of recording equipment for years.

WIRE DRIVES

Some wire recorders are equipped with a device called a "constant-angular-speed" drive. (The ordinary phonograph record turns at a constant angular speed.) In simple terms, this means only that the *center spindle* is turned at a constant speed. As the wire winds up, the spool diameter increases, the speed of the wire as it is drawn past the heads consequently increasing (Fig. 4-1). Thus the *linear* speed of the wire is *not constant,* but varies as the diameter of the reel or spool changes.

Hub diameters of wire spools are quite large in relation to the diameter of the roll of wire spooled on them. Therefore, although the constant-angular-speed drive does not produce constant linear speed, there is not enough difference between slowest and fastest speeds to cause any great difficulty in normal use. There would, however, be noticeable variation in wire speed (and, consequently, sound) if, for instance, the recorded inside layer of wire were to be cut off, spliced to the outside layer of another spool, and this section reproduced. The pitch of the reproduced sound of the spliced-in portion would be considerably different from that of the original sound, since variation in pitch occurs if spliced sections have been recorded at too-widely differing speeds.

Wire recorders require some means for distributing, or level-winding, the wire on the spool hub evenly so that there will be enough room, vertically, to permit winding of all wire on the spool. In addition, level-winding minimizes rhythmic variations in speed that are caused by unequal, lopsided, changing spool diameters. Level-wind mechanisms may be actuated by a gear and an eccentric cam, or by other means; such a device controls a guide that continuously directs the wire sections to their respective slots on the layer.

High-quality wire recorders overcome the problem of inconstant linear speed by means of capstan drives, which force the wire, by various means, against the surface of a motor shaft or a motor-driven roller. If the shaft (or roller) rotates without any wobble and if the wire does not slip, the wire's linear speed will be as constant as the speed of the driving motor itself.

The capstan drive has become popular in all kinds of recorders because it provides a simple means of approaching the constant speed necessary for good recording (Fig. 4-2). In wire recorders three types of capstan drives have been used: (1) the multiple-wrap drive, in which the wire is wound securely around the capstan three or four times, thus providing the capstan with a good grip on the wire and making it difficult for any slipping to occur; (2) the pinch drive, in which the wire is pinched by a pressure roller against the capstan; and (3) the jam type of drive, used in one of the first high-quality wire recorders, the Magnecorder SD-1, and in which the wire was forced into a groove circling the driving member, so that it moved at the desired speed without slipping.

As noted previously, wire is particularly adaptable for use on the magazine type of recorder. A complete spool may be recorded, the magazine removed for later playback, and another complete assem-

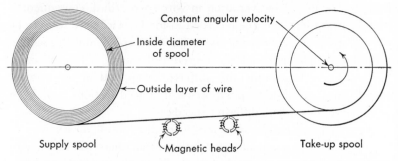

Fig. 4-1. Linear speed of wire cannot be constant in machines that employ a constant angular-speed drive but must vary in accordance with the changing diameter of the drive spool.

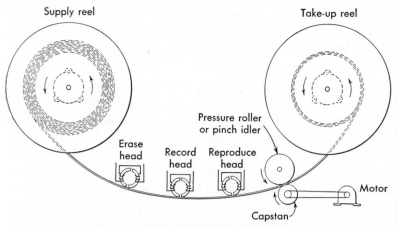

Fig. 4-2. Diagram of a constant-speed capstan drive.

bly inserted for more recording. In this way there is no period of waiting for the wire to be rewound and another spool to be threaded in. One of the first recorders to use magazines in the United States was built by the then Brush Development Company for the U.S. Army during the early 1940's, and its basic design was later much copied. In this recorder (KS 12016) the magazine, which was totally enclosed, contained two wire spools, the magnetic heads, the level-winding mechanism, an elapsed-time indicator, and the automatic stop. In fact, the magazine *was* the wire recorder itself—only the drive motor, the amplifiers, and their controls were mounted within the cabinet to which the magazine was clamped when the recorder was in use.

TAPE DRIVES

Many tape drives in use today have as their common ancestor the drive of the German Magnetophon, which in turn owed much of its design to its progenitors, the Stahltonmaschine of Stille and the Blattnerphone. The kind of tape drive now in use on most machines is shown in Fig. 4-3. The tape is fed from a supply reel on the left,

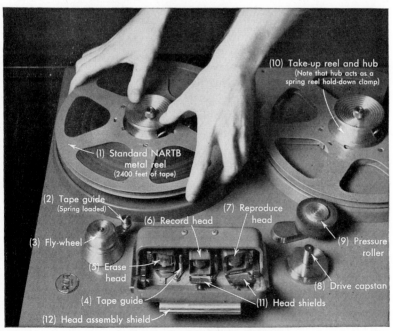

Courtesy of the Radio Corporation of America

Fig. 4-3. The top deck of the RCA RT-11A tape recorder.

pulled at constant speed with even tension past the heads, and then reeled up on the take-up reel at the right. On most machines the coated side of the tape, which is the magnetically active, dull-appearing side, faces the inside of the reels. In fact, this direction of wind has been standardized by the National Association of Radio and Television Broadcasters (NARTB).

The user cannot do very much about the design of his recorder, but he can get better recording by understanding its drive and by knowing what ills it is heir to and what he can, or cannot, do about them.

ELAPSED-TIME VARIATIONS IN TAPE SPEED

The modern tape recorder is designed to operate at constant speed, with the tape under equal tension all the time. The designers of the better, professional types of machine go to great lengths in trying to obtain constant speed, but owing to the nature of the medium they have not achieved perfection.

The speed of a drive may vary in two ways. The first relates to the variation between recording and playback speeds. Let us say you have recorded precisely 30 minutes of music. If your machine was as close to perfection as the better ones are now, the time consumed in reproduction would be 30 minutes plus or minus two seconds. That would be nothing to quibble about, and most of us would accept such a machine as perfect for almost all applications except synchronization with film. The second, flutter, is discussed in more detail below.

FLUTTER AND WOW

This type of variation in the speed of a tape drive is much more important than the first type in any application; it gives rise to the instantaneous speed aberrations that we call "wow" and "flutter." A momentary change of pitch in the reproduction of music (particularly piano music) from a tape is properly called a "wow." Wows are caused by low-speed variations that are perceptible to the ear. Flutter, on the other hand, is not perceptible as a change of pitch. It adds to the over-all distortion and contributes a "roughness" to music that makes it unpleasant to the ear. Following are some of the reasons for wow and flutter.

To begin with, all tape is slightly elastic in nature. As it is pulled through the head structure from supply reel to take-up reel, any undue strain will momentarily stretch or deform the tape slightly, the deformations being heard as flutter. Any vibration of the tape due to dirty head surfaces, a nonlubricated surface, a rough guide surface, or an out-of-round condition of the driving puck (pressure roller) or shaft may cause appreciable flutter. When pressure pads are used to press the tape against the magnetic heads, as is the case in many machines, the pads may on occasion fill up with wax and dust and cause chattering; this may create flutter-like distortion if the amount is not sufficient to be heard as a distinct tone. All these conditions, luckily, can be avoided. Within limitations imposed by cost, machines produced within the last few years have been free of most of these early troubles. The knowledge that they may occur, however, will serve to put you on your guard, and the following information may help you to eliminate flutter, wow, and chattering.

THE CAPSTAN DRIVE

You will notice that the capstan, as drawn in Fig. 4-2, is a metal shaft driven by a motor. Some capstans, such as that in the early Magnetophon, may be merely shafts attached to motors by a flexible coupling or elongations of the motor shaft. Other types of capstan are driven by rubber pucks, multiple belts, or rubber cog-belts. Whatever the design, the capstan must meet certain requirements: (1) to turn at a constant speed, (2) to run true, (3) to be capable of exerting at least five times the pull necessary to overcome the drag of the tape-drive system, and (4) to be connected in some way to flywheels which by their inertia will "iron out" any irregularities that may be contributed—by the drive system, sticking layers of tape, the motor itself, or the electric supply. Needless to say, the better the bearings on which the capstan turns, the smoother will be its operation.

Note that the capstan (unless the tape is wrapped around it as wire was in some early wire recorders) cannot, by itself, move the tape without slippage except when (1) the capstan's surface has appreciable friction and a comparatively large circumference, around which the tape wraps more than halfway or (2) there is a pressure roller of some kind to pinch the tape against the capstan and thus ensure against slippage at the point of contact.

The first method of capstan drive was tried and found wanting. The drives in almost all tape machines today use capstans and pressure rollers and maintain good constancy of speed. The pressure roller generally has a width about three times that of the tape and is made of a comparatively hard rubber compound. Considerable pressure is exerted on the tape as it passes between the roller and the capstan, but not enough, in most machines, to cause any deformation of the tape. The capstan continuously indents the roller's surface at the point of contact; thus, the capstan drives the pressure roller while the roller pulls the tape. The speed with which the tape is drawn may be affected somewhat by the drag (or resistance) of the pressure roller. Of great importance, the adjustment of the pressure roller for operation of the capstan at the correct speed is one of considerable nicety.

THE CONSTANT-TENSION SYSTEM

The capstan drive should have sufficient torque* to overcome easily the total drag of the tape system. An even drag should be presented to the drive capstan. In some early machines this was accomplished by means of special torque motors that would vary the drag in accord with the amount of tape on the supply reel. These motors, which were originally designed for use in the Magnetophon, were fed by an electric current that caused them to hold back the tape with the proper, varying amount of torque. In the latest designs, where the machines use standard reels in which the outside diameter is not much more than twice the diameter of the hub, such specially designed motors are not considered necessary for main-

---

* That which produces rotation.

taining constant tension. But considerable care is taken that nothing in the tape path contributes an *uneven* tension. The tape guides are generally either rotatable or faced with glass or sapphire to give minimum friction; the head guides are also glassy smooth, and reel platforms are balanced. In short, modern magnetic recorder design strives to achieve equal tension of the tape (or other medium) at all times.

SINGLE-MOTOR DRIVES

Since motors, especially synchronous motors used for driving the capstans of professional recorders, are expensive items, the makers of inexpensive tape recorders have tried to eliminate the need for three motors. These are the capstan-drive motor and the two other motors that respectively rotate the supply and take up reels. Most low-priced tape recorders utilize belt drives and a shifting arrangement by which to obtain normal and fast speeds forward and reverse at a speed between. In general, these machines maintain normal tension of the tape—as the tape diameter increases and decreases— by means of a friction clutch or brake. One type of friction drive, designed by R. E. Zenner and R. B. Vaile, Jr. of the Armour Foundation in Chicago, is used to some extent and performs remarkably well. The friction clutch in this case is gravity-operated, that is, the amount of friction generated between a driving disk and a driven disk is varied by and according to the weight of the tape on the reels. As Zenner and Vaile describe the action: "A metal disc is secured to the tape reel shaft. On top of this disc is an oiled felt washer. On top of the oiled felt washer is another metal disc driven by the shaft only through friction of the felt washer. A key projecting upward from this disc drives the tape-reel placed on it. With this arrangement the torque transmitted through the felt washer increases as the weight of the reel increases, taking up tape. This tends to keep the tape tension constant as the take-up diameter increases."*

Many other schemes have been concocted in order to avoid using

* Two-Channel Two-Way Drive Magnetic Tape Recorder," *Audio Engineering*, April, 1948.

three motors in a tape-drive system. Special clutches, slipping-belt systems, and belt-shifting systems are being used in recorders now on the market.

DUAL-TRACK DRIVES

The Zenner and Vaile recorder that used the type of friction drive described above was a dual-track, two-way-drive recorder. Recording was accomplished in either direction at the same speed, each track being recorded by its own recording head. Besides eliminating necessity of rewinding, which normally is done before removal of the recorded reel, this method of dual-track recording is also economical, and in modern recorders, very satisfactory. Fundamentally, however, the *amount* of recorded magnetic surface determines how much noise in relation to sound volume is present in the reproduction of the recorded sound; thus, a dual-track recorder, using standard quarter-inch tape, normally cannot produce a recording as quiet (noise-free) as can a machine that utilizes the full quarter-inch of tape surface as a single track, though the difference is small. In addition, dual-track recordings are difficult to edit and accordingly lack one of the major advantages of tape recordings. (Of course, it is possible to re-record-edit a dual-track tape recording, but this is not too practical.)

MULTIPLE-TRACK TAPE DRIVES

Multiple-track tape recorders employ drive systems similar in most respects to the normal three-motor drives previously described. Prototypes will be adequately described in a later chapter where specific uses of multiple-track tape drives will be pointed out.

SYNCHRONOUS MOTOR DRIVES

Three-motor machines in which the capstan-driving motor is called a synchronous motor have been mentioned earlier. Synchronous motors derive their name from the fact that they receive their rotational force from the pulsing of the alternating current that feeds their windings. The speed of a synchronous motor varies only with the frequency of the supply current, and not with voltage, as does the speed of the ordinary induction motor. Since well-made synchronous motors are expensive to manufacture, they are used only in expensive machines (Fig. 4-4). In some cases where the ac frequency varies, a synchronous-motor drive can be a liability unless precautions are taken.

Courtesy of the Ampex Corporation

Fig. 4-4. The underside of the transport plate of the Ampex 300 tape recorder. The large, rubber-rimmed flywheel is the capstan flywheel and is driven by the synchronous motor shown at left.

As long as a frequency-controlled device (like a synchronous motor) receives a voltage high enough to enable it to operate properly the device will be sensitive only to changes in the frequency of the supply current. Changes in frequency will give proportionate changes, in a recorder with a synchronous motor, in tape velocity. Frequency can be measured by a vibrating-reed frequency meter or a similar device, and can be controlled, if the need arises, by drawing the current for operating the synchronous-drive motor from a special power pack.

Several different kinds of power packs are available. They range from storage-battery-operated vibrator supplies to packs in which the frequency of the alternating current generated is held constant by means of a tuning-fork control or is varied by changing the frequency of an oscillating tube. In this latter type of pack, a small oscillator tube governs the frequency supplied. This frequency may be set to the exact frequency required for truly synchronous operation of the capstan motor or associated devices. The tiny amount of current delivered is then amplified until it is more than sufficient to drive synchronous equipment.

PICTURE-SYNCHRONOUS TAPE DRIVES

Various adaptations of the simple system with capstan and pressure-roller drive provided a degree of accuracy that for most purposes was completely acceptable—a few seconds of half an hour's playing time. However, a still higher degree of accuracy was needed if tape-recorded sound was to be properly synchronized with motion-picture film. In a system operating in tandem, such as this, sound reproduced from tape must be synchronized exactly with action if it is to be "lip-synchronous," as it is called. Anyone who remembers the first talking movies will recall the occasionally erratic synchronization of sound and picture. In the early talkies the sound was "played" from disks. In England in the 1930's one of the early steel-tape machines (the Blattnerphone—see Chapter 1) was used to provide "almost synchronous" sound for talkies. With the resurgence of tape as a magnetic medium, new attempts were made to synchronize sound with motion pictures, and several systems have emerged for the job.

THE RANGER SYSTEM

The first picture-sound synchronous system was that developed by Colonel R. H. Ranger (Rangertone Inc. of Newark, New

Jersey), who designed a comparatively simple method for keeping the picture in step with the sound. In the Ranger method 60-cy control signals are recorded on the tape *perpendicularly,* that is, *exactly at right angles to the sound* being recorded. These control signals are reproduced by a special head (which can be installed on any recorder) and serve to control picture-sound synchronization. In one method using the Ranger 60-cy control system, the motion-picture camera and the Rangertone synchronizing tape recorder are connected during recording to the same source of 60-cy power. Recorded on the tape are the signals corresponding to the frequency of the supply current. When the picture and sound are to be reproduced together, these signals on the tape are amplified and serve as the 60-cy supply current. Therefore, any variations from constant speed of the original camera film-drive cause the speed of the projector to vary accordingly.

Colonel Ranger developed a variation of his system described above; instead of controlling the film-projector speed, it controls the speed of the sound tape, itself, during reproduction. This system—the comparison method—makes use both of a system which controls the frequency of a 60-cy oscillator and of a recording head that records 60-cy sound on the tape perpendicularly (such sound cannot be reproduced by the normal reproducing head). This oscillator current is amplified so that it supplies enough current to operate the tape-drive motor. Thus, when the perpendicularly recorded synchronizing signals on the tape are exactly in accord with the frequency of the 60-cy current that drives the film reproducer, no speed change takes place because the two currents are "in step." When the tape gets ahead of the film-driving power source, or behind it, however slightly, speed is changed immediately and the tape is brought back into step with the film.

THE FAIRCHILD DRIVE SYSTEM—THE SYNCHROLL

The Fairchild Recorder employs a drive called the "Synchroll." The designers (W. D. Fling and D. G. C. Hare) recognized the fact that in a well-made tape-drive system there are two main objectives.

These are precisely constant speed during a short period of time and accuracy of timing over a long period of time. As we have seen, the normal capstan and pressure-roller system has proved to be accurate enough in both respects for most purposes, but there remained a certain amount of inaccuracy due to tape slipping or creeping at the driving point or at any point in the drive system ahead of the actual tape contact point between the capstan and the pressure roller. The Synchroll assembly, which combines the rigidity of a geared drive with the compliableness of a puck-driven flywheel, is designed to eliminate by means of its combination drive system many of the faults inherent in either type of drive.

In the Synchroll the puck drives the flywheel, which is geared back through soft couplings to the motor shaft, at the other end of which the mounting of the drive puck makes the full circle, each member driving the next. The system is so designed that the drive puck attempts to drive the flywheel slightly faster—only one or two per cent—than the gears will permit the flywheel to move. Thus there is continual tension throughout the system—this so-called "tight" system provides an extremely stable tape drive.

THE PIC-SYNC DRIVE

The Fairchild Pic-Sync Drive, based upon the idea of the Synchroll, is largely used at the present time in the production of television film programs. For this use the gear system of the Synchroll Drive is disengaged and a servomotor (two-phase) substituted for it. A drive puck is mounted at the top end of the servomotor's shaft and presses against the flywheel which is driven by the main synchronous-drive motor. In typical operation a 14-kilocycle (kc) tone, modulated by the supply frequency (which is approximately 60 cy per sec) is recorded with the program sound. This 14-kc tone does not affect reproduction of the recorded sound, which is cut off abruptly at 13,000 cy. Then, by means of a system we need not discuss here, the supply frequency actuates one phase of the two-phase servomotor, the amplified 14-kc signal the other, thus correcting instantly the speed of the main-drive flywheel. Since the Pic-Sync

Drive operates by a method of comparing the *phase* of the drive current during playback with that of the current at the time of recording, there can be no error in excess of one quarter of a picture frame; this should satisfy even the perfectionist.

THE AMPEX PICTURE-SYNCHRONOUS SYSTEM

The Ampex Corporation, now of Redwood City, California, which manufactures a complete line of tape recorders, also perfected a system for synchronizing tape with picture film that, like the Fairchild, makes use of a very high audio-frequency, 18 kc, modulated by the line current at the time of recording. This system has a "differential speed detector" that consists basically of two small synchronous motors (with their rotors connected). Both receive their current supply from a power amplifier connected to the 60-cy-modulated 18-kc signal which is reproduced from the recorded tape. One of these motors is rigidly mounted, but the other is permitted to move through a 180-degree arc. The movable motor controls a potentiometer that, in turn, varies the amount of dc voltage fed to a variable-frequency oscillator, whose output is amplified and fed to the main capstan-drive motor. Thus the speed of rotation of the capstan-drive motor is instantaneously controlled by the signals previously impressed on the recorded tape. Incidentally, the variable oscillator can by manual operation bring into correct playing speed a tape that has been recorded with other than 60-cy current.

COMPARISON OF SYNCHRONIZING METHODS

All of these picture-tape synchronizing systems were designed primarily to supplement sprocketed-film optical and magnetic sound systems. The movie-makers up to this writing have not adopted tape as the main sound medium. There are exceptions, of course, but the large production studios have continued to use sprocketed, magnetically striped or completely coated film for production purposes. As exponents of tape have pointed out, it is more expensive to use film than tape, and, theoretically at least, it is possible to get better sound from tape than from film. However, there are many reasons why the motion-picture industry still uses sprocketed film. A major reason is that its personnel, through long years of experience, have become familiar with handling film, and the time cost of production personnel is many times the difference in costs of film and tape. Another reason lies in the simple method of film synchronization. Both the camera and the magnetic-film recorder are sprocket-driven from the same current supply, which can be adapted in very short order to meet any exigency. Such exact, automatic synchronization results in an ease of editing, re-recording, and dubbing that is hard to duplicate by any other means. In addition, it is possible to re-use old film by clearing it and magnetically coating it, a procedure that reduces the cost of the medium considerably.

MAGNETIC-FILM DRIVES

Although magnetic recording had been considered for more than 30 years an ideal means of providing sound accompaniment of moving pictures, no practical system was built until 1946, when Marvin Camras* adapted a standard projector for use of magnetically striped film. Removing the optical system, exciter lamp, and photoelectric cell, he substituted the magnetic head assembly against the stabilized sound-drum. Some modern magnetic-film recorders are built in almost the same way today.

In order that better contact would be obtained with the magnetic surface of the film, the magnetic heads in later developments were placed in the loop path between two rollers that were part of the film motion-stabilization system. Use of this method enables manufacturers of magnetic-film recorders whose drive systems are stabilized by various devices to boast of flutter content in their recorders as low as several hundredths of one per cent (see Chapter 13).

ENDLESS LOOP DRIVES

Loop drives, whether the medium is tape, film, wire, or solid tape, have been used for years in test mechanisms, re-recording machines, and repetitive coin-operated devices. The drive system

* Of the Armour Research Foundation, Illinois Institute of Technology.

may be varied in order for it to accommodate the medium driven, but the principle of repetition governs its operation. We shall see loop drives utilized in different ways in later portions of this book.

ENDLESS REELS

In those cases where simple loop drives, because of the limited amount of recording time they afford, cannot be utilized for an application requiring more time, endless reels are used. Because of the fact that a flat medium, like tape or film, tends to abrade rapidly when it is arranged in endless form, systems employing endless reels have to be designed so that the recording medium is held to a definite path; sometimes the design provides for it to ride on a series of rollers or idlers. An endless reel may be used as part of the input or output system of certain types of computers. Such reels are also used in spot-advertising machines, in reverberation machines, and in similar applications.

MAGNETIC DRUMS

Magnetically plated or coated drums, or cylinders, on which limp sleeves of magnetically coated material are tightly supported, are used in many applications and are described in subsequent chapters. Their drives may be actuated by gears or belts—smooth, flutterless motion remaining the important criterion.

ACCESSORY SYSTEMS—BRAKES, SWITCHING

We would not be able to use any machine properly unless we were able to stop it easily whenever and wherever we want to. Professional tape machines must have rapid-acting brakes, since editing is commonly accomplished on the same type of machine that is used for recording. Stop, start, record, and reverse switching ma, be accomplished directly or through the action of relays. Braking and starting must not be abrupt enough to stretch or snap the tape, and all electrical switching must be accomplished without introducing noise into the recording or playback system.

SMOOTH MOTION ESSENTIAL

Regardless of the application or technique, the principles underlying the theory of magnetic recording require that the motion of the medium be as smooth, as free from random motion, as possible. With machines now being designed to perform work that requires finer and finer speed and flutter tolerances, we may be certain that drives will continuously improve in stability and accuracy.

5

Erasing

One of the primary reasons magnetic recording is preferred to other types of recording in so many applications is that erasing and recording can be repeated on the same tape, wire, or other medium many thousands, even hundreds of thousands, of times. This economy of use is the decisive factor in the growing acceptance of magnetic recording devices in industry. To a large extent, however, the efficiency of recording in many applications depends upon proper erasure.

The term "erase" was not used by the inventor of magnetic recording, Valdemar Poulsen. He preferred the word "obliterate," which seemed to him to describe better the action of his dc electromagnet in "rendering undecipherable" (as Webster defines "obliterate") the previous recording. Some technicians commonly use the word "wipe" instead of erase or obliterate, and some motion-picture engineers call erasing "degaussing," after Gauss, the early worker in magnetism. The different terms are used here interchangeably.

DC-SATURATION ERASE

The earliest form of erasure, called dc obliteration, was employed by Poulsen and others for many years. Erasure of this type was, and still is, a prerequisite to one kind of dc-bias recording. In dc-bias recording of this general variety, the magnetic medium is first saturated by the dc erase-head field. After leaving the vicinity of this field, the medium will lose some of its magnetization, and only a small amount will remain. When the medium is subsequently affected by the dc-bias field of the recording head, which is opposite in polarity to the erase field, the magnetization remaining on the medium is, theoretically, only that which has been recorded by the varying signal fields that have been superimposed on the bias field. The object, of course, is to cancel out all magnetization *except that caused by the superimposed signal.* But complete cancellation rarely takes place except in theory, and this method of dc erasure and recording is rarely used today (a few applications will be described later).

TWO-STEP DC ERASE

The two-step dc-erase method, which is still used with ac-bias recording to some extent, because of its economy, works similarly to the dc-erase method just described. It involves use of (1) two electromagnets opposite in polarity, (2) one electromagnet whose

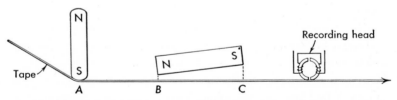

Fig. 5-1.   Illustration of the two-step dc method of erasure.

polarity can be reversed at the proper time, or (3) a permanent magnet or magnets accurately positioned in reference to the medium that is to be erased. This two-step dc erase—reversed dc or imitation ac—works as follows (Fig. 5-1).

Regardless of its state of magnetization, the medium, as it approaches the end of the first permanent magnet, which is strong enough to saturate the material, reaches a state of saturation—at point *A*. As the medium moves away, in its direction of travel, from this erase magnet, its magnetization is reversed by the slightly weaker and oppositely polarized field of the next magnet. As the medium next approaches this magnet's south pole, its remaining magnetization, theoretically, is cancelled—at C. Then, as the medium approaches and until it is recorded at the recording head, its magnetization, if the positioning of the erase magnets is absolutely correct, will theoretically be zero; it would then be in a completely demagnetized state.

Unfortunately, it is very difficult in practice to achieve top-quality results with this erasing method. Some noise always remains and, as W. W. Wetzel noted, " . . . the neutral condition is not stable. The noise level tends to increase with mechanical working of the tape after a wipe of this kind."*

There is one great advantage in the proper use of dc-erase methods: Regardless of its strength, the previous recording can be completely erased, a possibility not always offered by other methods. If conditions are such that overmodulation of the tape has occurred, dc erase or wiping on an ac bulk eraser affords the best means of complete removal of previous modulation. (See Chapter 9 on spurious printing for further discussion.)

AC ERASURE

A logical extension of the idea of the reversed dc-erase method is applied in ac erasing. This form of erasing is now used almost exclusively. Results vary, depending upon how well the erase system has been designed and constructed. In ac erasing the medium is effectively erased by alternate saturation, first in one magnetic direction and then in the other. The medium, by gradual removal from this saturating, demagnetizing field, is successively subjected to smaller and less powerful erasing fields until, when it is completely removed, it is completely neutral magnetically. If the medium is not neutral when recording takes place, distortion will be caused by the effect of the polarization of the incompletely erased medium on the recording ac-bias action.

* "Review of the Present Status of Magnetic Recording Theory," *Audio Engineering*, Dec., 1947.

For best erasure the magnetic medium should be subjected to a considerable number of reversals of the erase field, the fields gradually decreasing in strength. The frequency of the erasing current, therefore, should be high enough to cause a number of reversals of the erase field within the erase-head gap, and the wave shape should be symmetrical. If one part of a wave is less in amplitude than the other part is, the difference in amplitude has a direct-current effect that leaves the medium slightly magnetized, instead of neutral. To offset this possible cause of noise and distortion, some professional recorders provide a source of direct current that may be adjusted to balance the effective ac-erase field; if proper balance is obtained, the least possible magnetization will be left on the erased medium. (See Chapter 8 on maintenance.)

AC-ERASE HEADS

Alternating-current magnetic erase heads are commonly constructed of two separate cores. Made of very thin, laminated, silicon steel, the cores are butted together at the rear, an erase gap varying from a few thousandths to a few hundredths of an inch being left at the front. This gap is actually not an empty space but is filled with a proper amount of a hard, nonmagnetic material, generally beryllium copper. Each core is made of laminations from 0.004- to 0.014-in. thick; these laminations are insulated from each other in order to reduce the flow of eddy currents that waste (erasing) energy by converting it into heat. Some erase heads, made in Japan by a patented method, utilize cores made of compressed iron powder. The size of the gap, the frequency and strength of the erasing current, and the speed of travel of the recording medium together determine how well erasure will be effected. For instance, if the erase frequency were 100,000 cy per sec and the medium were moving at 15 in. per sec, the actual length in inches of one wave length would be

$$W = \frac{V}{F}$$

where W = wave length in inches
         F = frequency in cycles per second
         V = speed of the medium in inches per second

In the example mentioned the wave length would be

$$\frac{15}{100,000} \quad \text{or} \quad W = 0.00015 \text{ in.}$$

Let us say that the effective erase gap, which may be almost twice as wide as the actual physical gap, is 0.01 in.; then the medium, in passing through the erase flux field, is subjected to at least 0.01/0.00015 reversals, or 66 reversals.

DESIGN TRENDS

If the erase head is properly constructed and is fed by a symmetrical erase current that is high enough in power to saturate the medium, complete erasure will take place. (There is room for considerable doubt about "complete" erasure *ever occurring*.) Studies by Wetzel, Rettinger, and others of erasing methods indicate excellent ac erasure is possible even with comparatively low erase currents that do not heat the head cores excessively. Howell has patented an erase-head structure that is threaded by the recording medium (U.S. Patent No. 2,498,423, 1950); better erasure is claimed. Rettinger has devised a dual erase head permitting the medium to be erased first by one head and then by the other. The definite interval of time that elapses between the two erasings results, it is claimed, in considerably better erasure at lower power. (Recordists have, in the past, often erased magnetic tape twice in succession in order to produce a quieter recording.)

Erasing heads now in common use with all kinds of magnetic recorders may generally be depended on to produce good erasure compatible with the design and cost of production of the particular recorder on which the erase head is used. Note, however, that erasure of signals from a magnetic medium does not mean, in all cases, that they will remain erased. Some of the older kinds of magnetic tape that had high retentivity would erase quite well momentarily, but after a few days of storage the recorded signals that had been erased—but only temporarily—could be heard again—a sort of magnetic memory of the "erased" recording. Such effects occur rarely with modern, coated media, fortunately.

BULK ERASERS

Basically, bulk erasers, like the Cinema Engineering Company's* Degausser, are large electromagnets that draw their current supply directly from an ac line. For rapid and thorough demagnetization of all magnetic media in bulk form they are excellent. A reel of tape or film, or a thick batch of magnetically coated paper or plastic, can be quickly neutralized by proper use of any of these erasers. The tape or film should be rotated slowly and evenly within the demagnetizing fields;† then, while it is still in slow rotary motion, it should be *lifted upward and away from the fields gradually*. The medium should not be allowed to stop rotating at any time while it is within an erasing field, nor should it be slid off the eraser. Violation of either warning will cause the medium to be marked with magnetic imprints which may affect the quality of recording. Before bringing the medium within the erasing fields, turn on the eraser. Do not turn it off until the medium has been removed by about two ft from the fields. These bulk erasers draw considerable current (about 15 amperes or more at 120 volts ac). They should be kept on only long enough to erase a few reels of magnetic tape or film, because they tend to overheat after a few minutes' use.

It has become the practice in the radio and motion-picture industries to depend upon these erasers for wiping tape or film before recordings are made. Some magnetic recorders for magnetic-film field recording (recording on location) do not even contain an erasing head because it is possible to obtain much quieter recordings (better signal-to-noise ratio) by using bulk-erased film. Many radio

---

* A division of the Aerovox Corporation.

† A small, bulk eraser may contain only one electromagnet and, therefore, have only one magnetic field. Erasers now in use have two, and sometimes three, electromagnets, one placed beside the other(s).

broadcast and recording engineers disconnect the erase heads in their recorders and use bulk erasers, thus getting a much better signal-to-noise ratio.

PENCIL-TYPE SPOT ERASERS

Small ac erasers designed to spot-erase an unwanted click or syllable without affecting the rest of the recording have been on the market for a considerable time. The click eraser is made of an iron core, shaped like a pencil, over which a coil, suited to the alternating current supply, is wound. Unless the eraser is kept in motion while it is in use, it will cause a 60-cy signal to be recorded on the medium.

HEAD DEMAGNETIZER

Of a construction somewhat similar to that of the pencil type of eraser is the head demagnetizer (described more fully in the chapter on maintenance). As its name implies, this demagnetizer is designed specifically to demagnetize head cores that have become magnetized. When the head demagnetizer is used, the recorder should be disconnected from the ac supply or, if battery-operated, turned off. Again, as in all demagnetizing or erasing operations, the movements of the erasing mechanism should be gradual, that is, without jerks or stops. Turn the demagnetizer on, move it into contact with the head cores for a few seconds, then remove it gradually. Repeat this three or four times, and the core will be thoroughly demagnetized.

Other aspects of the erasure of magnetic materials will be treated in succeeding chapters.

6

Fundamentals of Magnetic Sound Recording

THE NATURE OF SOUND

The recording of sound by a magnetic, as well as by any other, method requires a working knowledge of the nature of sound. What is sound? How is it originated and how transmitted?

Sound is created by vibration of any material or matter in an elastic medium. Other waves, like those of light, are also vibratory in nature. One cycle of sound is made up of two excursions of sound, one advancing from nothing to its maximum and back to zero value in one direction, the other doing the same thing in the other direction. The number of cycles completed in the space of one second is the frequency of the sound. What we call "sound" is generally confined to the frequencies that lie between 20 and 20,000 cy per sec. Frequencies below 10 and above 20,000 cy per sec are not generally spoken of as audible sound, but as "subsonic" and "supersonic" sound, respectively. In this chapter we are thinking of sound objectively, as vibration in air or other media at audible frequencies. There is another meaning of sound—a subjective meaning—in which sound is considered as a stimulus to the sense of hearing. That phase of sound will be discussed later in Chapter 10 on editing.

HOW SOUND IS GENERATED

Sound can be generated in an infinite number of ways, but the final result is always a vibratory motion of some kind that can be heard. When you pull a string of a violin, for example, and let it go, you start a sound wave. As the string flies back past its former position it pushes the air in front of it. The particles of air that are pushed by the string push their neighboring air particles; these push their adjacent particles, and so on. When the force of the string's first forward push has been exhausted, the string is "pulled" in the opposite direction, both by its elasticity and by the partial vacuum in the space it has just traversed.* Another sound vibration then takes place, similar to the first one, differing only in direction and results. The first wave, or "push" wave, is called a wave of compression, since it caused compression of the particles of air in front of the violin string. The second wave is called a wave of rarefaction, or "pull" wave, since the string was pulled back, partly by its own tensional forces and partly by the pull of vacuum. This complete wave of sound will continue to vibrate, at a rate determined mainly by the string's properties, until all the energy stored in the string by the original pull given it has been expended.

FORCED AND RESONANT VIBRATIONS

Disregarding electron motion, materials normally are not in a state of vibration. They are caused to vibrate by motion communicated to them, generally by something external to themselves. Blow a whistle, strike a gong, pluck a string, or pound a drum—and sound ensues. It should be remembered that there are two kinds of vibration: forced and resonant. A forced vibration results when a moving object comes into contact with another object. If you struck a tuning fork and held its bottom firmly against a glass, the glass would vibrate at the *tuning fork's* frequency. The type of vibration illus-

---

* This phenomenon is merely an illustration of Newton's third law: every force is accompanied by an equal and opposite reacting force. Most readers will recall it from their secondary-school studies.

trated here is called forced vibration. But, if you struck the glass with a ruler, for example, it would vibrate, after the initial blow, at its (the glass') own *natural* frequency of vibration. However, if you *tuned* a tuning fork to the *natural* frequency of the glass, then struck the fork and held it *near* the glass, the latter would vibrate intensely. Strong vibration of the glass when the "attuned" tuning fork is held near is a result of resonance. Resonance is generally avoided, if possible, in all recording processes. In all kinds of recording, one material, circuit, or electronic component is forced to vibrate at a frequency (or frequencies) governed by the *driving force*.

For example, the ribbon of a velocity microphone is moved by the sound waves originated by someone striking the keys of a piano. If it is a good microphone and properly positioned, not much resonant sound will be added (any such sound would distort the piano's sound); therefore, a good microphone properly positioned will react to the piano's sound almost faithfully.

TRANSIENT VIBRATIONS

A material forced to vibrate because of the sudden application of an external force begins to vibrate violently at first. This violent initial vibration does not ordinarily have any special wave length but may range erratically over the entire audio spectrum. This state of erratic vibration is called the "transient period" of a material or piece of equipment. In recording we hope for as little "transient response" as possible and select equipment specified to create as little as possible. In sum, then, neither the artificial transients just mentioned nor resonance *should be generated in* good audio equipment, which should, however, respond faithfully to the *sound transients that are part of the sound to be recorded.*

Damping. The motion of any element of a transducer that is to remain as short a time as possible in the transient state must be damped by some means. Motion-damping is performed in any one of many different ways, depending upon the material that is to be stabilized. Microphones and loudspeakers utilize air chambers to help maintain steady, forced vibration. (This is called the "steady state" of vibration.) Viscous fluids, elastic solids, and other materials that do not permit too rapid motion of the particular part are used as motion dampers. Electrical circuits may be damped electrically by a process of "loading" with resistance. Thus, any sound that is to be transmitted faithfully must have as little resonance and transient response as possible and, therefore, as much damping as needed to enable it to reach the point where the sound transducer moves only when it is forced to vibrate. This point of damping is called "critical damping."

TRANSMISSION OF SOUND

Sound waves that are to be heard or recorded must be transmitted through some medium before they can move the microphone ribbon or our eardrums. (In this discussion the terms "sound" and "sound waves" are used interchangeably.) Sound may be transmitted through any solid, liquid, or gas but, contrary to light and other waves, it is not transmitted through a vacuum. In other words, sound transmission, or coupling, as we may call it, requires a medium of some density. The denser the medium, or the closer together the molecules of matter constituting the medium, the faster the waves of sound travel. At ordinary room temperatures sound travels about 1100 ft per sec. In water the speed of sound waves is roughly five times that in air, varying with the saltiness of the water, and in steel about fifteen times.

Sound waves are transmitted through a medium by means of the molecules of matter that comprise it. A wave is transmitted from one particle to an adjoining one, and so on. Imagine a series of rubber balls suspended by strings in a straight line and, when at rest, just touching each other. If you were to pull the first rubber ball back and let it go, its motion would cause all the other balls to move, each in turn. Each ball's motion would cause the next ball to move, and the last one would move almost as far as the one that was pulled from its resting position. The motion of the last ball, in swinging back to the series of balls, would be transmitted successively all the way back again to the first one. This oscillatory motion would continue until all the stored force (kinetic energy) was expended.

In a similar way sound is transmitted through any medium. Sound may radiate from a source in all directions, the directions in which it radiates its greatest force being dependent upon many factors that need not be dealt with here. One cycle, or complete wave length, of sound includes a wave of compression and a wave of rarefaction—a push and a pull. The number of complete wave lengths of sound occurring in one second is the frequency of the sound. The length of a complete sound wave at any frequency may be derived from the equation

$$\text{Wave length} = \frac{\text{velocity}}{\text{frequency}}$$

Thus, the wave length of a sound that vibrates 400 complete waves per sec at room temperature would be

$$\text{Wave length} = \frac{1100}{400} = 2.75 \text{ ft}$$

where the velocity at room temperature is 1100 ft per sec.

HOW SOUND IS DISTORTED IN AIR

Practically no source of sound ordinarily encountered produces pure tones in air—harmonics and overtones are generated at the same time. It is important to understand the distinction between sound traveling in air (or a similar medium) and electromagnetic waves representing sound in amplifiers and other equipment. Sound in air is subject to cancellation and addition; it mixes with other sounds, but it is not as subject as electrical transducers are to the form of distortion called "intermodulation distortion."

One phenomenon deserves the recordist's attention. Ideally, if identical notes were sounded by two identical tuning forks in free space a few feet apart, struck at the same time, two waves of sound of identical frequencies would be set up. If a compression wave emanating from one fork met a compression wave emanating from the other fork, the opposing waves would cancel each other; at the frequency and at the point where the two waves met, no sound would be heard. The opposing waves would be out of phase and would exactly cancel each other at their meeting place. But, at another point, the compression wave from one fork might coincide with a wave of rarefaction from the other fork; at that point the sound would be twice as intense as that of either original wave.

Now, suppose that instead of identical notes being struck on the two tuning forks, notes having a frequency difference of 10 cy per sec are struck at the same time. The opposing waves would be *almost* identical, and there would be, momentarily, *almost* complete cancellation at the point where the two compression waves meet during the out-of-phase condition. When they are in phase, the waves aid each other slightly; the compounded sound from the two forks, at the different points where the waves are in phase, thus gets louder and softer at a rate corresponding to the difference between their frequencies, in this case ten times a second. Placement of microphones should be made with this phenomenon in mind.

REFLECTION AND DIFFRACTION

Interference between waves of sound takes place when there is only one source of sound in an enclosed place. Sound is reflected from walls, ceilings, and floors in the same way that light is reflected from mirrors. Thus a sustained note can periodically cancel itself as reflected waves of the same wave length as those of the sustained note first "compression-cancel" and then "rarefaction-aid" the original wave. When a sustained wave of this pattern occurs (this is called a "standing wave") and the microphone happens to be located in the "canceled"-phase area, very little sound at that wave length will be picked up. The opposite can also happen: If the microphone is placed in a location from which it picks up a reinforcement (or aiding) phase at a particular wave length, a disproportionate amount of sound at that wave length will be picked up. Another difficulty caused by such standing waves, which occur at radio frequencies as well as at sound (audio) frequencies, is the picking up of noise and hum in a microphone cable from frequency-modulated, television, and other radio-frequency waves.

Sound waves tend to cancel one another when they bend around objects of lengths identical to their own. This phenomenon—diffraction—causes microphones as small as possible to be used when the highest quality of work is desired.

DISSIPATION

Although interference between sound waves may take place in an enclosed space, in free space (which actually seldom occurs), sound will not be reflected but will die away as its energy becomes dispersed. Such dispersion occurs in inverse ratio to the square of the distance. Thus, if we are 10 ft away from a source of sound, a certain amount of energy will reach us. If we move to a point 20 ft away only 1/4 of that amount of energy will reach us. At a spot 30 ft away, the amount will be 1/9 the original amount, and so on. The energy of a sound is finally dissipated in overcoming the inertia of air-particles, but apart from the dispersion effect just discussed, in almost all space* sound is reflected by natural or artificial means. Echoes occur in nature when sound is reflected (after the original sound has almost died away at its point of origin) from various surfaces or bodies such as a hillside or a building. Multiple echoes, as in rolling thunder, occur when sound is reflected several times from various surfaces.

REVERBERATION

Reverberation is caused by a series of echoes occurring in such rapid succession that overlapping results. Echoes do not normally occur in small auditoriums, but reverberation in such places is common. Excess reverberation can be lessened by acoustic treatment of the studio or room. Heavy tapestries (monk's cloth), rugs, absorbent hair felt, acoustic tile, and many other sound-absorbent materials should be judiciously used to remove *unwanted* reverberation. Re-

* All space except a vacuum and anechoic chambers.

verberation time is ordinarily computed as the length of time it takes, after production of a sound has stopped, for reverberation to die away. It is, actually, what we call "acoustical damping" that causes a sound to stop reverberating, and we may think of it in that way. Audiences in a studio or auditorium can be quite a large factor in damping reverberation. When rehearsing, prior to recording, in an audience-free room, one must allow for a considerable loss of reverberation that will occur after the hall fills with the audience.

The amount of reverberation that will produce pleasing sound varies with conditions. Speech ordinarily requires, for good perception by the audience, a short reverberation time. The requirements for music will differ according to the kind of music, the kind of orchestra or music source, the musical director, and what the audience expects, depending upon its musical experience and tradition. Ordinarily, more reverberation will make sound appear brighter and brilliant—"live"; less reverberation will make it appear duller and "dead." Radio broadcasting studios have been built to provide a means of varying reverberation time at will—by the utilization of wall vanes, absorbent on one side and reverberant on the other, which are moved by motors controlled by the audio engineer.

The knowledge of acoustics is still far from complete, and experimentation is still going on. Studios and auditoriums with unequal walls, curved walls, angled ceilings—all kinds of treatments of rooms are being tried in attempts to get controllable and predictable acoustics. For our purposes, however, the practical method of "cut and try" and the lessons of experience will suffice in our consideration of recording. Microphones and acoustics should be manipulated so that the *sound desired* will be recorded.

MICROPHONES

One should always remember, when recording, that any number of microphones that feed only a single amplifier constitute, effectively, a *single ear*. Most present audio systems are based upon the "single-ear" or monaural pickup. A single-microphone pickup can, at best, give the listener the impression of hearing intimate sound (by using it close to the sound source) or reverberant sound (by using it farther away).

Binaural, or "two-ear" systems, require that the positions of two microphones simulate those of a person's ears, that the sounds they pick up be amplified separately in phase all the way, and that sounds picked up by the microphones be listened to through headphones clamped on both ears of the listener, one headphone for the sound from each microphone. In order to get good binaural results, the pickup fields of the microphones selected should approximate those of the human ear, and the headphones should be of high quality with the ability to reproduce equally all audible frequencies of sound. Properly speaking, true binaural reception can be obtained *only* by using headphones.

Stereophonic systems require two or more complete sound channels right through to the associated loudspeakers, which are so placed that each will duplicate, in position and angle of sound dispersion, the position and angle of pickup of one or a group of the original microphones.

Microphones perform the function of converting sound into electrical energy and are subject to all the laws governing the transmission of sound. They should not produce peaks at any audible frequency and should be highly damped so that they will translate sound into electromagnetic waves with great fidelity. There are four main types of microphones in present use: the velocity (ribbon), dynamic, condenser, and crystal microphones.

MICROPHONE PICKUP PATTERNS

A graphic drawing of the manner in which a microphone picks up sound is called its pickup pattern. These patterns are generally plotted in polar form, the microphone serving as the nucleus, or pole, and the line surrounding the pole delimiting the microphone's directional sensitivity, or characteristic. All microphones are most sensitive to sound hitting the microphone diaphragm, or ribbon, broadside. Therefore, a microphone that is shielded from sound coming from every direction but one will have a pickup pattern that will show the microphone (the pole) at the small end of a pear-shaped oval pattern. A ribbon microphone whose ribbon is hung so that its flat sides are exposed to sound coming from two directions has a polar pattern in which the microphone (the pole) is shown between two circles drawn contiguously; such a pattern is called a "figure-8" pattern.

THE VELOCITY MICROPHONE

The ribbon microphone utilizes a crimped, nonresonant metal ribbon placed between two permanent magnets. The ribbon's movement is controlled by the *velocity* of the particles of air striking it, and this motion generates an electrical voltage in the ribbon. Ribbon microphones are bidirectional, picking up sound in something like a figure-eight (8) pattern. The sides (where the involutions of the figure eight cross each other) are, for all practical purposes, dead. Ribbon microphones can be ruined by blasts of air taking the "crimp" out of the ribbon and causing the ribbon thereafter to hit the permanent magnets when the ribbons are actuated by sound; actual contact of ribbon and magnet produces severe distortion. For that reason the ribbons are generally shielded by a fine mesh fabric underneath a punched metal shield. It is not a good idea to employ ribbon microphones for rugged, outdoor recording. They are quite fragile and require careful handling. *Never blow into them.*

THE DYNAMIC MICROPHONE

Dynamic, or moving-coil, microphones, are a rugged type suitable for all kinds of recording. They are made like tiny, permanent-magnet loudspeakers and operate like loudspeakers in reverse. They are pressure-sensitive and are not extremely directional, since they are actuated by the varying *pressure* of the air around them, not by the *velocity* of the sound. Sound strikes a metal or plastic diaphragm attached to a coil that moves with varying sound-pressures within a magnetic field created by permanent magnets. The electric current produced thus is fed to a pre-amplifier.

The velocity and dynamic types are essentially low-impedance devices, and the microphone cables can be as long as needed—at least up to approximately 100 ft. Longer microphone cables, even at low impedance, should be avoided in full-frequency-range recording.

THE CARDIOID MICROPHONE

A microphone that is a combination of the velocity and dynamic types of microphone is called the "cardioid" because its pickup pattern looks like a heart. It is used for work where its wide angle of frontal pickup and its negligible pickup at the rear are extremely useful, especially in locations where public-address systems are used. In such cases, the loudspeakers, although producing adequate sound, do not cause enough sound to feed back into the microphone to build up into destructive oscillations and "howl."

THE CONDENSER MICROPHONE

The condenser microphone, after quite a period of disuse, is coming back into popularity. The first commercial model of a condenser microphone was made by E. C. Wente in 1922. This type of microphone was used a great deal during the early years of radio and the "talkies." But complications inherent in amplifying its tiny pickup voltage and difficulties arising from its size resulted in its being supplanted by the dynamic and velocity types of microphone, both of which are easier to handle. However, design engineers, as we shall see, overcame these troubles.

One of the facts of acoustics, as applied to microphones, is that the *volume* of sound picked up varies; it is related inversely to the square of the distance from the sound source. The volume also depends upon the reverberant properties of the studio and upon microphone placement. When a microphone is *directional,* it obviously picks up more sound from one direction than another. Since a microphone picks up only a small fraction of the total volume of sound in the room, amplification is employed to bring the sound up to a usable level. Naturally, then, designers attempt to make the microphone pick up enough sound so that the always-present tube noise and hiss in the amplifiers will not be too evident in the sound picked up. When the microphone is made physically big, it becomes frequency-selective because of its very size. Frequency distortion of the sound a microphone picks up is in part due to diffraction. There are other design problems that have to do with the mass and resonance of the diaphragm, ribbon, or condenser plate, but with these we are not concerned here. Miniature condenser microphones (designed by Wente, Veneklasen, and others) have minimized these difficulties.

All condenser microphones depend for their operation on the variation in voltage occurring in a condenser, which is formed by the diaphragm (that moves with the varying pressure of the sound waves impinging on it) and a backplate (on which a small electrical voltage is placed). This voltage varies with the movement of the sound-sensitive diaphragm. Sound-pressure changes are thus translated into corresponding voltage changes in the voltage between the diaphragm and the backplate which, amplified by a tiny tube in the microphone base, are then conducted through a cable to the regular recording pre-amplifier. The small physical size, less than 1-in. diameter, of these miniature condenser microphones makes them able to pick up sound at most audio frequencies from any angle with a minimum of diffraction loss and also a minimum of consequent variation in response in accordance with frequency.

THE CRYSTAL MICROPHONE

Crystal microphones may be constructed in several ways, but basically they are all similarly actuated. Most are made of Rochelle salt crystals driven by small diaphragms which, when struck by sound waves, cause the crystals to bend or twist; in so doing the crystals give off electric voltages proportionate to the sound striking them. Since the crystal microphone is a high-impedance device, the cable connecting it to the pre-amplifier must be short; otherwise hum and noise and loss of output would result. Crystal microphones become inoperative after they have absorbed an excess of moisture or have dried out completely. It is not, therefore, good practice to use crystal microphones in very hot (over 120° F.) or in very humid climates. Microphones employing ceramic cartridges, which work much the same way as crystals do, are not seriously affected by either heat or humidity.

THE CARBON MICROPHONE

Carbon microphones are now used mainly for special purposes. A carbon microphone works on the principle of the varying electrical resistance to current flow that is offered by carbon (treated coal) granules subjected to varying degrees of pressure. A typical carbon microphone has a single "button" or carbon-granule-filled cup, across one side of which is mounted a movable diaphragm made of metal. A direct current is made to flow through the carbon granules. This current *decreases* in strength as the button's resistance increases—when the diaphragm bends outward—but *increases* when the diaphragm moves inward. These changes in current flow are then amplified as usual, as is any noise created by the continuously changing electrical contact between one granule and the next. Because of this noise, the tendency of the carbon granules to stick together, high distortion, and generally poor frequency response, carbon microphones are now rarely used except where their great sensitivity furnishes an economical means of picking up sound whose fidelity is not a factor.

SPECIAL FORMS OF MICROPHONES

Microphones of standard types are manufactured in several special forms. "Lapel" microphones, about 2 in. wide or smaller, may be pinned to a coat lapel or hidden under a jacket. Hearing-aid microphones are still smaller. A "machine-gun" microphone, which utilizes the air-resonance of different lengths of tubes, has been devised for highly directional uses. A hydrophone, a device that picks up sound under water, consists of a microphone or a number of microphones, generally crystal, inserted in a waterproof, generally oil-filled, flexible compartment. Contact microphones, made in a variety of forms, are used to pick up sound through solids and from stringed instruments and any vibrating body.

The Parabolic Microphone. The parabolic reflector microphone is extremely valuable for recording sound from a distance. As you know, the energy of sound waves decreases inversely with the square of the distance between the microphone and the sound source. If one were to intercept a larger percentage of the sound than usual with the microphone, it should be possible to pick up more energy than usually picked up, even at great distances. The parabolic reflector is a stiff, concave disk, curved according to a formula, with a hard surface and a very low resonant period. By suspending a microphone with its diaphragm or other sound-sensitive element facing the center of this disk at the focus of the parabolic curve, one can reflect intercepted sound into the microphone. The frequency band of sound waves that can be intercepted in this way depends, of course, upon the diameter of the disk. To reflect a sound adequately into the microphone, the reflector must have a diameter longer than half the wave length of the sound. The use of the parabolic microphone is described by Dr. Peter Paul Kellogg in the following chapter, "Recording Sound in Nature."

Microphones may be adapted to serve any purpose in any surrounding. When the exigencies of a situation call for a solution, one can be found by the reader who uses his common sense. It would hardly be profitable to go into a lengthy discussion of special setups for various kinds of sound—music, conversation, sound effects, battle sounds, and others. Every situation should be analyzed; no general conclusions can be drawn except those that are implicit in the laws of the propagation of sound. The recordist should take care not to be misled by theoretical assumptions. Tonal balance should be attained by listening to the sound coming from the loudspeaker and comparing it with the live or actual sound. When it sounds like the original, go ahead and record.

MEASUREMENT OF SOUND

DECIBELS

Before we begin to discuss the amplifiers that magnify the sound picked up by the microphone, we should learn the terms used in measuring sound. The term used to compare different magnitudes (or "levels") of sound is the decibel (one tenth of a "bel"), so named in honor of Dr. Alexander Graham Bell, the inventor of the telephone. The decibel (abbreviated "db") is the unit agreed upon (originally by telephone engineers) to express the ratio between two amounts of power, for instance, the amount of electric power at the beginning of a telephone line and that at the termination of the line.

Intensity of sound can be measured in "dynes" per centimeter squared. By this method is actually measured the pressure of sound waves as they pass, every second, through a measured area that is perpendicular to the direction of the motion of the sound waves. This amount of acoustic pressure is measurable in millionths of a watt, or microwatts. It was found, by experimentation with normal human hearing, that the intensity of the sound we hear, or more properly its "loudness," can best be expressed by the decibel notation. In other words, our appreciation of changes in loudness is logarithmic, for the relative intensity of two sounds is equal to the logarithm, to the base 10, of the ratio of the two sounds' powers. (The logarithm of any number to the base 10 (log 10) is the exponent indicating the number of times 10 must be multiplied by itself to obtain that number; thus $\log_{10} 1000 = 10 \times 10 \times 10$, or $\log_{10} 1000$ is 3.) The use of decibel notation permits us quickly to express differences in power, adding and subtracting decibels instead of multiplying and dividing microwatts. For instance, the energy of sound in the form of loud speech is about 1000 microwatts. A low voice might produce an acoustic power of one microwatt. Since one power is 1000 times the other, we may say: $db = 10 \log_{10} (P_1/P_2)$, which is: $db = 10 \times \log_{10} (1000/1) = 10 \times 3$ or 30 db. Therefore, the ratio of the power of one sound to the other is 30 db, or, the difference between the two sounds is 30 db.

By means of decibel notation we may quickly and easily find out the amount of power required to perform any work we may have to do. In ordinary sound work, the db reference point, zero, is equal to one milliwatt of power (0.001 watt). At this power level, usually called zero level, one may be almost deafened by listening with a pair of good headphones to sound. As an example of the facility provided by decibel notation, we are going to use a microphone that delivers a power of —55 db. In order to amplify a sound picked up by this microphone to zero level, we require 55 db of amplification. A good two-stage amplifier might do the job adequately, or we might need two amplifiers—their specifications, expressed in db, would tell us exactly what to expect. Another example: A sound force of one dyne per centimeter squared is equivalent to 74 db above the point where a tone of 1000 cy per sec can barely be heard by the average young adult human ear. This point is called the threshold of hearing. The range of human hearing, from this threshold point to the point where pain is experienced, is normally 120 db, or about a million million times the threshold power.

THE "DBM" AND "VU"

Power level *measured* in decibels with reference to a one-milliwatt zero level is properly designated in "dbm," which means "decibels referred to a zero level of one milliwatt," and the use of the term "dbm" in a measurement automatically indicates that the level being measured is referred to a one-milliwatt zero level. Telephone practice is to use a reference level of 6 milliwatts of power. The numerical difference of 8 db between the two reference levels is a constant, that is, any reading in the dbm system will always read 8 dbm higher than in the telephone system; therefore, a level of +8 dbm is equivalent to zero db (referred to 6 milliwatts).

A "VU," or volume unit, is a unit of program-level measurement, as opposed to steady-state signal measurement. The term VU implies the use of a standard indicating meter whose ballistics conform to a carefully controlled set of conditions. The VU meter system was developed for use primarily in the radio broadcasting industry. (See Bibliography: Chinn, H. A.) When the VU meter is used to measure a single-frequency sine wave, which is a pure tone, it indicates the result in dbm.

SIGNAL-TO-NOISE RATIO

The "signal-to-noise ratio" is a comparison of the amount of noise and musical sound present in an audio system. Noise of all kinds in a system may be lumped and expressed as being so many decibels below or above reference level. If a recorder's specifications say that "noise is —55 db," you may be sure that normally you would not hear the noise or would barely hear it, depending upon the frequency range within which the noise was produced. (The human ear is most sensitive within the range of about 800 to 2500 cy per sec, sensitivity falling off on both sides of these frequencies.) Recorders for top-quality results should have a signal-to-noise ratio of 70 to 80 db, thus permitting absolutely no noise to be heard during reproduction of very low-level passages of music and even silent periods. Very few machines and media are capable of this degree of quietness. Good equipment should be capable of a signal-to-noise ratio of 50 to 55 db.

EQUALIZATION

In order to record and reproduce sound we employ a "flat" system. This is a system in which all frequencies are reproduced with equal intensity. No method of recording, however, is naturally a flat system, not even the magnetic recording method. Somewhere during the recording and reproducing cycles some frequencies have to be emphasized and others depressed in order to produce a total result that will be flat. This process is called "equalization," and it may be effected in a number of ways. Basically, however, equalization consists in adding corrective circuits during recording and also reproduction. These corrective elements or controls, which compensate for deficiencies in the magnetic recorders and media, can be incorporated in the recorder or may be separate equipment.

Without equalization, reproduced magnetic sound would increase by 6 db every octave (every time the frequency of sound is doubled) up to a definite point determined by many factors, such as the speed of the medium, the thickness and kind of coating, the length of the reproduce-head gap, and so on. At 100 cy per sec the oxide coating will record, without excessive distortion, a certain amount of magnetism within a given length of the medium. At 200 cy, within the same length of medium, although the strength of a single magnetic impression may be the same, there are twice as many impressions as at 100 cy, and these impressions induce current in the reproduce head *twice as fast* as do impressions at 100 cy; the result is four times as much power at 200 cy as at 100 cy. Depending upon the speed of the medium and other factors, this increase in number of impressions continues up to the point where the output from the tape or film drops again because of gap-effect, self-erasure, and other causes. Thus, in order to achieve "flat" over-all response, the very low and very high frequencies have to be emphasized in some way. Ordinarily the high frequencies are accentuated during the recording process and the low frequencies during reproduction. Equalization during recording is called "pre-emphasis" and during playback, "post-emphasis." Sometimes "de-emphasis" circuits are used to remove some, or all, of the "pre-emphasis" during reproduction.

THE GAP-EFFECT

The gap-effect, referred to above, is the cancellation of a recorded wave length that takes place when the effective magnetic gap of the reproduce head is equivalent in length to one wave length of the recorded sound. (It is similar to the "slit" effect in optical recording.) What happens may be easily visualized; one phase of the recorded wave on the medium is entering the gap as the other phase of the same wave is leaving it; thus they effectively cancel each other. For this reason the gaps in magnetic heads are made as short as possible; maximum cancellation then takes place in some part of the audible spectrum above the working range of the machine. The gap effect thus becomes serious only at high frequencies. The best reproducing heads now available have gaps about 0.00025 in. long and must be made very carefully. If good results are to be achieved, the opposing faces of the gap must be perfectly straight and parallel, and the surface of the head core must be perfectly smooth, straight, and perpendicular to the opposing faces of the gap.

SELF-ERASURE

Self-erasure of magnetically recorded sound (or other recorded waves) takes place when some recorded waves are close enough to others to affect the magnetic state of the recorded waves. If we should double the speed of the medium, these magnetic marks would be twice as far apart for a given frequency as they were at the original speed, and therefore much less self-erasure would take place. Such reduction of self-erasure is one of the phenomena that make it possible to reproduce a wider band of high frequencies at higher speeds. The higher the speed in recording, the smaller is the amount of equalization needed to obtain a given output at high frequencies. There is a point of diminishing return, however, which it is not important to discuss here.

The amplifiers associated with a recording machine are equalized in order to make possible equal reproduction of the recorded sound at all frequencies within its range. Of course, it is not necessary that equalization be built into the recording and reproducing amplifiers. "Flat" amplifiers—a flat amplifier is one that amplifies all frequencies equally—followed by equalizers of the permanent or variable variety, may be used just as well. All amplifiers, however, should be able to transform, with a minimum of distortion and noise, the signals generated in the microphone of the recording machine.

DISTORTION OCCURRING
IN THE RECORDING PROCESS

We have already dealt with frequency distortion, which is any departure from equal amplification at all frequencies. If we get out of a recording what we put in, frequency-wise, there is no frequency distortion. Phase distortion need not concern us very much, since it is not noticeable to the average listener. However, an excess of phase distortion makes sound appear unreal—it loses naturalness. Phase distortion is due entirely to unequal delays in amplifying, recording, and reproducing sounds at various frequencies. Phase distortion is a considerable problem in data recording and other kinds of magnetic recording, as we shall see.

In well-designed and operated systems there will be very little amplitude distortion. This is the kind of distortion where the output of a system contains harmonics and sum- and difference-frequencies which were not contained in the original sound. We may avoid amplitude distortion if we do not overload, or overmodulate, our system of recording, beginning at the microphone. The experienced recordist finds out, by testing, the distortion-free limits of his equipment and then keeps well within these limits. If a microphone, for example, is placed too close to a singer, both the microphone and the first tube of the first amplifier, or preamplifier, may be overloaded, or overmodulated. The microphone may distort as a result of wild mechanical motion of several kinds, depending upon its construction. The first tube of the pre-amplifier will be overloaded by the high voltages passed on to it from the microphone and will create, within itself, sounds that are not contained in the original sounds. *Almost all poor-quality magnetic recording is caused by overmodulation of this kind.*

Overmodulation occurs when too much voltage for the tube to handle without distortion is sent to any tube of the amplifier and also when audio-recording current exceeds the permissible recording limits of the magnetic medium. By inserting a variable resistor or potentiometer between the microphone and the first tube, we obtain some degree of control over the audio. This kind of control, or "gaining," is called "low-level" gaining, since it necessarily takes place at a very low level, approximately —55 db. Low-level gaining is not used very much because it is a noisy method of control. Ordinarily, level is controlled in a stage after the first amplifier; the sound from the microphone has already been magnified by about

45 db, and the noise created by the moving contacts of a potentiometer will not be noticeable.

Intermodulation distortion in magnetic recording is created during the recording process by the many other frequencies resulting from interaction between signals of different frequencies of sound. It will be more fully discussed in Chapter 8 on maintenance.

LEVEL INDICATORS

In order to permit recording with a minimum of distortion, most machines have some way of indicating visually how much power is reaching the recording head. The indicator may be a db meter, an ac voltmeter, or an indicating neon or "magic-eye" tube. This indicator of "level" should be placed in the circuit where it will show the amount of current reaching the recording head. Since the current at the recording head has already been equalized, the indicator circuit should contain compensation for whatever equalization is in the recording circuit so that a true reading may be obtained. Otherwise the indicator might show a level that would be very high at high frequencies and quite low at low frequencies. The amount of recording current that can safely be recorded at all audible frequencies must be correctly indicated, and the operator should never allow this current to be exceeded. If the indicator is an "eye" tube, the manufacturer's instructions should be consulted in order to learn just how much the "eye" should close or move at the proper level. It is always preferable to have a meter which can be marked and easily observed during the recording operation. But meters consume electrical energy and in most cases require amplifiers if they are to be operated properly. When a manufacturer has to cut costs in the production of a magnetic recorder he cannot afford the extra cost of a meter and amplifier, using an indicator tube instead. Experience in recording with machines using "eye" indicators has shown that sometimes very slight fluttering of the eye is an indication of sufficient level for good recording. The most practical way of testing a recorder to find out whether the recording level is correct is to record tone from an oscillator at 100 cy per sec, later reproducing it on an oscilloscope screen. When the level recorded is too great, the wave shape on reproduction will be distorted. If the level is too low, the wave shape may be good, but random noise will be high. If an oscilloscope is not available, tests may be made by comparing the reproduced tone by ear with the original tone. When they are the same in *quality*, the recording level is correct. Generally speaking, if the recording machine is in good condition, poor recording results are obtained either from overrecording (in level) or underrecording. Overmodulating (one may call it by that term although it is not strictly correct) will produce heavy distortion of a recognizable kind. Low-frequency sounds will sound muddy and flat; highs will be raspy and piercing in quality. Experimenting in recording at various levels, as shown by the indicator meter or eye tube, will soon show you what the optimum recording point is for your machine. You can then mark the meter, or the tube face, to indicate the point beyond which you should not go.

Overmodulating will result in effects other than distortion. A medium containing too heavy recording may be difficult to erase on the ordinary machine's erasing head; after the next recording you make on the same medium, you may be surprised to hear a jumble of two programs. (Of course, a good bulk eraser *will* erase it.) A more severe effect, partly due to overheavy recording, is spurious printing, which will be fully described later. The effects of underrecording are not serious. There will be more noise compared to the signal strength when the level of the reproducing amplifier is increased to compensate for the low signal level recorded. If there is any doubt, however, it is far better to underrecord then to overrecord.

THE MAGNETIC HEAD

Probably more know-how goes into the making of magnetic-recording heads than into any other component of a recorder, with the possible exception of the drive. The magnetic-recording head is an electromagnet through whose coils flow two kinds of electricity. One current is that which is to be recorded in the form of magnetic markings; the other current is the direct or alternating "bias" current that creates the right climate in which comparatively distortion-free recording can take place. Most magnetic heads in use now are of the "ring" type. As the name implies, they are made of magnets arranged in the shape of a ring. For ease in manufacture and because of design considerations, ring heads are generally made in two sections and, after assembly, clamped or resin-molded together. Heads used in wire recorders may contain a groove which holds the wire. Heads made for recording on magnetic tape and film vary considerably in respect to the widths of magnetic track they are designed to record. For greater fidelity a wider track is recorded; when only recorded information is the object, a narrower track is used. Heads (for tape) that will record tracks varying from 0.250 in. to 0.003 in. and even less are available. Magnetic recorder heads for use with film generally make a track either 0.100 or 0.200 in. wide. Many very narrow tracks may be recorded simultaneously by stacking specially made heads one on top of the one below. Heads like these are used on different kinds of information recorders (data recorders). New kinds of magnetic head assemblies, now coming into use, do other specific jobs well.

The magnetic head is a fundamental part of the mechanism in which it is used and should not be carelessly used or transferred to another recorder before the results are considered. Everything about the head—the metals of which it is made, the magnetic gap, the impedance of the coils, the shape of the head surface—all these factors are parts of the design of the particular machine. For instance, if a recorder is built to drive 1/4-in. tape at a certain speed, with a certain pressure of the tape against the head, no other speed and no other pressure will produce the results intended. If the recording medium is radically different from that for which the recorder was designed, many changes may have to be made to accommodate it. A magnetic recorder provides for a chain of electronic and mechanical events; not one link of the chain can be changed without disturbing the whole, generally for the worse. This applies more to magnetic recorders than to almost any other piece of audio-frequency apparatus.

The magnetic head that reproduces the recorded sound is almost the same as the recording head. As a matter of fact, one reputable manufacturer of high-grade equipment installs two heads of the same type to perform both functions. Reproducing heads, to give high quality at fairly low speeds, must have very short magnetic gaps. These have been made as small as 0.00025 in., or even less. Whether they can be made any shorter than this must be determined by the expert machinists and engineers of the future. Right now, it appears that this is as fine as head gaps can be made mechanically if they are to discharge their magnetic functions. Possibly in the near future we shall be using focused magnetic beams in air to reproduce and record magnetically.

After the recorded sound has been picked up from the magnetic medium by the reproducing head it is first amplified, then equalized (post-emphasis), amplifying the entire frequency range of sound equally, and finally amplified again. How much amplification is finally needed depends upon whether the sound is to be heard by one person wearing headphones or by thousands of people via a public-address system.

7

Recording Sound in Nature

Contributed by
Peter Paul Kellogg, Ph.D.
Professor of Ornithology and Biological Acoustics
Cornell University

RECORDING SOUND IN THE OUT-OF-DOORS

COMPARISON WITH STUDIO RECORDING

Fundamentally, the problem of recording sound in nature is not greatly different from that of recording sound in a good studio. The equipment, the general techniques in using it, and the type of power used are essentially the same for recording in the studio or out-of-doors. The chief differences arise from the fact that acoustics, extraneous interferences, equipment maintenance, and performers are more or less under control in the studio, whereas in the field they present constantly changing problems. Perhaps the best way to record sounds made by a bird or other animal is to invite, or to entice, it into a good studio, place a microphone before it, and have the animal render its various songs and call notes, repeating these until the engineer and the biologist are convinced that the recording is satisfactory. Unfortunately, very few animals will cooperate to this extent, and even when one does, some naturalist is sure to remark that the sound is different from that heard out-of-doors in the animal's natural habitat. Very few animals will perform naturally or normally when they are in unfamiliar surroundings; therefore, we are usually forced to take our equipment into the field and seek out the animal whose voice is to be recorded in natural surroundings, be this mountain top or open meadow, deep swamp lands or densely wooded areas.

The farther we get into the field, away from the technical conveniences of the studio, the more do certain problems begin to emphasize themselves. In general, many of the problems are the same as those with which we cope in the studio, but oftentimes, these problems as present in the studio have been so effectively solved that we no longer think of them as being annoying. For example, in the studio the problem of acoustics and microphone placement requires for its solution no more than the judgment necessary to put the microphone in the best position. Control of sound source is easy in the studio—a word to the performer and he changes his position, but wild animals and other sources of sound in nature do not react in this manner.

Studio equipment, without consideration of size or weight, may be the best available, but in the field both size and weight are necessarily limited.

The source of power in the studio is taken for granted, and usually the power supply is so constant that its frequency may be used as a standard for running and timing all studio equipment. In the field, power for recording must be generated, and the control of both frequency and voltage presents problems.

Maintenance of equipment in the studio may seem quite commonplace and is often reduced to a routine, which is carried out by specialists. In the field problems of maintenance are always emphasized, partly because of the rough treatment to which the equipment is subjected while in normal use and partly because it is almost impossible to have a maintenance specialist always at hand.

SPECIAL PROBLEMS

An additional problem—which arises whenever one tries to record birds or insects and which is seldom met in the studio, where conventional sounds are recorded—has to do with the distribution of energy throughout the sound spectrum. Normally, in human speech and music, high-frequency energy is present and contributes much to the quality and recognition of sounds, but by far the greatest amount of energy is found in the low frequencies, below 2000 cy per sec. This is often referred to as the natural roll-off of high-frequency energy content in speech and music, and advantage is frequently taken of this phenomenon to achieve a better signal-to-noise ratio in recording. The results are the presently accepted standards of equalization, resulting in emphasis of the high frequencies during recording and de-emphasis of the high frequencies during reproduction.

Unfortunately the bird and insect worlds do not conform to this characteristic of speech and music. In fact, a bird may, and often does, put out, in the form of sound, a tremendous amount of energy that lies within the very region of the audio spectrum which the designer of a modern recorder had planned for very little energy; when this happens, severe distortion of the recorded sound results. This phenomenon explains in part at least the very great difficulty encountered in recording some bird and insect sounds. The tape recorders that operate at higher tape speeds and those having shorter effective magnetic gaps in the record and playback heads (therefore requiring less pre-emphasis of high frequencies in recording) give the best results. For these reasons, it is at present often impossible to record satisfactorily many bird songs at tape speeds below 15 in. per sec. Even at this tape speed and with the best available equipment, considerable difficulty is experienced in recording some bird songs. Modification of the standard equalization-response curve of the recording and playback amplifiers in a way to correct this difficulty, in part, will be discussed later.

SOLUTION OF PROBLEMS—BASED ON EXPERIENCE IN THE FIELD

The manner in which problems of field recording have been met will make up the subject matter of this discussion. There are probably many other ways of solving these same problems; those given are the result of more than 20 years of experience in field recording and were, and are, influenced by the current stage of the art. Advances in the art of recording have frequently removed problems entirely, but, on the other hand, they may set up new problems which must be solved.

In the studio portability or mobility presents no problem. In the field one must always be ready to move; everything must be carried along; and arrangements must be made to prevent delicate equipment from being injured. Whether the equipment is to be carried by hand, perhaps in a suitcase, or in a pack on one's back,—whether it is to be built into a car or truck, in effect providing a traveling studio—or is to be transported in a box in a passenger car, thus permitting the car to be used for other purposes—problems are presented which must be decided by one who wishes to record sounds in the out-of-doors. In our work at Cornell, our basic equipment has always been built into a light truck or passenger car, but so arranged that it could be removed readily, if necessary, either for transportation to locations not accessible by car or to permit the car to be used for other purposes. Even though a recorder is used in a car only occasionally, we have found it advisable to determine carefully, considering convenience and hum or other noise pickup, the best position for all units, and then to stick precisely to this arrangement when the car is being loaded.

Even the individual who proposes to record the sounds of nature presents a special problem, for in him or in his team of not more than one or two other people, we should find something of the artist with an ear for the beauty of natural sounds and the feeling for the best place in which to put the microphone to pick it up; we should find something of the naturalist or the biologist with an interest in the accuracy of names of the animal forms which will be recorded; and finally, we must find in this individual, or his team, something of the engineer, if the most is to be obtained from the recording equipment.

ACOUSTICS OF THE ENVIRONMENT

In general, the out-of-doors is more "dead" than almost any studio is. This is especially true of woodland, open fields, and bodies of water. Canyons and city streets lined with buildings often produce annoying reflections of sounds. Also, outdoors, less dependence may be placed on reflections to give reinforcement than is usually the case in a studio. On the other hand, because the microphone, of necessity, must usually be so much further from the subject—from a bird high in a tree—small amounts of reflected sound are often in evidence and prevent these recordings from having the characteristics of sound recorded in a too-dead studio. Extraneous and man-made sounds, which cannot be controlled in the out-of-doors, create a very serious problem. This is especially true if it is impossible to place the microphone reasonably close to the subject, and sometimes such sounds make recording impossible. Under this heading come such things as wind strong enough to cause fluttering of the microphone diaphragm, leaves that rustle even in very light airs, running water in brooks, distant waterfalls, airplanes, traffic noises from nearby roads, and the general noise that is always present near urban centers.

Acoustically, the out-of-doors can generally be counted on to be "deader," but much noisier, than a studio. Choosing a time, usually early morning, when man-made sounds are least and when birds often sing best will help greatly in solving the noise problem, but it is seldom that conditions are ideal in all respects at the same time.

MICROPHONES, THEIR USE AND ACCESSORIES

CHOICE OF MICROPHONE

For most of the serious work of recording the sounds of nature, a high-quality, low-impedance dynamic microphone is probably best. A good dynamic microphone is usually a very rugged instrument. It has a broad, flat frequency response and low distortion, and it is not adversely affected by either temperature or high humidity. Another distinct advantage of this microphone is that it may be used several hundred feet away from the recording equipment without noticeable loss of sound and without the use of auxiliary equipment, such as pre-amplifiers.

The newer types of small condenser microphones may be even

better than the dynamic microphone in respect to frequency response wanted and lack of distortion, but so far most of these instruments require rather bulky, special power supplies and pre-amplifiers located relatively close to the microphone. This circumstance necessitates running power lines into the field along with the microphone cable or improvising special battery supplies.

Some satisfactory results may be obtained with crystal microphones, but these instruments are normally very sensitive to changes in temperature and therefore are not always suitable in the field. Also, they often have poor frequency characteristics and sometimes very high distortion. The high impedance of crystal microphones requires that they be used close to the recorder, or that, whenever the distance is more than a few feet, pre-amplifiers or transformers be used.

In recording sounds under water, crystal microphones, or hydrophones, are used almost exclusively. In such work the crystal element is housed in a rubber compartment which is completely filled with castor oil. The rubber housing and the oil are sufficiently similar in their sound-transmission characteristics to those of sea water for a very effective coupling to be achieved between the water and the microphone. Usually, in order to secure the best possible frequency response and also to provide transmission over a long line, as is necessary when the microphone is used at great depths, a pre-amplifier of the cathode-follower type is used as close as possible to the crystal element.

DIRECTIONAL MICROPHONES

Most microphones are to some extent directional, that is, they will have more output, or better frequency response, when picking up sound from one direction than from another. Some microphones, such as velocity-sensitive ribbon microphones, are much more sensitive along the axis perpendicular to the face of the ribbon than they are at right angles to this axis. Because of their extreme sensitivity to air movement, ribbon microphones are infrequently used outside the studio.

Some type of directional microphone is definitely needed for outdoor recording, especially for recording bird songs. Concentrating the song of a distant bird onto the microphone by means of the parabolic reflector is one of the most useful techniques in natural-history sound recording, but there are several limitations which must be recognized if one is to use the reflector intelligently. Sound, being a wave phenomenon, tends to diffract around objects that are of about the same dimensions as a wave length of the sound. This means that if a parabola is to reflect a low-frequency sound, it must be proportionately large. A parabola 3 ft in diameter is a very poor reflector of sound below 300 or 400 cy per sec, but its efficiency increases rapidly as the frequency goes up. Because of this characteristic, a man's voice is picked up by a small parabola with much distortion. For the same reason low-pitched roars of the black howling monkeys as recorded with a parabola are very disappointing. Likewise, when any sounds with a wide range of frequencies, such as those made by a concert orchestra, are picked up with a parabolic reflector, the high frequencies will be emphasized much more than the lower ones.

Fortunately, most bird songs are high pitched and seldom extend much over an octave in range; therefore they are recorded very well with a parabolic reflector.

We have tried many sizes and conformations of parabolic reflectors and have found that a parabola 40 in. in diameter, with a focal length of 10 in., effects a good compromise between the ability to reflect and the ability to concentrate low frequencies; we have also found that a parabola of this size can be conveniently handled in the field (see Fig. 7-1).

Reflectors may be constructed at home from papier-mâché and plaster, then reinforced with strips of burlap or canvas. A ring of lightweight steel tubing around the edge gives additional support and facilitates mounting the reflector on a tripod. A light but rigid bracket mounting holds the microphone at the focal point of the reflector. (Aluminum parabolic reflectors, originally used for directing radar beams, may often be found in war surplus supplies.)

In addition to being highly directional, parabolic reflectors concentrate a large amount of sound energy onto the microphone from the direction toward which the reflecting surface is pointed. In the frequency range within which most birds sing, this gain in sound power will often amount to as much as 25 db more than the energy received by the microphone without the reflector. This gain is approximately equivalent to a stage of amplification, and since it often

Photo by, and courtesy of, A. A. Allen

Fig. 7-1. A parabolic microphone in use by Professor Kellogg.

represents sufficient gain to enable the bird's song to be heard over other sounds in the environment, use of the reflector is indeed very worth while.

Another type of directional microphone—the machine-gun microphone—consists of a bundle of hollow metal tubes, perhaps fifty, each about 3/8 in. in diameter, and each of a different length, varying from about 1 in. to 5 or 6 ft. These tubes all arise from the chamber in which the microphone is placed. The device works on the principle that a sound originating directly in front of all the tubes will travel down all the tubes simultaneously and arrive, in phase, at the microphone. Sound arriving from directions not on the axis of the tubes will necessarily travel different distances, depending on which tube is entered; accordingly, sounds from such directions will arrive at the microphone out of phase, and cancellation will result.

Although this microphone type is highly directional, it does not concentrate the sound from a large area as the reflector does, and therefore gives no gain to the signal. Actually, instead of a gain, there is a loss of about 12 db.

WIND SCREENS

Wind screens made of silk, nylon, or other cloth and placed over the microphone or over the entire parabolic reflector are helpful when a recording must be made in the wind. The wind screen smooths out the sudden changes in pressure (due to the wind) that otherwise would cause the microphone diaphragm to flutter violently and produce sounds not present in the environment. Wind screens, however, do not eliminate sounds set up by the wind moving past objects, and these sounds, if the wind is strong, may be very annoying.

Good wind screens produce very little, if any, frequency distortion, but many types of cloth that one may be tempted to use to reduce wind noise are very selective in the frequencies they transmit. Accordingly, considerable care should be exercised in selecting the materials and in making the screens.

MICROPHONE PLACEMENT

Microphone placement in the field calls for much more originality, initiative, and patience than are usually needed in the studio. Only by studying each species of animal sound to be recorded and the problems of each locale as they arise, can one hope to get a really satisfactory recording out-of-doors.

When recording most subjects out-of-doors, the rule is to try to place the microphone as close to the subject as possible, much as would be done in a studio. Occasionally this rule can be carried too far, as sometimes happens with insects (which permit a very close approach) or with frogs. However, the fault is usually the other way about, and it is almost impossible to get the microphone close enough to obtain a really good recording. A bird, for example, singing 20 ft from a microphone in the field would be considered close, but in the studio a director would be horrified at a singer who wished to sing from a distance of 20 ft. With birds and animals, the more one knows about their habits, the easier it is to guess what they will do next and what the chances are of getting the microphone close to them.

With birds—the wild creatures with which we at Cornell have had most experience—there are many tricks that sometimes help to get an acceptable recording. A study of the habits of birds reveals that many of them have favorite song perches. If these perches can be located, the microphone can be placed near one of them, and then it is only necessary to wait until the bird chooses to sing from that perch. Song perches often seem to serve as the "fence posts" outlining the area that a male bird considers to be his own territory, and in which he will not tolerate any other bird of his species except his mate. Often the most singing takes place along the boundaries of adjacent occupied territories.

When microphones are to be placed near song perches, an ability to climb trees or to heave a line over a selected branch above the perch is desirable. Sometimes it is a good idea to place two or more microphones at perches where the bird may be expected to sing; once the bird arrives, the appropriate microphone may be plugged into the recording amplifier or the appropriate microphone gain control opened up. If it is necessary to leave the microphone out for long periods, such as overnight, some precautions should be taken to protect it against rain or heavy dew. For this purpose we often tape a small cone, made of waterproof paper, to the microphone cable just above the microphone.

Sometimes a bird shows great interest in a reproduction of its own voice. While listening, the bird appears to be very conscious of his territorial rights and interested in driving out the other songster. One of our earliest experiences of this kind occurred with a mockingbird in Florida in 1935. We were reproducing a mockingbird's song in the house when we noticed a mockingbird at the window. We moved the loudspeaker into the yard and prepared a small perch for the bird in front of the speaker. As the song was reproduced, the bird first tried to find his rival, walking around the speaker and looking into the rear opening. Finally, perhaps in exasperation, perhaps in an effort to show that he was the better singer, the bird sat on the prepared perch and sang continuously for several minutes. It was a simple matter to shut off the loudspeaker and open the gain control of the nearby microphone through which an excellent song was recorded.

We now carry with us a small loudspeaker with about 50 ft of cable attached to it. The speaker can be used in the car to monitor the recorded sound, but we prefer to use earphones for this purpose unless there are visitors present who also want to hear the sounds. The primary purpose of the loudspeaker is to permit the bird to hear its own song in order to entice him to come closer (Fig. 7-2).

An almost perfect recording of a winter wren's song was secured in this manner. A winter wren was heard singing, high in a spruce tree. Normally these birds prefer the tangled roots of an overturned tree. Because we were anxious to record the song, we used the parabolic reflector, and except for wind whistling in the treetops, the recording was satisfactory. But hoping to do better, we placed our loudspeaker and a microphone without the reflector in the most likely looking spot among the roots of an overturned tree. The speaker had hardly started to reproduce the wren's notes when the bird came down to investigate. After a moment, the speaker was silenced and the recorder started. Almost at once the bird commenced to sing. He was not more than 2 ft from the microphone and was well protected from any wind by the towering forest and the tree roots. He continued to sing in the same spot for over half an hour.

Some birds sing best on the wing. We have occasionally solved the problem of recording the songs of such birds, for instance, the woodcock and chimney swift, by suspending the parabolic reflector from a tripod 20 ft high by means of a soft cord, which would prevent noise as the reflector was aimed about the sky.

One bird, the water ouzel, of the Western United States, seems to prefer to sing on a boulder in the midst of a rushing, roaring canyon torrent. The problem of obtaining a recording under these

Photo by, and courtesy of, A. A. Allen

Fig. 7-2. "The primary purpose of the loudspeaker is to . . . entice him to come closer."

conditions was solved by placing the microphone on the boulder. The bird returned, and finding this new and slightly higher perch, hopped upon the microphone. The only difficulty was the noise of his feet picked up by the microphone as he twisted about on it during his song on this new perch.

Some birds sing from high trees, and other from stones in the middle of a grassy field. Most birds prefer to be conspicuous when they sing. Perhaps the most difficult animals to record are those of the jungle, where the foliage is so thick that birds are seldom seen. In such a habitat the best one can do is to point the parabola by ear until the sound is heard loudest in the earphones. Often the remainder of the day is then spent trying to find out the kind of bird that has been recorded.

Photo by, and courtesy of, A. A. Allen

Fig. 7-3.   Professor Kellogg is shown in the process of recording frog songs.

When one is recording frogs, toads, or insects, it is often possible to place the microphone very close to the singing animal without disturbing his song for more than a moment (Fig. 7-3). The advantages are that little amplification is required and background sounds are reduced to a minimum. After recording such species, many of which occur in great numbers and may easily be captured, we usually bring home specimens so that there will be no question about identification.

When animals sing in chorus, as birds sometimes do and insects and amphibians often do, some experimenting must be done to determine the best balance between the nearest singers and those more distant. An effort should be made to create a recording that gives a true concept of the concert. It is quite possible to place the microphone so close to an individual that the song is unrecognizable, simply because it is never normally heard at such close range. On the other hand, it must be remembered that it is always much easier to create a medley of sound from individual recordings than it is to get the sound of an individual from a group recording. Whenever possible, good recordings of individuals should be secured. Background sounds may always be added later.

Although the very best recordings may be expected in the field when conditions approach those of a good studio, it is seldom that this ideal is reached. Usually, because of the many difficulties encountered in the field, the best recordings of birds will be those made with the aid of a parabolic reflector. Even with a reflector, a close approach is desirable. Under quiet conditions a bird's voice may sometimes be recorded satisfactorily from a distance of 100 yards; frequently a song recorded with a reflector is indistinguishable from one made at close range without the reflector.

RECORDING EQUIPMENT

GENERAL REQUIREMENTS

Today, when rather good recorders may be purchased even in drugstores, anyone can record sounds out-of-doors. Occasionally, a truly fine recording of a natural-history subject is "caught" by an amateur with such equipment. But usually, as with a beginner taking photographs of birds or other animals in the wild, it is necessary to have an interpreter to point out the creatures from the wealth of other detail that finds its way in through the lens or microphone.

For serious natural-history sound recording, however, a recorder with professional possibilities should be chosen. This means that although it will probably have to be a compromise between the best available and the best that the purchaser can afford, it should be portable and capable of giving service comparable to that of a good studio machine. The relatively inexpensive machines that are available today will produce excellent results compared to those of the very expensive and less efficient recorders of even a few years ago.

Until recently, field sound recordings were made on photographic film, which had to be developed before the recording could be heard, or on acetate phonograph disks, which were very sensitive to dust. Since neither of these media permitted re-use, they were basically more expensive than magnetic tape, which is now employed almost exclusively for this type of recording.

In selecting a tape recorder the choice of tape speed is quite important. The National Association of Radio and Television Broadcasters has chosen a tape speed of 15 in. per sec as the standard speed, with 7.5 in. per sec and 30 in. per sec as substandard speeds. Because of the economy of the 7.5-in. speed over the 15-in. speed, most broadcasting stations use 7.5 in. per sec. This speed is probably adequate for most broadcasting purposes. It is perfectly satisfactory for voice and gives a pleasing, though not a very high, quality of reproduction for music. Many home recorders use a speed of 3.75 in. per sec, and some operate as slowly as 1.875 in. per sec. These slower speeds of tape definitely do not produce high quality, and they have come into existence entirely for economic reasons. Machines with higher speeds do not necessarily have high quality simultaneously with low distortion and low flutter, but these desirable characteristics are more easily achieved at higher tape speeds.

Recorders that permit the recorded sound to be heard or monitored immediately after the sound is recorded are especially desirable for recording sounds in nature, since many natural sounds do not follow the pattern of man-made sounds. The high-frequency energy in the songs of many insects and in some bird songs is so great that a recording medium may be greatly overloaded long before the meter or recording indicator shows that the sound is of even normal loudness. The ability to listen to the recorded sound immediately—as it is recorded—enables the operator to adjust the gain far more intelligently than it could be adjusted while he was watching any type of indicator. Unfortunately, the recorders that permit immediate playback while recording are much more expensive than those without this feature.

FREQUENCY RESPONSE REQUIRED

The frequency range encountered in recording subjects out-of-doors is very great, extending all the way from the basso of a bull alligator or the drumming of the ruffed grouse, around 80 cycles, to the staccato trills of the blackpoll or the black-and-white warbler, which are above 12,000 cycles per second. The sounds made by many animals can be recorded satisfactorily with a machine that does not have a wide frequency response, but some of the sounds encountered out-of-doors tax the capabilities of the very best recorders which have been developed to date.

At 7.5 in. per sec, we have been unable to record many bird songs and many insect sounds; even at 15 in. per sec we have had difficulty in recording the songs of some birds, especially of warblers. This is true, not only because of the high frequency of bird voices and insect sounds, but because of the unusual distribution of energy throughout the sound spectrum that was mentioned earlier. However, some workers have had considerable success in recording songs of a few birds and some amphibian sounds at 3.75 in. per sec. As improvements are made in the science of recording, we may expect better recordings to be made at lower speeds; at the present time, however, it does not seem probable that high-quality recordings will soon be available at a tape speed lower than 7.5 in. per sec.

SIGNAL-TO-NOISE RATIO

The ratio of desired sound to other sounds that are introduced into the recording during the entire recording process is another consideration of importance. The more expensive machines may be expected to offer a somewhat better range of selectivity in this respect than do the cheaper machines, but cost is not always a good criterion. Among the various cheaper machines on the market today there is a great difference in this respect, and careful consideration should be given to this characteristic.

It has been found that the erase current on many recorders contributes a great deal of noise. Some workers find it desirable to erase the tape carefully on a bulk eraser before they go into the field and also to disable or by-pass the erase head, thus reducing noise from this source. The elimination of hum and other amplifier noises, which are probably responsible for most undesirable noises, is discussed later.

HAND-PORTABLE RECORDERS

Some progress is being made in the design of truly portable tape recorders of high quality. Such a recorder should weigh not more than 20 lb. It should have a flat frequency response up to 15,000 cy per sec with low distortion and a signal-to-noise ratio of at least 50 db. The recorder, which should be independent of commercial power lines, should not require battery changes more often than once a week in normal hard service. The recorder should serve as a reproducer, at least for the purpose of checking the recording process. Ideally, meters should show the recording level and also battery condition.

Several commercial recorders now on the market approach these requirements. The most successful ones drive the tape by means of a spring motor; this may be wound during operation without affecting the tape speed. A spring motor has two great, inherent advantages over an electric motor for service in outdoor recording of natural sounds: Its source of power is always available, and, secondly, it sets up no electric or magnetic noise which could be picked up by the amplifier. This second point is especially important, since the entire recorder is so small and the amplifier must have more than average gain for outdoor recording. The proximity of parts and the high gain make it most difficult to filter out any disturbance originating in an electric motor (see Fig. 7-4).

All amplifiers used to date in these small recorders have tubes of the directly heated filament type. These tubes, compared to those with a separate heater sleeve, are inherently noisy and very sensitive to vibration. The only advantage of the filament tube is the economy of "A" battery power. Even with filament tubes, however,

Courtesy of the Amplifier Corporation of America

Fig. 7-4. This spring-driven recorder, the Magnemite, was designed and developed in accordance with Professor Kellogg's specifications.

a signal-to-noise ratio of 50 db is claimed by some of the manufacturers. Before these tiny recorders become really satisfactory, new amplifiers will have to be developed especially for them. Such amplifiers would employ subminiature tubes available and possibly would be entirely enclosed in a block of waterproof plastic, permitting their use as a plug-in unit when desired.

Spring motors, too, will need the attention of the development engineer. Ball bearings will eliminate much of the present friction. Better gears and more appropriate gear ratios and mechanical filters will result in smoother and longer operation. Present governors are surprisingly good, but with better workmanship throughout, even these will perform better.

FIELD PRE-AMPLIFIER

Although it is possible to use a dynamic microphone (without an amplifier) 500 ft or more away from the recording equipment in the field, it is better to use a small battery-operated pre-amplifier whenever the performer is over 100 ft or so distant from the recorder. The pre-amplifier has three stages and normally is used quite close to the microphone.

The use of the pre-amplifier confers several advantages. The first two stages serve to amplify the signal from the microphone and transform it to an impedance of 500 ohms. The signal thus amplified is sufficiently strong for it to be transmitted over an open-wire line to the recorder without loss and without picking up any extraneous electrical noises. The third stage of the pre-amplifier is bridged across the output of the second stage and serves to amplify the signal still more for earphone monitoring. In this way, the man in the field can hear, through earphones, a well-amplified version of exactly what is coming in over the microphone; if the microphone is being used in conjunction with a parabolic reflector, sounds heard through the earphones may be used as an indication of whether or not the reflector is properly pointed, whether or not the source of the sound can be seen. Another advantage of this setup is that the man in the field with his earphones can hear any signal that has been put on the line at the recorder. This provides for two-way communication between the man in the field and the operator of the recording equipment in the sound car. This type of communication is a decided help, especially when the distance between the recorder and the microphone is great.

The total weight of the pre-amplifier and the earphones, under

15 lb, is light enough to be easily carried. Normally the field man transports this equipment by means of a shoulder strap. The 6-volt lantern battery, which operates the three heaters of the tubes, will last for more than a week in normal service. Although the use of a pre-amplifier is not absolutely necessary, another of its advantages —in addition to those mentioned above—is that it often serves to reduce hum, providing, as it does, a very clean signal reaching the recorder, a signal so strong that it does not need great amplification. The use of a pre-amplifier offers little, if any, inconvenience, in contrast with the many advantages it provides. Using a pre-amplifier, we have recorded over an open-wire line more than a mile long. In an emergency we have even used two strands of a barbed-wire fence to carry the signal for a considerable distance without noticeable loss or noise pickup.

POWER SUPPLY FOR FIELD RECORDING

GENERAL NEEDS

When one elects to do recording beyond the reach of an extension cord plugged into a commercial supply of power, an entirely new responsibility must be assumed. From reading advertisements about portable power equipment one gains the impression that supplying a constant source of electric power with unvarying frequency is a simple matter. Actually it is not easy to accomplish this in the field if the recordings made there are to compare with the best that may be obtained in the studio.

VOLTAGE REQUIREMENTS

Since the usual procedure is to take a standard recorder into the field, there is need of a constant power source of at least 115 volts at a frequency of 60 cy. Usually this power is obtained by means of a small rotating converter driven by storage batteries. The voltage from such a machine is likely to be far from constant. When the batteries are fully charged the voltage may be 120 volts or higher, but as the batteries lose their charge the voltage may.fall below

100 volts. This voltage drop is not too serious so far as the amplifiers or the motors are concerned, because there is usually more than enough power to operate the recorder. But since in most tape recorders both the bias voltage and the erase voltage vary directly with the line voltage, this variation becomes a very serious problem. Many recorders will not erase properly with low voltage, and almost all tape recorders are very sensitive to changes in bias voltage. It is true that if we are after only such quality as is so often heard on the air with apologies and attributed to the great difficulties under which the program was recorded, or if the program is intended only to amuse our friends, such severe voltage changes may be tolerated. On the other hand, if field material is to be recorded that will stand up against the best recorded in professional studios, voltage variations of more than a very small percentage cannot be tolerated.

FREQUENCY REQUIREMENTS

The best tape recorders have very smooth tape motion, and often the speed control is better than 0.1 or 0.2 per cent. The average speed of these machines is controlled by the line frequency. Of some small rotary converters, it is claimed that the speed may be controlled within one cycle; that is, one part in sixty, which is almost two per cent. This variation is enough to cause a clearly audible change in the pitch of an organ pipe, for example. Again, if the field work is to compete with that of the studio, the variation in frequency of the line voltage must be controlled and held to less than one cycle, perhaps to as small an amount as one quarter of a cycle.

BATTERY-OPERATED POWER SUPPLY

The power supply such as that shown in Fig. 7-5 is able, by means of normal adjustment, to give a voltage of any value between 100 and 125 volts throughout the useful charge of the batteries. The design is not original; in its present form it was suggested by members of the staff of the School of Electrical Engineering at Cornell

University. The rotary converter is rated at 300 watts output, more than sufficient for almost any of the various tape recorders on the market today. The novel feature of the circuit is a filament transformer designed to supply 31.5 volts at 10 amperes from a 110-volt line. The voltage to the primary of this transformer is sup-

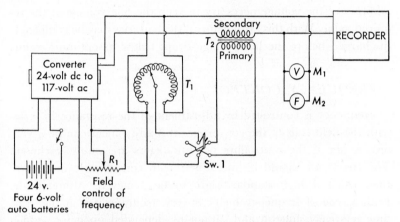

Fig. 7-5. Circuit diagram showing the method by which the frequency and the voltage supplied to an ac-operated field recorder are controlled.

$T_1 =$ General Radio Variac, 100 watts, controls the ac voltage transmitted to T_2.

$T_2 =$ A 115-volt to 31.5-volt, 10-ampere filament transformer. It controls the addition or subtraction of voltage in accordance with the position of Sw_1.

$R_1 =$ The rheostat, by controlling the speed of the converter, controls the frequency.

$Sw_1 =$ Double-pole, double-throw switch. In accordance with the position of Sw_1, voltage is added to, or subtracted from, the ac line to the recorder by T_2.

$M_1 =$ A 0-volt to 150-volt ac meter.

$M_2 =$ A 60-cy Frahm type of frequency meter.

plied by the smallest-sized Variac (a voltage transformer which is variable), which gets its energy directly from the output of the rotary converter. The double-pole, double-throw switch serves to change the polarity of the transformer output so that the low voltage which is in series with the rotary-converter output may either be added to or subtracted from the line voltage. Thus, when the batteries are freshly charged and the line voltage is likely to be high, the Variac may be adjusted to cause subtraction of the excessive voltage. As the output of the converter falls, the Variac is turned closer and closer to its no-output voltage until it is completely inoperative, at which time the switch is thrown. As the voltage of the converter drops still further, the Variac is again adjusted to cause addition of the voltage necessary to keep the line voltage at the required value. With this arrangement, the batteries may be completely discharged before the line voltage drops below its optimum value.

FREQUENCY CONTROL

Frequency is controlled by adjustment of the resistance in series with the field coils of the converter—this adjustment can be a very precise one if the controlling potentiometers are carefully chosen. The frequency should be monitored with considerably more care than usual if high standards are to be achieved. Although the Frahm type of frequency meter is very accurate, it is at the same time relatively sluggish and cannot be depended upon for sudden changes in line frequency. The dynamometer type of frequency meter, such as the Hickok model S-49, is very sensitive to frequency changes but is likely to experience considerable drift with temperature. The use of these two types of frequency meters in parallel, which results in possible control of better than a quarter of a cycle, is desirable.

Another type of frequency monitoring that could probably be used to advantage would be a stroboscopic disk mounted on the flywheel of the capstan and illuminated by a flashing light driven by an oscillator with exceptionally good frequency stability.

Even when every effort is made to achieve good frequency stability, a further precaution should be taken, that of occasionally sounding the note of a good pitch pipe near the microphone while the recorder is running. We use a pipe sounding "A," 440 cy per sec, for this purpose. This additional check is desirable since it will expose any error in tape speed stemming from any cause and occurring at any time during the recording and reproducing processes.

ROTARY CONVERTERS AND BATTERIES

Rotary converters that supply 115-volt alternating current are available in models which may be operated from almost any dc voltage. It often seems easiest to operate the converter directly from the sound-car battery, but this is not always wise. Usually a single storage battery will operate the converter for about one hour, but if the battery is discharged too much, it will not start the car. On some modern cars the generators are referred to as high-output generators. These have a maximum output of about 35 amperes at a motor speed equivalent to about 35 miles per hour. This type of generator may be used for charging the recording batteries, but it is slow-charging and must be operated at high speed if it is to be very effective. Having used most combinations of from one to twenty 6-volt storage batteries, we have now settled on four standard 6-volt car batteries—standard because they are available anywhere—and these are a workable compromise.

LEECE-NEVILLE SYSTEM

Charging batteries for the sound car used to present an annoying problem, if not a real chore. This has been solved in a most satisfactory manner by replacing the car generator with a Leece-Neville alternator and associated equipment. Heavy, double-pole, double-throw switches connect the recording batteries in series for recording, and in parallel—across the car system—for charging. A voltage regulator tends to keep the batteries at a predetermined voltage, usually about 7 volts, and the Leece-Neville system supplies sufficient current, up to 100 amperes, to provide this voltage. Two very great advantages of this system are that it will furnish about 25 to 35 amperes of current at idling speeds of the car's motor and reaches full output at a motor speed equivalent to 12 miles per hour. Under these conditions the batteries recharge in less time than was required to discharge them, and usually they are kept fully charged by the normal operation of the car.

It would seem, from our experience in the field, that any setup for recording out-of-doors should be able to operate at full efficiency for at least one hour before it becomes necessary to recharge the batteries. The power-supply system described above will operate most recorders continuously for four or five hours at full efficiency.

SPECIAL DESIGN

Somewhat greater efficiency in the use of battery power may be achieved by designing the recorder, or rewiring it, so that the tube filaments operate directly from the 6-volt storage batteries. Motors may be chosen that will also operate directly from storage batteries; thus one may avoid the loss which always occurs whenever power is changed from direct to alternating current. The high voltage necessary to operate the amplifiers with this modification is usually obtained directly from dry batteries or from a very small dynamotor or vibrator-power pack operated by the storage batteries. The difficulty with either of such systems is that it is almost certain to be very special and unique. The various units of the system will operate only in conjunction with the components for which they are designed. Neither the power supply nor the recorder may readily be used with other equipment, and consequently, the problem of maintenance becomes much more complicated. Using a power supply that produces 60-cycle current and a commercially designed recorder has many advantages. Whenever commercial power is available, plugging the recorder into the line directly will save batteries and also the trouble of monitoring the voltage and frequency. With a good supply of 60-cycle power in the field, any recorder may be given a trial, or in the case of breakdown, another recorder may be used while the regular one is being repaired.

MAINTAINING FIELD EQUIPMENT

SPECIAL REQUIREMENTS

The best equipment that one can afford requires constant care to keep it working properly for optimum results. Even radio broadcast professionals tend to overlook faults until the defects become obvious enough to be apparent to nontechnical listeners. But distortion or trouble on a radio program is seldom serious. At worst, the penalty is a few thousand dollars for missing a big commercial. But to miss the chance of a lifetime out in nature, when every special condition in the field for the rarest of rare recordings is at hand—except that the recorder won't work—is quite a different matter. The combination of unusual animal performance, perfect habitat, and weather conditions may never be experienced again.

TESTING AND CHECKING

Only the best-run studios carry out a routine of regularly testing and checking all equipment, but those that do are rewarded by serious trouble occurring only infrequently. The average naturalist, amateur or professional, is not equipped, either through training or by possession of good service equipment, to handle all the technical problems that may be encountered with modern recording equipment. But it is almost a necessity that a naturalist, realizing he cannot anticipate or solve these problems, cultivate the acquaintance of local engineers or technicians who may be called upon for help. Good service equipment costs more than most recorders, but regular checks of field equipment with oscillators, oscilloscopes, and other measuring equipment are almost inescapable if the recorder is to be kept at its best. Many of the technical tests are best performed in a laboratory and by competent engineers.

The naturalist who is using recording equipment should diligently study his equipment. Practice in using and adjusting it should enable him to develop critical, though perhaps nontechnical, listening tests that will permit him to evaluate the performance of his recorder. He should be able to check incipient faults before they become serious. Almost anyone can learn to check and align the heads of a recorder by means of a standard test tape, and such a tape should always be carried if the equipment is used far from service facilities. It is incredible how distortion and other faults can slip by unnoticed until the recording is listened to later, when one can concentrate on the recorded sound without the necessity of watching the bird, watching the recorder, and trying to make everything operate perfectly.

USE OF EARPHONES

Good earphones are important maintenance equipment in the field, since through their use symptoms of trouble may often be heard long before it begins to show up on the meters. Low-frequency response in earphones is not usually important so far as recording most sounds in nature is concerned, but such response is very important for detecting hum, which may not otherwise be observed until the recording is played back later on a wide-range system. It is advisable to have a long extension cord available for use with the earphones when one is trying to correct hum or other trouble in the equipment. If the earphones are worn while working on the equipment, it is relatively easy to make adjustments and to observe immediately whether they help the situation or make it worse.

ELIMINATION OF HUM

One of the most common faults of amplifying systems is unwanted noise, most of which, because of its low-frequency character, is classed as hum. Because of the unorthodox power sources used and the proximity of the various elements of the recording system when used under field conditions, hum—or, rather, its elimination—is a special problem almost invariably closely associated with recording in the field. Although most hum can be traced directly to the ac source of power, there are some exceptions to this statement. For example, hum may result from an uneven movement of the recording medium, such as sometimes occurs in motion-picture recording when the sprocket jerks the film while moving it. Occasionally hum will be observed in a recorder that is entirely operated from direct current. Hum in such instances may be caused by commutator ripple in the recording motor, or it may be picked up by the input lines from adjacent power systems.

Usually hum can be traced to one of three sources: The high-voltage power supply may be defective; the filtering may be inadequate; or the generator may be too close to the amplifier. As to this last, most input amplifiers or pre-amplifiers are very sensitive, and hum is readily picked up by them, either by magnetic induction or by electrostatic transfer of hum voltages.

When 60-cy power is being generated very near the recording equipment, strong magnetic fields are always present in both the primary and secondary circuits of the generator. Since these varying magnetic fields are readily picked up by input transformers or by input lines, great care must often be exercised in running the lines or in positioning the equipment in such ways that the hum voltages will be kept very low, or if possible, will be completely balanced out. Sometimes placing a low-resistance choke in series with the storage-battery leads helps greatly and tends to suppress the high-frequency ripple from the commutator, which often flows through the batteries and the primary leads. If the equipment is housed in a car, some improvement in hum-reduction is often secured by grounding one side of the storage-battery system to the car frame. This can be determined only by trial and error. The best method of fighting hum is to set up the system as though a recording were being made and then to turn the gain control up to full volume. Wearing earphones with sufficiently long cords, experimentally determine ways of increasing or decreasing the hum—by rotating or moving the various pieces of equipment and/or by moving the cables about. No matter what changes are necessary, hum must be eliminated before any recorder can do a first-class job.

USING AND PRESERVING NATURAL-HISTORY SOUND RECORDINGS

IDENTIFICATION

One of the first uses to which recordings of birds and other animals were naturally put was that of identifying sounds out-of-doors. At first the recordings were used mainly in giving classroom instruction at Cornell University, but as information about their existence became more widely known, there was a general demand for them, and several albums of sound recordings of birds and amphibians have been published. These recordings are used in schools and camps, museums, and by individuals. Many persons find them useful for refreshing their memory of the songs and calls in nature that they haven't heard for a long time. Especially enthusiastic about such recordings are sightless people, to whom the recordings open up the whole field of natural-history sounds. Often a blind person will learn, through sound alone, much more about birds and other animals in their environments than will others through good vision in addition to sound. The Library of Congress has made available to the blind, through its *Talking Book* series, many natural-history recordings published to date.

USE IN TAXONOMY

Many species of birds and other animals are more easily distinguished from their close relatives by the sounds they make than by any other means. Taxonomists have long recognized this fact, but until sounds could be faithfully recorded, it was not possible to study them objectively and compare critically the songs of closely related groups. Now, as a result of high-quality recordings, graphic representation of the songs of birds, for instance, may be used to show the pitch, duration, and loudness of each note. The audio spectrograph, which has also been used for this purpose, shows not only pitch and duration of the notes but also their harmonic content. Such graphic analyses may be charted or printed on paper. Even now it is agreed that many common birds sing differently in different parts of their respective habitats. How constant these differences really are is not known because of the difficulty of comparing songs objectively. It may well be that many birds may be recognized by their song differences to the extent that we can tell in what part of its habitat the bird originated. Only future studies that include analyses of sound recordings will reveal this. Taxonomists are only now beginning to use these new tools, but the future is very promising.

BEHAVIORAL AND PSYCHOLOGICAL STUDIES

Very little is known about the language of animals, but some progress is being made in this field through sound recording. Calls or other sounds of animals observed in connection with specific activities may be recorded. These same sounds may then be played back to the same or other animals, and the responses noted. Sounds associated with fear, pleasure, hunger, or distress may be recorded, analyzed, and studied in much the same way.

MAKING AND PRESERVING NATURAL-HISTORY SOUNDS

Although recording sounds of nature requires more time and patience and perhaps more skill than does any other type of recording, there are many incentives, chief among which are the scientific value, the aesthetic satisfaction, and time advantage afforded. This last makes it possible to listen to and study these sounds at any time of the day, month, or year. Being able to listen to or study bird song in midwinter, for instance, has both educational and aesthetic merit, at least for students of ornithology.

There is only a small demand for the publication of these sounds, and no one in this field of recording has ever come near to making his expenses. Since restricted educational uses and personal satisfaction and pleasure are about the only rewards, the work must be carried on in connection with scientific studies or as an avocation. That it offers fascinating challenges no one can doubt.

Now that the advent of tape recording makes possible the recording of these sounds more easily, it is probable that many biologists and others interested in natural history will begin to make contributions of recorded material for study. The role of the biologist or naturalist is important, for all sounds recorded in nature must be identified authentically if they are to prove of greatest use. Unless the biologist is willing to delve deeply into the engineering aspects of the problem, he will have to work closely with someone who has the ability to keep recording equipment in good operating condition. This fact cannot be overemphasized. The possibility that unfaithful or distorted recordings will give wrong impressions—or even lead to wrong conclusions—is greater in the field of natural-history sound recording than it is in natural-history photography, since sounds, unlike photographs, cannot be readily subjected to critical analysis and comparison with originals. When pictorial analyses of sounds are made for study, the form of the picture presentation is usually such that it cannot readily be resynthesized into sound. Therefore, if the original sound recording is defective, the analysis of it and the conclusions drawn from it are likely to be inaccurate.

Natural-history sound recording is a relatively new art, but it is not too early to give some thought to the problem of preserving recordings for future generations and for future study. Some recordings of sound will naturally be published as disk recordings, and these, if they achieve wide distribution, will be relatively permanent. But many important sound recordings will never be published. Compared to books or periodicals, they demand a wider audience before their production and distribution become economically practical. Unlike periodicals, they have no advertising to carry much of the cost.

Since observations of sound cannot be published in journals in a manner that permits the sound to be recreated, some other way must be found for preserving important recordings, or they will be lost. It is not conceivable that a periodical publication of phonograph disks of natural-history sound observations would, at the present time, have wide appeal or adequate support; it does seem that a magnetic-tape library of natural-history sounds might be a very practical solution to the problem of preserving and making available this unique fund of knowledge.

A magnetic-tape library of natural-history sounds would have as one of its important features a catalog listing all the recordings of each separate species with complete data for each recording. These data would include, with the catalog number, the place, time, temperature, type of sound, quality, person recording, authority for identification, and restrictions on use. Wide distribution of the catalog among libraries and educational institutions would enable anyone interested to learn much about these recordings. Listings for later recordings would, of course, be added in revisions of the catalog. Insofar as possible, the recorded sounds of one species of animal would be kept, in the order of accession, on a single reel; each recording unit would be identified on the reel by a corresponding number announced prior to its recording on the tape.

Anyone wishing to obtain copies of any of this material could do so by sending one or more reels of magnetic tape to the library, and high-quality copies of the desired reels would be made on the user's own tape. This would greatly reduce the bookkeeping usually associated with a lending library, since no return of material would be involved.

Ideally, such a library would be set up under a continuing grant or an endowment that would cover the costs of housing and operation. A service charge could be made to cover the actual time charges for re-recording, but these charges should be kept small to avoid discouraging use of the collection.

Cornell University, as a result of its 35 years of natural-history recording, has a large collection of sound recordings that could serve as a basis for this kind of library, but it is hoped that others doing field recording would wish to store copies of their recordings in the library. This procedure would automatically make their work more widely useful and would also provide a degree of permanence and a workable system of preservation and use not ordinarily available to such material. Ownership protection would be given to the respective contributors of recorded material. Users of the material would understand that the primary purpose of the collection was for scientific study and that the material might not be used commercially in any manner—whether for radio, television, motion pictures, or as illustrative material of public lectures—without written permission from the owner of the original recording.

Unless some orderly method of preservation, such as is suggested here, becomes an actuality, many recordings of high scientific value will be lost. Unpublished recordings may be referred to in literature, and even diagrammed with considerable accuracy, but up to the present, and probably for a long time to come, there is no substitute for a recording, since it alone permits reproduction of original sound. It is conceivable that, when reports of studies involving sound are published in the literature, reference would be made to specific tapes in such a central library, and further, those interested could secure for critical study recorded copies of the actual sounds on which the original study was based.

Tape recording has opened to naturalists a new field of investigation. Every effort should be made to coordinate the activities of those interested so that the results of past, current, and future recordings of sound in nature may be used most effectively.

8

Maintenance

Magnetic recorders are subject to the same kinds of trouble that afflict any electronic apparatus. In addition, a recorder is a machine with moving parts, some requiring lubrication and others that do their work properly because of friction. To top it off, we have to deal with magnetic fields, which we can hardly measure without special equipment. We must, therefore, adopt such practices in maintaining recording equipment as will stave off its major failures; we can do this if we become familiar with indications of approaching troubles and forestall them.

Consider that our example in this chapter is a professional tape recorder in daily use. Other kinds of recorders suffer from troubles similar to those we shall consider, and they will respond to the same kind of care, whatever the magnetic medium. Wherever the instructions in this chapter are at variance with the instructions issued by the manufacturer for the care and maintenance of your equipment, follow the service manual's instructions. There are generally good reasons for its specific instructions.

MAINTENANCE ROUTINE

Maintaining equipment in good operating condition requires painstaking attention to details, and this is doubly true where rotating mechanical parts are integrated with the equipment. (Flutter must be reduced to a maximum of 0.1 per cent at 3000 cy per sec for best results. To maintain this condition requires excellent mechanical know-how.) Maintenance in a well-ordered magnetic-recording studio may be divided into four general categories: the daily routine examination, the periodic test and lubrication, repair methods, and care of associated parts and media.

DAILY ROUTINE EXAMINATION

The daily routine examination should not take more than 30 minutes, once the recordist has become accustomed to it. During this time the machines should be warming up so that they will maintain proper speed when recording begins. Before the machines are used the first time during the program day they should be loaded with tape and allowed to run for at least 15 minutes. The ordinary tape recorder will not run at normal speed unless all bearings are at operating temperature, which is at least 65° F. Most homes and studios will be at this temperature or higher. Any doubt as to whether the machine is running at the proper speed may be checked by the pitch-pipe or tone-comparison test that is described later in this chapter.

The magnetic head surfaces and the surfaces of all the tape guides, rollers, and stabilizer arms contacted by the tape in its normal path should be cleaned thoroughly at least once every day. Most tape that is now manufactured does not leave much residue, but occasionally you may use tape that does. This residue may become thick enough on the heads to hold the tape away from the head surface, resulting in poor recording of high frequencies. When it accumulates on the switch-actuating arms or tape guides, it can cause periodic "sticking" that will produce "wows" and irregularities in recording or reproduction. Unlubricated tape may vibrate, causing strange "squeals."

Improperly spliced tape may deposit some adhesive bits on a head surface, thus making that particular head practically unresponsive to any but very low frequencies. There should be good contact between the head and the magnetic coating—even infinitesimal spacing will cut down the high-frequency response tremendously.

Composition-rubber rollers and drive pucks should be cleaned with the cleanser specified for those parts in the manufacturer's service manual. One maker suggests grain alcohol for the purpose, another, soap and water. Carbon tetrachloride may soften the rubber compound and, in time, change its driving dimensions (besides loosing injurious vapors).

The capstan itself should be kept free of oil or dirt. This capstan is generally a metal shaft against which the pressure roller is tightly pressed, thus driving the tape held between them. In some early recorders the pressure roller was not used. Instead, the capstan was of quite large diameter and was surfaced with a gripping material like cork-rubber compound. If such surfaces are not kept clean, the result will be constant slipping of the tape.

Soft camel's-hair brushes should be used to brush away free dirt and dust around the heads. Lintless cloths or wooden sticks with tightly wound cotton batting at one end may be used to clean the heads. Avoid scratching the head surfaces or leaving any lint or carbon tetrachloride residue on them. If carbon tetrachloride is used for cleaning, be sure to wipe the surfaces with a dry soft cloth after the surfaces are *dry*.

Head Magnetization. A record head that becomes magnetized will make distorted recordings; these will be very noisy. Higher-than-normal noise noted when reproducing a tape recording may be due to magnetization of one of the heads. Heads may become magnetized accidentally in a number of ways. A simple test to ascertain whether a head is magnetized can be made in this way: Load some new or freshly erased tape on the recorder. Provide yourself with some means of measuring the output from the recorder, either a decibel meter or an ac voltmeter with the proper range. Play the tape for about 20 sec or just long enough to permit you to note the reading of noise on the meter. Then after rewinding the tape, play back *the same section of tape* as before, and note the noise reading. If the noise *increases by any amount* after this operation has been repeated about ten times, one of the heads is magnetized. The magnetization may be slight or serious—the noise reading will give a fairly good indication of its extent.

Note that the test for magnetized heads will not tell you *which* head is magnetized, merely that *one* of them is. The erase head can hardly become magnetized because it normally erases when actuated by the alternating current. If, however, through some defect in the erase oscillator or amplifier, direct current is fed to the erase head, it may become magnetized. In that event you will have to search for the cause of the trouble, which will probably be found in

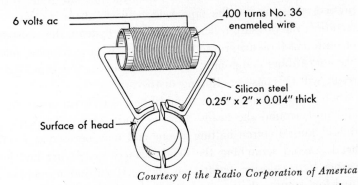

6 volts ac

400 turns No. 36
enameled wire

Silicon steel
0.25" x 2" x 0.014" thick

Surface of head

Courtesy of the Radio Corporation of America

Fig. 8-1. Diagram showing the construction details of a head demagnetizer. (From the instruction manual for the RCA RT-11A Professional Magnetic Tape Recorder, MI-11912-A, page 27)

a leaky condenser. Magnetization of the head may also be caused by a faulty condenser allowing direct current to leak through the record head's coil, thus making a dc electromagnet out of it. These kinds of faulty components are not common, however. Most magnetization of head cores occurs accidentally. Remember that *direct current* magnetizes the head cores; therefore, avoid testing the head coils with a dc ohmmeter.

Heads may become magnetized by surges of current (transients) during motor switching, proximity to a magnet, a lightning discharge, or undue mechanical strain in head cores because of faulty annealing. Heads are sometimes magnetized also by their proximity to poorly shielded drive motors. In any event, it is not difficult to check periodically to find out whether there is a magnetized head. The cure is positive and practical.

Head Demagnetization. Heads may easily be demagnetized, just about as easily and as quickly as we erase tape. The recorder should be disconnected from the supply current, and the head should properly be disconnected from its associated circuit, although heads have been demagnetized while connected. A head demagnetizer (such as the Audio Head Demagnetizer) can be purchased from any large supply house of radio and electronic materials and used as indicated in the instructions, or you can make one. A unit, suggested by the RCA RT-11A Magnetic Tape Recorder Service Manual, may be constructed as follows (see Fig. 8-1):

1. Obtain a silicon-steel transformer lamination 1/4-in. wide, 2 in. long, and at least 0.014 in. thick.
2. Wrap insulating tape or paper around the center portion, and wind approximately 400 turns of No. 36 enameled wire on it.
3. Bend the iron strip into a U-shape so that the ends can be placed in contact with the surfaces of the head.
4. Connect a 6-volt ac source to the windings (this may be obtained from a heavy-duty 6-volt filament transformer).
5. Bring the ends of the U-shaped lamination against the head surface slowly. Then remove the lamination from the vicinity of the head very slowly, taking several seconds to move it completely away. Repeat this operation several times, being careful not to scratch the surface of the head. It is a good idea to wrap one or two layers of cellophane tape around the lamination tips that come in contact with the head surface to avoid any accidental scratching.
6. After having performed the demagnetization operation, remove the demagnetizer from the vicinity of the head, and then disconnect it from the ac source.

All demagnetizers, whether the source voltage is 6-volt or 110-volt alternating current or higher, should be used in the same manner. The time a demagnetizer should be left against the head surface varies with the magnetic field of the demagnetizer. If the manufacturer's instructions are not closely followed in this respect (as they should be), the time needed to demagnetize the head should be determined by tests.

Pre-recording Check. The pre-recording routine should include a rapid check of the noise level of recorded tape. Load the machine with new tape (or tape that has been erased) and, with the input control turned off or short-circuited, record for two or three minutes. Then run this part of the tape back, and play it with the monitor loudspeaker turned on full. The amount of "hiss" should be very little more from the freshly recorded tape than from a playback of new or previously erased tape. The noise or "hiss" that you hear should be smooth in character and free from erratic noises or "bumps."

If the noise level from the recorded tape is satisfactory, record the tone from an oscillator at a level 10 db less than normal level for the recorder (which is usually adjusted so that the indicating meter will read at zero decibels for peaks of volume). The tone should be recorded at least at three different frequencies, depending upon the frequency range of the recorder. For ordinary professional work, tones of 100, 3500, and 10,000 cy will do very well. These tone signals should be reproduced at the same level as that at which they were recorded.

One further precaution, before actual recording is begun, is needed only when recording away from the studio. That is, a check of the ac voltage and frequency. If these are not standard, make a notation on the reel or reel label so that the conditions of supply voltage and frequency may be duplicated when you get back to the studio and re-record the tape for later use. Of course, if a variable-frequency power pack is available, it is a simple matter to bring its frequency to 60 cy per sec or to the frequency of the studio's current, and to set the voltage at the amount needed, ordinarily 115- to 120-volt alternating current.

Some manufacturers of coated tape recommend that, before it is recorded, the tape be run off to the take-up reel and then rewound. If desired, one may perform just half of this operation: run off the tape to another reel and use this reel as the supply reel. The reason for this operation is that tape may be too tightly or too loosely wound, depending upon the conditions under which it has been stored since leaving the factory. Some rounds of tape may be under stress, which will be relieved by the unwinding process. If the stresses are not relieved, they may give rise to vibration or jerking that may mar the recording, depending upon the type of drive system the recorder employs and its mechanical condition. Also, some kinds of tape tend to stick, layer to layer, after long storage, and the rewinding operation will alleviate this condition.

The unwinding operation also gives the careful recordist an opportunity to check the tape for kinks and poorly made splices and to clean the coated surface. If tape has been properly spliced (in the way specified in Chapter 10 on editing), with all materials cut at 45-degree angles or less, there will be no sticking or adhering of the tape at the splice to the next layer of tape. Occasionally new tape contains splices, made at a 90-degree angle, from which adhesive has exuded, owing to extremely tight winding or improper storage conditions, to the adjacent rounds of tape. It is necessary either to cut out the affected portion and make a proper splice or to wash off the adhesive carefully with a cloth dampened with carbon tetrachloride. Dusting the splice with a tiny dab of talcum powder, after the splice has been cleaned, will generally prevent further sticking at that point. In most studios, however, badly spliced tape is cut out and thrown away. Tape may be cleaned by running it at high speed past a lint-free pad, dry or dampened with carbon tetrachloride.

PERIODIC TEST, CLEANING, AND LUBRICATING

After every hundred hours of use, approximately, the magnetic recording equipment should be thoroughly cleaned and lubricated according to the manufacturer's specifications; the tubes should be tested; and tests should be made that will reveal any condition requiring replacement of parts or extensive repairs. It is recommended that flutter measurements be made at this time and that commercially available flutter-test units be used.

Dust and dirt should be vacuum-cleaned from every part of the recorder. All tubes should be removed and tested, and the tube prongs should be cleaned, first with carbon tetrachloride or alcohol, and if corroded, with "crocus cloth" (a very fine abrasive cloth). (Very frequently buzzes and hums are traceable to poor contact between a tube prong and its socket.) Plug-in connectors should be cleaned in the same way. Where possible, rotating switches may be cleaned by spraying them with carbon tetrachloride while they are being rotated. Do not attempt to adjust or clean relay contacts unless you are familiar with this exacting operation. More relays are ruined by inexpert repairmen than are repaired by them.

The brake bands and other dry frictional surfaces, drive belts, and so forth should be wiped clean with a cloth moistened with carbon tetrachloride unless other instructions are given by the manufacturer.

Lubricate the machine as the manufacturer specifies, always, and *do not substitute another grade of oil or grease for that which is specified*. The viscosities of the lubricants have a direct bearing upon the speed of travel of the tape at normal temperature and upon the wear at bearing points. Do not drip oil anywhere but where it belongs. Oil or grease in the wrong places can do considerable damage; oil should never be allowed to get on frictional surfaces, on contact surfaces, or in a coil winding.

In a well-designed machine the tape should bear only on the head surfaces and guides and on itself while the recorder is in operation. There should be no scraping against the top plate of the recorder. The tape should ride smoothly between the capstan and pressure roller, without any tendency to ride up or down on the pressure roller. Wear of the tape guides may cut slots in them in which the tape may tend to jam or stick; these guides should be replaced when necessary or rotated in a way that will prevent the tape from falling into the grooves.

A professional recorder in good condition should be able to record piano music without noticeable flutter (less than 0.1 per cent is within reach), wow, or any kind of excessive distortion. With machines of the "home" type, recording of piano music shows up imperfections in the drive. Wows are long-lasting changes in speed;

flutter is the term used for fast changes, instantaneous in nature, which are not ordinarily heard as a change in speed but which contribute to the total distortion. Any irregularity in the drive mechanism can cause these phenomena.

A clump of dirt or a bit of adhesive on a driving or driven member, an out-of-round condition of a rubber roller, a belt with a wide spot—any of these can cause troublesome irregularities. Much can be done to eliminate out-of-round conditions in the drive merely by the judicious use of a file and sandpaper, provided one is very careful to correct an existing fault and does not file enough to change the speed of tape travel excessively. A drive irregularity or imbalance is self-proclaiming. If a wow occurs once every second, for instance, we should look for something that revolves once a second. We may find that a tape reel is bent and is sticking periodically or that a rubber drive wheel, which has been ruined by oil, has a flat spot. Common sense will almost always point to the cause of trouble. When found, the cause can be corrected by replacing the defective part, or by remachining if the maintenance of exact tape speed is not an absolute necessity.

Pressure Pads. Varying speed in machines that use pressure pads to hold tape in contact with the heads is often due to variation of the friction of the pressure-pad surface. Pressure pads, if kept clean and at the proper tension, should permit smooth travel of the tape. If they do not, the pressure should be checked by means of some kind of pressure-testing gauge and should be adjusted according to the manufacturer's instructions. Note especially that the pressure necessary for proper operation depends a great deal upon the kind of tape used. Paper tape requires more pressure than does plastic tape, and different types of plastic tape will operate best at particular pad-pressures. (If your recorder uses pressure pads and requires frequent adjustments, you should own a tension-measuring gauge that reads in ounces of pull.)

Other kinds of mechanical troubles are encountered in all kinds of recorders. It is hardly necessary to detail them here, since they are noted in the service manual that can be obtained from the manufacturer of your recorder. But a final word of warning should be inserted: Do not attempt to repair your recorder unless you are qualified and equipped to do so.

Head Wear. Most magnetic recorders in use now require that the medium be in close contact with the head surfaces for optimum results. Another fact that we must consider in our use of magnetic recorders is this: The headcore metal must be made of magnetically soft metal, that is, metal that will *not* retain magnetism and become a permanent magnet, thus begetting noise. Magnetically soft metals are also inclined to be physically soft in comparison to the hard steels. Thus we are confronted with this situation: If the contact of the coating to the head surface is good for recording, we get head wear; consequently the higher the speed of travel of the medium, the faster the wear takes place. Even with polished and lubricated tape surfaces, the heads wear considerably. (We are considering now the usual magnetic recorder; for special purposes there are both noncontact heads and even very hard-cored heads.) Head wear may or may not have serious effects on the recording, depending upon how the head core is constructed. Some head cores are so constructed that as they wear the gap becomes wider and wider. In the record head, *unequal widening* of the flux path results in poorer recording; in the reproduce head *any lengthening* of the gap results in a drop in the output at *higher frequencies*. You can understand now why all manufacturers warn: *Do not operate the recorder at high speeds while the medium is in contact with the heads!*

Noncontact heads (at present used in specially constructed machines that will be described later in this book) are, of course, not subject to physical wear. In the future, probably, newly designed noncontact heads for audio recording and very hard-cored heads (contact type) will come into general use.

The kind of wear that takes place follows directly from the fault —in design or operation or media—that produces the wear. If the machine is a tape recorder, for instance, and depends upon electric braking of the supply platform to keep the tape under tension so that tape-to-head contact will be good, the following may happen: (1) If the braking tension is too great, the tape will curl, thus wearing the head surfaces unevenly. (2) If the heads are not properly aligned, they will wear at an angle. (3) If the tape is consistently run, in contact with the heads, at high speeds, it will wear "shelves" in the cores. The same effect is also noticeable after long use.

Tape recorders that rely on pressure pads to keep the tape against the head cores are heir to other kinds of head wear. If the pressure pad contacts the tape at an angle, the tape will wear the head concavely.

From what we have seen so far, uneven and rapid wear of magnetic heads can be avoided by reasonable care and careful handling of the machine. We must never forget that, from the crudest and cheapest machine to the most expensive professional apparatus, the magnetic recorder is a complicated piece of equipment in which many different components affect each other for good or ill, depending upon how well their interrelated functions are discharged.

Head cores that have worn down unevenly *can* be reground to specification if the magnetic gap has not been unduly enlarged. However, the process of finish-grinding and lapping of a magnetic head surface is fraught with peril for even the expert machinist who has precision grinding equipment and all the "know-how" in the world. One must be careful not to overheat the core metal nor destroy the insulation between laminations; a ragged or uneven edge should not be left at the gap. These are only a few of the cautions. "Shelves" worn in the head-core surface may be removed by grinding the surface by hand on a fine stone, preferably wet.

Some magnetic heads of recent manufacture are reversible. We would expect that the ordinary magnetic head could be reversed, after one side is worn and that the other side could then be used. But such is normally not the case. One side of the head-core assembly is spaced properly and polished, but the other side contains no spacer in the gap, is left rough, and in some instances, the gap is soldered together for the attachment of a grounding strip at that point. The employment of heads with the reversible feature would be an innovation welcomed by the great majority of recorder users.

It was mentioned, in Chapter 3 on recording media, that tape or film that has been stored under poor conditions of humidity and temperature tends to curl, the coated side becoming slightly concave. Since the coated side contacts the head surfaces, this condition of the medium makes for uneven head wear as well as for poor recording.

Head Alignment. The manufacturer of your machine is the proper source of exact instructions on methods of adjustment for proper head alignment. But we can discuss the various adjustments here in general and learn how they affect the quality of recording.

In the first place, the magnetic coating on the medium should "track" accurately. This is especially critical if the medium is a narrow stripe coated on a film base or if it is wide tape with as many

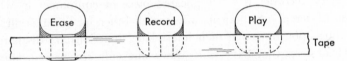

Fig. 8-2. Horizontal alignment of heads. Note that the reproduce head core (play) has been drawn slightly narrower, and the erase head core slightly wider, than the record head core. This design, it is reported, results in a better quality of recording.

as 20 or 30 recorded tracks. In other words, you must be absolutely certain that the heads are in perfect alignment and that the medium does not wobble from bottom to top in its guides. Thus, in the normal full 1/4-track tape machine with erase, record, and play (reproduce) heads, the heads should line up horizontally, as shown in Fig. 8-2. If they do not line up properly, any of these things may result: (1) If the erase head were out of line sufficiently, there might be part of a previous, unerased recording in the background of the newly recorded material. Some distortion might also result, owing to poor erasure. (2) If the record head were out of line, the recorded level would be lower than normal. (3) If the reproduce head were out of line horizontally, the same effect, namely loss of level, would result.

For good contact, in most recorders using flexible media the medium "wraps around" the head surface slightly. The amount of "wrap" is determined by the designer and should be kept to that limit. Wrap-around gives the kind of intimate contact that results in the best possible high-frequency reproduction. As you know, the higher in frequency we reach, the shorter become the magnetic marks in the medium. Not only are they short in the horizontal plane, but their flux fields are also very close to the surface of the medium. To these very tiny fields 1/10,000 in. is a tremendous distance. That is why, sometimes, a dirty head can result in such a loss of high-frequency sound and why, even with a clean head surface, it is necessary to have either wrap-around or head pressure pads. Wrap-around may be effected in the manner illustrated in

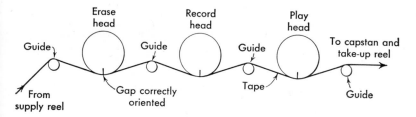

Fig. 8-3. Diagram of head-wrap and orientation.

Fig. 8-3. No matter how it is done, intimate and unvarying contact must be effected between the magnetic coating and the surfaces of the magnetic heads. The magnetic heads should, then, be so oriented that each has its gap in the exact center of that particular arc of the medium in which it is positioned and also has the same "wrap" on both sides of the gap, under tension. Luckily for most of us, this positioning rarely gets out of adjustment.

The next alignment adjustment we have already touched upon under head wear. This becomes necessary when the head is accidentally tilted backward or forward. The cure is an obvious one, and your service manual will cover it. Depending upon its design, there will be some means for bringing the head into exact position vertically.

The last alignment is called the "azimuth" adjustment. It is a

very important one, especially if different heads are used for recording and reproducing. The azimuth of the head gaps should be
exactly at a right angle to the path of tape travel (Fig. 8-4, A and
B). If the recorder has only one head, which first records and then,
when switched, reproduces, incorrect azimuth can be tolerated.
Even here, however, it is preferable that the azimuth be correctly
adjusted in order that the tape can be reproduced properly on other
machines.

In the normal three-head recorder and in the two-head recorder
(where no erase head is incorporated), a definite method has been
established for azimuth adjustment. The means for making the ad-

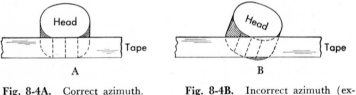

Fig. 8-4A.   Correct azimuth.   **Fig. 8-4B.**   Incorrect azimuth (exaggerated).

justment may differ from one recorder to another, depending upon
the way in which the heads are mounted in place. The adjusting
member may be a screw or a slotted nut; your service instructions
should be consulted. The proper adjustment may be made as follows: (a) Obtain a standard alignment tape and reproduce (play)
it, noting the output level on an indicating meter. Adjust the
azimuth adjustment on your machine's reproduce head for maximum response. (b) Take off the standard tape, next record a tone
of 15,000 cy per sec at a tape speed of 15 in. per sec at low level on
a *fresh tape*. The level should be approximately 10 to 20 db *below*
normal maximum for your machine. (c) Adjust the azimuth adjustment of the *recording head,* while playing back to the indicating
meter, for maximum output. (d) While still recording, check the
azimuth of the reproduce head again; it should not require further
adjustment. (If it does, it indicates either that the standard tape

was recorded improperly or, what is more likely, that your adjustment of the record-head azimuth was slightly wrong.)

Equalization. The specific method given in the manufacturer's instruction manual for re-equalizing the frequency response of your recorder should be followed. The ordinary low-priced recorder does not have any controls for varying the response of the tape at different frequencies; although it may be furnished with controls for low and high boost, these do not work in the same way. Most professional machines incorporate variable controls for varying the high-frequency response, either in both the record and reproduce amplifiers, or in the record amplifier only. Low-frequency response is ordinarily set by the equalizer switch, which may be thrown when changing speeds, or is unchangeable except after a change of wired-in components.

Equalization of a professional machine is performed as follows: A standard frequency-response test tape, or film, made on a machine of exactly the same type or on the same machine at a previous date, is played back, and the levels of the output at representative frequencies are charted on graph paper. A series of frequencies, with 1000 cy per sec as the reference point, ranging from 50 to 15,000 cy per sec is ordinarily recorded on the standard tape. If the output from this standard tape falls below the level of the 1000-cy reference tone, the particular reproduce-amplifier equalizer controlling that frequency should be varied to bring the output up to the reference point. Next, remove the standard tape and record from an oscillator the same series of frequencies on a fresh tape of the same type at the same levels, and observe the reproduced output. When any reproduced frequency varies from the reference level, manipulate the indicated equalizer control, or controls, of the record amplifier sufficiently to bring that particular frequency up to normal. The response in good professional equipment, when red-oxide plastic tape in good condition is used, should not vary more than plus or minus 2.0 db between 50 and 15,000 cy per sec.

As you have perhaps noticed, the operation for equalization is quite similar to the operation of adjusting for proper head azimuth.

First, we obtain a standard that is known to be right. We play it through the machine and adjust the *reproducing* equipment. *Thus we have eliminated one chance for error in the machine itself.* Then we record on the machine, checking the recording equipment against the reproducing section *which we now know to be correct.* It is very important to realize the implications of this method, that of proceeding from one known *true fact* to another equally true.

One must remember, in making the foregoing tests and adjustments, to use throughout the same kind of medium in approximately the same state of preservation. That is to say, if the test tape with the standard response frequencies recorded on it is red-oxide plastic of a certain type, the fresh tape should be of the same type. Any plastic of the cellulose-acetate type should be kept in an atmosphere of close to 50 per cent relative humidity and between 60 and 80° F in temperature. The standard response tape, especially, might well be kept stored in an airtight film can. In respect to machines that do not have variable equalizers, a major change of medium may require re-equalization by removal of some components and replacement with others. Information about making such changes should properly be obtained from the manufacturer of the equipment, and the change should not be attempted unless complete test facilities are available.

The accepted method of equalization, followed in general by most manufacturers, is to pre-emphasize high frequencies and to postemphasize low frequencies. The optimum result desired is equal response with minimum deviation over the frequency band for which the machine is designed. There are simple reasons for this procedure. At low frequencies, there is a limit to the amount of magnetization the oxide will accept without distortion and general "muddiness" in response resulting. At high frequencies, both the self-erasing effect that takes place during recording and the "skin effect" require that *more* power be given them originally. Besides, if high frequencies are emphasized in recording, they can be de-emphasized in reproduction, and less high-frequency noise thereby results. Some popular recorders, however, divide the necessary amount of equalization, both pre- and post-, in half, applying one-half during recording and the other half during reproduction.

One need not emphasize that whenever a recording or reproducing head is replaced, the whole series of head-adjusting and re-equalization operations must be performed. In addition, the bias and erase currents should be checked. In the home type of machine, generally no provision is made for varying the bias. Evidently the manufacturer feels, and rightly so, that the adjustment of such critical currents should not be left to the novice. Moreover, to add these controls would increase the cost of the present low-priced equipment.

Bias Adjustment. Bias current adjustment may be performed in several ways, and each manufacturer specifies a method that should be followed for his recorder. But a general method that can be used with any machine satisfactorily is this: Record a low-frequency signal of 100 to 400 cy per sec from an audio oscillator (the writer prefers to use the 100-cy signal), and adjust the audio level of the reproducing system to register near the mid-scale of the output-level indicating meter. Then, while observing this meter, increase the bias current control until the maximum output reading is reached and further increase results in a *decrease* in the output level. This point is the optimum recording point for all frequencies. However, because of the possibility of some instability, it is generally recommended that the bias current be increased slightly beyond this maximum-level point, enough to decrease the signal by 0.5 to 1 db.

When bias current is increased much beyond the maximum-level point, as described above, the distortion at low frequencies decreases, but the frequency range becomes compressed. In other words, owing to the bias-erasing effect during recording, the bias, as it is increased, erases more of the high frequencies. The individual user, therefore, should make his choice—less distortion at low frequencies and less high-frequency response or more distortion at lows and extended high-frequency range. One cannot have both at the same time. The writer prefers an overbiasing of approximately 1.5 db and feels that cleaner low frequencies (and, incidentally, less over-all noise) are preferable to an extended frequency range.

If, after being checked, the bias adjustment has been changed from its previous position, the equalization routine must be repeated, since a change in bias upsets the equalization.

Measurement of Bias Current. The amount of bias current required to give optimum recording varies with the magnetic qualities of the medium used. The precise amount required to get the best results from the medium you are using can be ascertained from the

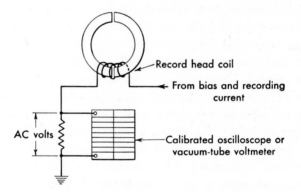

Fig. 8-5. Diagram of one method by which bias current may be measured.

manufacturer of the tape or film involved. The multi-reading meter of some types of recorders is connected to a switch which permits the user to check the bias current at any time. In machines where no provision is made for measuring bias current, a measurement may be obtained in the following way: Connect a resistor (any value from 10 to 250 ohms) in the ground return side of the record head coil (see Fig. 8-5). Across the resistor connect a calibrated oscilloscope (calibrated in volts). Then the current through the resistor, with some negligible error, can be computed by using Ohm's law, $I = E/R$. For instance, if the voltage on the calibrated oscilloscope reads 0.050 volt, and the resistor has a value of 10 ohms, then $I = E/R = 0.050/10 = 0.005$ ampere, or a 5-milliampere bias current. Be sure, when making this measurement, that the recorder is properly grounded, that the measuring equipment is at ground potential, and that there is no audio current present; otherwise a false reading may be derived.

EFFECTS DUE TO OVERHEATING

In the summer of 1948 the writer operated a bank of recorders at Convention Hall in Philadelphia. The recorders were equipped with air-blowers with which to dissipate motor heat, which otherwise would have heated the heads. Trouble of many kinds due to overheating was thus avoided. But one incident remains in memory. An engineer recording a speech on tape rushed in and cried, "My recorder is distorting horribly! What shall I do?" He was told to cool the heads by any possible means. He did! He rushed back from the downstairs bar with an ice bag, which he laid on the heads—and the day was saved. This is an extreme example of the effect of heat on magnetic recording heads. No one at that time and place was equipped to find out what the actual trouble was or how the heat had caused distortion. One guess was that the core structure had become so deformed by the heat that it short-circuited the magnetic gap. The writer is fond of the theory that possibly, when heat invades the tape coating, there is less effect from magnetism. It has been observed that recording is cleaner and less distorted at low temperatures than at high temperatures. Whatever the true theory may be, there is no practical guide except experience. And experience indicates that recorders should be kept as cool as possible for best over-all results—but not so cold that the oil or grease in the bearings congeals.

If heads are overheated, the tape tends to stick to them, especially to the erase head; the tape or film also sticks to guides. When a medium that sticks is jerked away by the drive, there is audible "screeching," caused by the resulting vibration, which records as heavy flutter or even as a tone. Internally or externally lubricated tapes are not subject to this trouble under conditions of operation ordinarily encountered.

In all locations that are very hot and in tropical and subtropical climates, cooled air forced from a small blower in such manner that its stream hits the head assembly will contribute to better recording.

TROUBLES DUE TO EXTREME COLD

The aggravating troubles that occur in a tape recorder during extremely cold weather have driven more than one experienced engineer to distraction. Rubber friction drives get hard and slippery; tape becomes brittle and breaks easily (with the exception of Mylar tape); and the drives do not reach speed until the bearings are warmed up. The cure for all these troubles reminds us of our earlier discussion. These machines are primarily meant to operate in normal temperatures. When the temperature gets low enough to congeal grease, no attempt should be made to record until the machine has been warmed. It can be brought to normal temperature in any convenient way—by inserting an electric heating element or bulb within the cabinet near the capstan shaft, by using a chemical heater (alcohol-aluminum), or by keeping the recorder near an old-fashioned wood fire. But, one may ask, how can the operator know when the recorder is up to speed? He can find out by any one of several ways. The easiest way is to take along a tape recorded with pitch-pipe tone and the pitch pipe itself. Playing the tape back, blow the pitch pipe at the same time. If there is any difference in frequency—such difference indicates a speed different from that at which the original recording of the pitch pipe was made—the recorder is not up to speed. You can make a similar test by using an oscillator to produce the tone, but oscillators can vary considerably in their dial settings under different conditions and are subject to drift. If an oscillator is used, *it also* must be warmed up before using, whereas the little pitch pipe can be carried in a pocket; since the pipe has been warmed to some extent, probably, its frequency should vary but little.

The facts that the capstan-drive motor is a synchronous motor and that the supply current is of the correct frequency will not prevent the motor from running too slowly if the temperature is *low enough to congeal the grease*. Dry-lubricated drives may lessen this difficulty somewhat, but not entirely. The rule to follow is: Bring the mechanism up to normal temperature, and then play back an accurately recorded tone against the *same tone* produced on the spot. If both blend together in sound, all is well; if they do not, (they will produce beat notes) do not record unless accurate reproduction of sound is not required.

FLUTTER

Flutter in a drive system may come from any of a variety of causes. It is a recurring instantaneous speed variation, and, although not necessarily heard as such, it can cause considerable roughness and distortion of the reproduced sound. A number of flutter-measuring equipments available today will give a fair approximation of the amount of flutter in a drive system and the rate at which the flutter occurs. In one accepted method of flutter measurement, a 3000-cy tone is recorded, and the output from the tape reproduction system is compared to the input tone. Rhythmic flutter components may then be measured and noted, graphically if desired. Excessive flutter can generally be traced to out-of-round parts in the drive, vibration of the medium in any direction, or any other condition that contributes to uneven motion of the medium.

RELATIONSHIP OF MEDIA-HANDLING TO GOOD RECORDING

If machines are maintained properly and proper care is observed in handling and storing the media, there is no reason why consistently good results cannot be obtained. A few observations may be made, however, regarding obvious faults existing at this writing.

Many machines now rewind tape too tightly; this condition is generally the result of too rapid rewinding under tension. Tape should be rewound at a speed not exceeding approximately 90 in. per sec. At this rate, if the back tension is properly adjusted, the result will be a fairly loose, evenly rewound reel of tape that will record well for many thousands of times, assuming proper storage. If high-speed rewind is essential to operation, the sideways excursions of the tape should be limited; this can be done by using reels with 0.270-in. inside spacing between flanges instead of the usual NARTB reels, which measure 0.345 in. between flanges. The glass-filled plastic reels now obtainable are made with this 0.270-in. inside spacing. When the tape winds unevenly, no harm is done, provided that it is reused immediately—and provided further that winding tension has not been great enough to stretch the tape unduly. But if a tight, unevenly rewound reel is stored under dry conditions, the loss of moisture from the plastic base of the tape in its unevenly compacted form will result in poor quality of subsequent recording and reproduction. The tape will have "ruffles" and kinks, more or less permanent; these will *not* be removed even by a tight drive. Consequently, the tape will be forced away from the heads by its own distorted shape. Tape in this condition is useless for good quality of recording.

Tape will rewind more smoothly if it is rewound slowly. Most machines may be reworked, according to manufacturers' instructions, in a manner to obtain a slower speed in rewinding. The speed may be slowed a bit by means of a motor field rheostat controlling the motor's speed, or by use of reduction gears. Most simply, if time is no object, the reel may be rewound at normal playback speed after the reels are changed, the loaded take-up reel placed in the supply position, and the tape played "backwards" onto a blank take-up reel. Actually, there is no reason why the tape should not be stored *reversed,* without rewinding, and rewound just before playing.

SOME TEST AND REPAIR METHODS

Brittleness Test for Tape. The best nontechnical way of telling whether tape is too dry and brittle for good recording is by its "hand." Tape in good condition is very limp; if you hold a section of it between your thumb and forefinger, the tape will droop around and touch one of the two. If it is too dry, it will droop but will stand away from your finger or thumb. If you suspend a strip of brittle tape in a closed mason jar containing just enough water to cover the bottom, leave the tape there for an hour or so, and then repeat the above test, there will be no doubt in your mind as to the difference in "feel" between dry, brittle tape and pliant, limp tape.

Measurement of Distortion. Nonlinear distortion (usually shortened to "distortion") in a recorder means that the unit generates additional tones within itself, which are mixed with the tones originally recorded and hence appear in the recorder output. To the ear, the presence of distortion imparts a disagreeable harshness or fuzziness to the tone and results in considerable fatigue of the listener.

Kinds of Distortion. Two kinds of distortion possible in a typical audio system are harmonic and intermodulation. In the measurement of harmonic distortion a *single* tone is fed into the audio system, and the amplitudes of tones in the output at frequencies other than the original are measured. These additional tones (usually two or three) created by harmonic distortion are harmonics of the original frequency—whence the name. When one is measuring intermodulation distortion, *two* tones are fed into the recorder, and the result of interaction between the two is measured. In the most popular method, the so-called SMPTE (named after the standards of the Society of Motion Picture and Television Engineers), the modulation of the higher frequency tone by the lower is measured. In effect, this takes account of the many distortion products that may be caused by intermodulation and, because they are *not* harmonically related, are particularly offensive.

In comparing the two methods, we may judge by similarity to actual conditions of audio-system use, by mathematical studies, by comparative listening tests, and by certain problems peculiar to the magnetic recorder. We are struck by the fact that the harmonic method of test bears small relation to actual use. Little music except a flute solo resembles a single tone. Most sounds are typically complex in nature—and the distortion effects parallel those measured by the two tones of the intermodulation method. If harmonic distortion is low and intermodulation high, then a solo instrument will sound all right, but a full orchestra at the same audio level will sound muddy and distorted.

Originally it was thought that intermodulation and harmonic

distortion were interrelated in a 4:1 ratio, but this has long since been disproved. The two types of distortion are truly interrelated, the mathematicians tell us, but by so complex and flexible a law that it is not ordinarily practical to calculate the intermodulation from harmonic distortion data compiled from measurements of an actual system.

Exhaustive listening tests were run by the motion-picture industry at the time it abandoned the harmonic method for most measuring. The harmonic readings bore little or no relation to the "opinion" of the ear, but SMPTE intermodulation data correlated reliably. That is why the intermodulation method has been the major method in use by the motion-picture industry for over 15 years.

The magnetic recorder presents special problems of measurement, caused by two characteristics of commercial machines: (1) small but rapid changes in speed (flutter) and (2) bias leakage.

Flutter produces a continuous variation in frequency over a narrow band. Unfortunately, virtually all modern harmonic distortion meters use a very sharply tuned circuit to remove the fundamental frequency tone whose distortion products are being measured; this circuit is too sharply tuned to remove the entire band of fundamental frequencies produced by the flutter.

Recorders usually contain some means of removing bias leakage from the output, but whatever the means, it is seldom effective enough to remove bias completely. Since a harmonic distortion meter must pass the higher harmonics of the highest audio-frequency used (15 kilocycles), it may have considerable response at 40 to 60 kilocycles or higher, that is, in the bias frequency region.

A combination of these two faults makes the accuracy of a typical modern distortion meter highly doubtful, when such a meter is used for magnetic recorder measurement. On the other hand, the accuracy of an intermodulation distortion meter is not injured by these and other special characteristics of a magnetic recorder.

Distortion Measurement as a Maintenance Tool. A magnetic recorder is especially dependent on the proper functioning of its electronic system, for it contains a bias oscillator as well as the usual amplifiers. A loss of only 30 per cent of oscillator output is sufficient, in most professional machines, to reduce the bias to a point where a slight further decrease will produce a radical increase in distortion. Thus, systematic measurement of the amount of distortion, under fixed level and frequency conditions, can reveal failure while incipient and before it has progressed to a dangerous point.

Setting the Correct Recording Level. Connect the magnetic recorder to an intermodulation meter (Fig. 8-6). Set the latter for

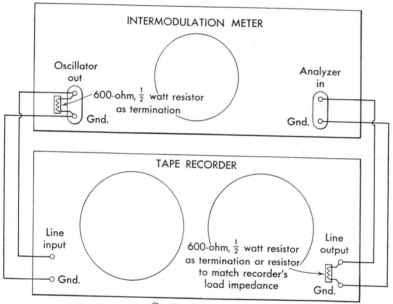

Courtesy of the Audio Instrument Company, Inc.

Fig. 8-6. Connections to the Model 165A intermodulation meter are shown diagrammatically.

frequencies of 60 and 2000 cy per sec, and a 4:1 ratio. Increase the recording level in steps of 1 db, measuring the distortion at each level, until the level producing 10 per cent intermodulation is reached. The volume indicator should preferably be set so that it reads zero VU at a level 7 db below this 10 per cent level. If the machine has a poor signal-to-noise ratio, it may be necessary to use a margin of 4 or 5 db instead of 10 db in order to keep reproduced noise to a minimum, but recording quality will suffer, and the peaks of musical crescendos will tend to be clipped, leaving the music somewhat tasteless.

The above procedure is based on two factors: 10 per cent inter-modulation is considered to be the minimum detectable by the ear without a special comparison procedure, and a 7-db margin above the VU meter reading is necessary to allow for instantaneous peaks. If the measurement were made on a harmonic basis, a 10-db margin would be necessary.

Maintenance Measurement of Intermodulation Distortion. In the ideal case it would be desirable to make measurements of inter-modulation distortion at 10 db above normal recording level and under these two conditions: (1) 60 and 2000 cy per sec, 4:1 ratio, and (2) 150 and 7000 cy per sec, 1:1 ratio.

In practice, a single measurement at 60 and 7000 cy per sec, 4:1 ratio, will usually be found sufficient for routine checks.

Linear-Speed Test. Every so often an absolute linear-speed check of the recorders should be made. A test of this kind may be made in a number of ways, even by measuring off a length of tape, then marking each end of the measured portion, and finally observing how long it takes for the machine to pull the tape from the beginning mark to the end mark. A more rapid check may be made by holding, or fixing, a mechanical counter against the tape so that the tape motion is transmitted, without slipping, to the counter drive. The counter should indicate totals preferably in feet and tenths of a foot, for easier calculations. A counter made so that it will measure in multiples of 15 in. per sec for 15-in.-per-sec tape recorders, totaling in minutes and seconds, is a handy item for checking rapidly both absolute linear speed and length of tape program. A Keuffel & Esser map-distance counter may be adapted for this purpose very easily, as may a number of the Veeder-Root counters.

It is *not* recommended that a stroboscopic disk cemented to the top of the capstan and scanned by a lamp be used as a speed check. This method will reveal whether (1) a *capstan* is operating at the right number of revolutions per second and (2) a stroboscopic disk has been made properly, but it will not indicate accurately the

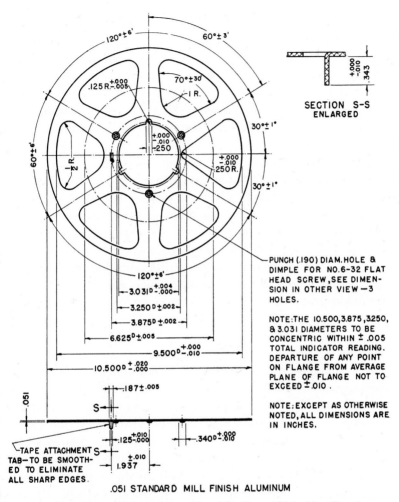

SECTION S-S
ENLARGED

PUNCH (.190) DIAM. HOLE &
DIMPLE FOR NO. 6-32 FLAT
HEAD SCREW, SEE DIMEN-
SION IN OTHER VIEW —3
HOLES.

NOTE: THE 10.500, 3.875, 3250,
& 3.031 DIAMETERS TO BE
CONCENTRIC WITHIN ±.005
TOTAL INDICATOR READING.
DEPARTURE OF ANY POINT
ON FLANGE FROM AVERAGE
PLANE OF FLANGE NOT TO
EXCEED ±.010 .

NOTE: EXCEPT AS OTHERWISE
NOTED, ALL DIMENSIONS ARE
IN INCHES.

TAPE ATTACHMENT
TAB—TO BE SMOOTH-
ED TO ELIMINATE
ALL SHARP EDGES.

.051 STANDARD MILL FINISH ALUMINUM

Courtesy of the National Association of Radio and Television Broadcasters

Fig. 8-7. Diagram of a flange of the NARTB standard 1/4-in. magnetic tape reel. (From *NARTB Recording and Reproducing Standards,* revised June, 1953)

actual linear speed of the tape. Stroboscopic methods may be used to good advantage if they are based on printed marks on the tape itself. Indeed, pulse-counting systems may easily be designed, based on electronic counters actuated by pulses at supersonic or subsonic frequencies recorded on the tape. However, for practical use a mechanical measuring device is simpler to use and far cheaper to obtain or make.

Care of Reels. Tape reels (see Fig. 8-7) should be carefully handled and not bent or, in the case of plastic reels, cracked. A bent metal reel, in combination with a careless operator, can cause periodic "wows" as the bent side drags on the machine's top plate. Discard or straighten bent metal reels, and either cement or discard the cracked plastic reel. Bent plastic reels should not be used. The new glass-filled plastic reels will shatter, possibly, but will not bend; they permit a smoother tape wind at high speed than does the standard metal reel.

SUMMARY

This chapter has described some of the common troubles of all magnetic recorders. In later chapters, troubles that affect, or have affected, the kind of machine under discussion will be described more fully. The maintenance of a recorder may become more complicated as the machines grow more complicated, so that, typically, one might expect a never-ending array of "bugs." The great majority of troubles, excepting those that are due to defective tubes, worn heads, and mechanical components, can generally be traced to improper cleaning and lubrication. It is surprising how well made are even the low-priced recorders of the present day. If the user accustoms himself to clean and lubricate his machine carefully, to use it as directed, and to test tubes and measure bias current and distortion about every hundred hours of use, no major troubles need be anticipated.

9

Spurious Printing

The "printing-through" of a signal from one layer of a magnetic tape to another has been termed "magnetic" or "spurious printing" in the literature of magnetic recording. Such printing is an exact copy of the desired signal, lacking in fidelity, it is true, but still an echo of the original sound.

This effect had been observed in wire recording and in recording homogeneous tape; in fact, it was one of the reasons why the use of this kind of tape, which is permeated by iron particles, has almost entirely ceased. It was too prone to the accidental printing effect that we are now investigating.

It is only in those forms of magnetic recording where the magnetic medium is wound up on reels immediately after recording that the phenomenon of spurious printing takes place. Although the same effect may occur in different media, such as wire, solid steel bands, homogeneous tape, coated tape, and coated film, we shall confine this discussion to coated tape.

Magnetic tape consists of a plastic base 0.25 in. wide, ordinarily, coated on one side with a thin layer of magnetic oxide. The particular kinds of oxide used by various manufacturers in the coating may vary in magnetic qualities, as may also the methods of manufacturing and application of the coating to the tape base. There is as yet no universally accepted standard, but in the United States and several European countries, the tape is cellulose acetate coated with red oxide of iron. The ratio of the thickness of the base to the

153

coating is approximately three to one, and the tendency is to make the coating of the minimum thickness that is consistent with the magnetic and mechanical characteristics desired.

As the reader has observed, the tape is fed from a supply reel past the recording and reproducing heads and is then immediately reeled up again on the take-up reel. Thus signals recorded on the tape are quite rapidly placed in close juxtaposition to another layer of tape on the receiving reel. When one realizes that, after all, a magnetically recorded signal is a series of small magnets that radiate magnetic fields, one can readily appreciate how spurious printing originates. One is almost tempted to wonder, not that it happens, but that it can be prevented from happening.

Printing of this nature can take place either on the layer of tape preceding that on which a given signal is recorded or on the layer succeeding, or on both. It can be a very embarrassing phenomenon, especially if one does not know when it is going to manifest itself.

If these "echoes" are heard, on reproduction, before the true signal, they are called "pre-prints"; after the true signal, they are called "post-prints." In most cases printing is so low in level that it goes by unobserved except in those instances when the tape is very lightly recorded or is quiet either before the pre-, or after the post-, print. In either case there is a feeling that the noise is higher than it should be and that the record is not as clear as it might be, but no distinct echoes are noticed.

METHODS FOR THE REDUCTION OF SPURIOUS PRINTING

Accidental or spurious printing has been investigated intensively for several years past, and the results indicate that several conditions of operation are in the main responsible for its occurrence.

INCREASE OF PRINTING EFFECT WITH TEMPERATURE

Most researchers agree that there is at least a 1-db increase in the level of the spurious print for each 10 degrees (Fahrenheit) of increase in temperature of the tape. After considerable time has elapsed, this increase in the level of spurious printing can reach disturbing proportions at very high temperatures. In test tape that was heated to 250° F, the printing level had increased by the end of an hour by almost 20 db. It would seem that the least amount of spurious printing, therefore, will take place when the tape and everything it contacts are kept cool during recording and subsequent storage. In normal recording machines the tape passes an erase head before the record head, and with continuous recording, the erase head may become quite hot. (Our modern machines have not copied the early Magnetophon's blower system, which forced a stream of cooling air through the machine.) Accordingly, under certain conditions tape may reach comparatively high temperatures *during recording* and may print excessively. Some magnetic-tape recorders, which eliminate erase heads, are not subject to this hazard. For best results, then, keep the tape cool and store it in a cool, properly humidified, dust-free room or in sealed cans. (Note that pre-erased tape, recorded on a machine from which the erase head has been removed, has been from 5 to 8 db quieter than comparable tape recorded under identical conditions on a recorder having an erase head. Whether this will continue to hold true with improvements in erase heads and coatings is problematical.)

EFFECTS OF STRAY MAGNETIC FIELDS

When a tape, after being recorded, has been subjected to a magnetic field (either while it is being reeled up or after it is stored), the amount of transfer of a signal from one layer to others in either case will increase. Although the strength of the magnetic field required to effect spurious printing is considerable, it is not more than is likely to be caused by power lines conducting heavy currents, or by motors, magnets, and the like. Some early models of tape recorders were plagued by a great deal of printing, which was probably due to excessive heat and the heavy magnetic fields thrown out by overloaded motors and power transformers. Stray magnetic fields may be detected in a number of ways, by a compass or by a radio-frequency probe, for example. A few turns of wire, connected to a sensitive amplifier (about 80- to 100-db gain), will indicate the strength of any ac magnetic field, such as those set up by power lines or transformers. A heavy dc field is most easily detected by means of a sensitive compass. The tape should be subjected to only one magnetic recording field, that of the recording head. Any subsequent fields in the recorder itself, such as those radiating from overloaded motors and improperly shielded or oriented transformers, should be eliminated. Tape should be stored in a place found free of magnetic fields by test.

EFFECT OF RECORDING LEVEL

Overmodulation of tape will cause a proportionate increase in spurious printing. The writer's opinion, backed by practical experience, is that the known dangers resulting from overloading the tape make it foolhardy to record any more level than necessary to obtain signals sufficiently above the general residual noise of both the tape and the recorder to be satisfactorily reproduced. The frequencies at which overloading occurs are different with different machines, depending upon equalization, heads, and type of amplifier. It may be safely asserted, therefore, that the general rule of *avoiding overmodulation* is still the best, even though the new low-print tapes provide a print reduction of 8 db.

EFFECT OF STORAGE TIME

Tape stored under the best possible conditions will still print layer to layer, but in very minute quantities. The increase of printing at the end of three days of storage may be 2 or 3 db, but thereafter the increase *due to storage alone* will not be very great. It is recommended that a reel taken out of storage for reproduction purposes be played and rewound two or three times before it is restored. The very tiny magnetic fields generally present about the record and reproduce heads actually will erase a slight amount of the spurious signal, and sometimes will entirely remove the transferred signal.

EFFECT OF TIGHT SPOOLING

The normal effect of tape-tension systems is to cause the tape to spool up cleanly and fairly tightly. Under normal tension no bad effects will take place. However, if tape is spooled up while warm and cools on the reel, distorting strains may be set up in the tape, causing especially tight contact between layers. Whatever printing has taken place can be increased by such contact. The cure is to keep recorders *cool*. Winding tension should *never be greater* than the manufacturer specifies, and generally can be less.

EFFECT OF THICKNESS OF THE BASE MATERIAL

The amount of spurious printing is directly proportionate to the distance between the iron-oxide coatings. The thicker the base, therefore, the less printing will take place. There is much to recommend a tape with a high ratio between base and coating, because both thinner coatings and thicker bases produce generally better recordings. Of course, the base must be pliable enough to wrap around a head, maintaining good contact without too much tape tension or pressure. All things considered, however, it seems best to use the thickest tape with the thinnest coating that will measure up to your specifications as to frequency, storage space, and recording time needed on one reel.

EFFECT OF DIFFERENCES IN COERCIVITY OF COATINGS

According to several tests, the high-coercive-force tapes, which are now rarely used, were more susceptible to printing than are the present low-coercive tapes. Much more spurious printing occurred at the same temperature and, moreover, was retained for a longer period of time.

PRINTING DUE TO SPEED OF TAPE TRAVEL

No investigations into the possible variation of the amount of spurious printing that may occur when the tape is traveling at different speeds have come to the attention of this writer. It is possible that, in longitudinal recording at least, less accidental printing will take place at high speeds than at low speeds. The foregoing, one must hasten to add, is just a guess with no observation to back it up. It seems reasonable to expect, however, that the depth of magnetization, and therefore the resulting printing at low frequencies, will be less at 30 in. per sec than at 15 in. per sec, for example.

It should be emphasized here that the foregoing causes of spurious printing are infrequent and due to the unusual conditions respectively mentioned. Under the conditions of operation generally prevalent, not enough magnetic printing will occur to be noticed.

For those of you who are inclined to experiment, there is a way in which unwanted printing may be erased, that is, by running the tape past a *very* lightly energized erasing head. It has been suggested that this can be done by separating the head from the tape, by erasing from the base side of the tape, or, best of all, by passing the tape through the center of some form of energized, helically wound coil in order to effect the partial erasure. You must be warned, however, that slight erasure of the true signal will take place and will be greater at high frequencies than at low frequencies, even though it is little, if properly controlled. The amount of current needed to erase printing without affecting the true signal considerably will vary with the type of coating.

10

Editing

This chapter deals primarily with tape editing or cutting, since tape is at present the most common medium in many applications. Rules that govern tape editing also apply, with slight changes, to the cutting of magnetically coated and striped film. Some methods now in use for cutting and splicing magnetic-film track will be found in Chapter 13 on Motion-Picture and Television Techniques. The basic principles of editing, as explained here, are valid regardless of the medium and may be followed whether the recording is on wire, tape, or single-track film.

WIRE-SPLICING METHODS

Wire may be edited by cutting out the length of wire containing the recorded sound to be discarded and splicing the remaining pieces of wire together with a square knot. The knot should be tied loosely while the wire is cold and then tightened while the knot is held in or near a flame hot enough to soften the wire sufficiently to tie it in a tight knot; a lighted cigarette will do, or the two loose ends of wire can be welded together by means of a small spot-welder. Either process requires that the loose ends protruding from the knot be trimmed off, leaving the knot smooth enough to pass through the head assembly without sticking. No matter how wire is spliced together, the splice makes a noticeable "click" when that part of the wire passes through the play head. When heat is intense enough to soften the wire sufficiently to allow tight knotting, it will also demagnetize the wire at the point of knotting. The resulting magnetic state is heard as a click or a thump; because of this wire is rarely used as an editing medium.

TAPE-CUTTING AND -SPLICING

Single-track magnetic tape can be cut and spliced very easily with present-day equipment. There was a time when the physical act of cutting tape required quite a bit of dexterity on the part of editors. After the tape had been cut at an exact angle with scissors, the unwanted length was removed; then the tape had to be cut again at an identical angle and the two ends patched together with adhesive tape applied on the back of the magnetic tape. After that, the editor had to trim away the excess adhesive tape with scissors so that the splice would pass through the heads without sticking.

ANGLE OF TAPE CUT

No matter what method of cutting tape is used, the tape should be cut to make an angle of 45 degrees or less to the side of the tape, rarely more than 45 degrees (Fig. 10-1). The reason for this is that

Fig. 10-1. Tape on which sound is being edited should be cut at a 45-degree, or sharper, angle.

at ordinary tape speeds a cut at more than a 45-degree angle may be heard as noise. (We shall go into this phase of the matter more thoroughly later in this chapter.)

CUTTING WITH SCISSORS

Some of the best tape editors in the profession have edited with scissors. Although more dexterity is required than with other methods, good splices can be made in this way, and with practice, a "scissors editor" can edit as quickly as those who use other methods. It is done in this way. When the point at which the tape is to be cut has been reached,* mark the *back* (base side) of the tape with a black or yellow grease pencil (whichever is more easily seen) exactly at the center, or magnetic gap, of the reproduce head. If you intend to remove only a word or two, or a comparatively short length of tape, do not cut the tape, but proceed to the next point at which you want to cut. Make another mark on the back of the tape at that point. Then, after pulling out enough slack tape, line the tape up so that one mark is on top of the other and the edges of the tape are parallel, and cut through both marks with the scissors at a 45-degree angle. Cut off a piece of 1-in. No. 41 Scotch Tape, or the equivalent, and after placing the two ends of tape tightly together with no gap between, place the Scotch Tape across the ends, allowing about 3/4 in. of tape on the back side of each magnetic-tape end. The splicing tape should be laid down, or applied, at an angle, too. After rubbing the splice a few times firmly with your thumb, making certain it is gripping properly, trim off the excess Scotch Tape with scissors, cutting *into* the splice very slightly (not more than 0.002 in.). Such undercutting is recommended for several reasons. Tape has to be pliant enough to maintain contact while wrapping around the heads. After a thickness of adhesive tape is added to the thickness of the recording tape, the tape is not as pliant and conformable as it was before the addition. Undercutting helps to maintain the normal amount of pliability at the spliced point, thus lessening the possibility of poor playback because of a stiff splice. Undercutting also decreases the chance that the adhesive compound will "bleed" out from under the edges and cause one layer of tape to stick to the next.

There is a good reason for cutting and patching the splicing adhesive diagonally. After the tape has been spliced and rewound, considerable pressure generally exists between adjacent layers of

---

* The tape has to pass over the reproduce (play) head of the recorder at the speed used during recording in order for a listener to hear the sound as it was recorded.

tape, varying with the degree of tautness produced by the drive tension. This pressure may force a tiny bit of adhesive from under the edges of a splice, causing the spliced area to adhere to the next layer of tape at two points: the beginning and end of the splice. If the splice has been patched at an angle of 90 degrees to the recording tape sides, these straight edges may, on re-use, stick to the next layer of tape enough to stall the capstan drive momentarily, thus causing an audible "wow" or "gurgle." If the splices are made at 45-degree angles or less, the sticky points, if any, will peel away from the next layer of tape without stalling the drive. This is only a minor point in editing, but it aids a great deal in producing a "smooth" piece of work.

CEMENTED SPLICES

Overlapped cemented splices on tape have been used in Europe with machines operating at a speed of 30-in. per sec., at which even imperfect splices are almost inaudible. The lapping method is similar to that used in film-splicing but is not advocated for tape operating at 15 in. per sec. or less for several reasons: The cement, unless carefully applied, may disturb the binder in the adjacent magnetic coating, causing imperfect audio response at that point. In addition, an overlapped splice is neither as accurate nor as quiet as a butt splice.

VULCANIZED OR "HOT" SPLICES

Good splices may be made by the application to the butted tape ends of perfectly controlled heat under pressure for a measured length of time. The theory is that the heat will melt enough of the plastic backing to produce a perfect bond. Some advocates of this method use additional plastic at the bonding point. This method has several advantages. There is no chance of adhesive "bleeding" that will cause layers of tape to stick together. It is rapid enough for general use, and if everything works as it should, a very good job results.

TAPE-SPLICING BLOCKS

Several makes of tape-splicing blocks are now on the market. The principle of design is simply to provide a block of nonmagnetic material with a groove in which the tape is held, either by clips or by other means. At some point in the block is a transverse cut, generally at a 45-degree angle, wide enough to accommodate a cutting edge. The tape is cut while in the groove and is then spliced at the same point, after the tape has been precisely "lined up" in all directions. The writer developed one of the first blocks of this type in the United States and invented an improved model several years ago. A description of its design and proper use follows.

USE OF THE EdiTall TAPE-SPLICING BLOCK

The EdiTall Tape-Splicing Block (U.S. Patent No. 2,599,667) was designed to ease the task of splicing tape ends together accurately. Before its invention splicing had been a time-consuming and tedious job. By using this block, anyone can splice tape with a minimum of waste motion.

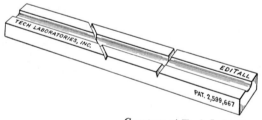

Courtesy of Tech Labs, Inc.
Fig. 10-2. The EdiTall tape-splicing block.

The EdiTall block is so designed and constructed that the physical properties of coated tape are utilized, that is, the block holds the tape tightly while it is being cut. Tape, like most coated magnetic media, is coated on one side only. When marking it for editing, we normally mark the base side (generally the glossier side). Then, when ready to cut the marked tape, we place it in the groove of the block with the base, or marked side, facing up. Figure 10-2 shows the curve in the bottom of the tape groove. The two slightly protruding "shelves" on the sides of the groove near the top are so shallow that they are not visible in the illustration.

The tape is placed in the groove and forced down by running the finger lightly over it; thus it has to conform to the curved bottom of the groove. Tape narrower than normal will not touch the bottom of the groove solidly, but its edges will still be held firmly under the narrow shelves. Wider tape (up to the limit of a quarter of an inch) will touch bottom firmly. The fact that the tape, whose tendency is to remain flat, is bent slightly causes it to exert enough pressure against the side ridges to prevent its moving during the cutting operation. Because of this, it is possible to assemble in the groove many bits of tape for splicing at one time, an operation performed in some phases of phonetics demonstrations.

After the section of tape to be discarded has been cut out, the cut pieces of tape are placed in the groove, and the two ends, which have been cut (in the transverse cut across the groove of the block) at a precise 45-degree angle with a razor, are butted together firmly. To obtain the best possible splice, push the tape ends together until there is a slight bulge where they butt. Then a length of splicing tape 1 1/2 in. long and 7/32 in. wide (No. 41 Scotch Tape, made in the 7/32-in. width, was originally made especially for use in the EdiTall block) should be cut with both ends at acute angles; this piece should be placed with its center over the butted tape ends in the grooved block. The splice should be smoothed down firmly with the finger. To remove the spliced tape from the block, grasp the tape at both ends of the block and pull the tape taut. While it is taut, snap it up and out of the groove; the splice is finished. Note that the spliced tape should be held *taut* and *snapped* up and out of the groove. Do not attempt to "peel" it out or you will ruffle the tape edges. After you have practiced this operation several times, it should not take you more than ten seconds to make a splice.

The cutting groove in the EdiTall Block was designed to accommodate any single-edged safety-razor blade. A scalpel or fine wood-carving knife can be ground down to fit. Many editors use these renewable-edge tools. Make certain, however, that the cutting tool is demagnetized. Should it become magnetized, it will cause a tiny "click" in the sound when the edge of the splice passes the play head. This calls for erasure of the click by an erasing tool or re-cutting at the same point to remove it. (See page 263.)

The writer always uses a slicing motion in cutting tape, since it provides the cleanest edges. If the tape is dry and brittle, the cutting edge should be especially sharp. Ordinary razor blades will give about eight hours' satisfactory service in cutting tape.

Establishing the Tape-marking Point. Tape is marked with a pencil for cutting at the reproduce-head gap, which is in the center of the front surface of the reproduce head. Note that repeated markings at this point will in time leave the head surface soiled with grease-pencil marks, which will affect the operation of the head. Tape recording requires intimate contact of tape to head; even grease-pencil markings can create trouble. They can be easily avoided, and considerable time can be saved in editing, if the following marking method is used. This marking method is simply a means of measuring the distance between the reproduce-head gap and a point established on the tape recorder.

With tape threaded through the heads, mark the tape precisely at the reproduce-head gap (X in Fig. 10-3A). Make another mark on the tape at a *convenient marking point* in the direction of tape travel (Y in Fig. 10-3A). On some machines, where the head assembly is enclosed in a shield, the edge of the head-assembly shield, or housing, can double as the marking point. On the home type of recorders, where marking at the head is sometimes very difficult, a marking point may be made by cementing a little block of wood or a brass right-angle to the top plate a few inches away from the head.

After you have marked the tape at these two points, take it out of the head assembly and put it in the groove of the EdiTall block (see Fig. 10-3B), the mark that indicates the head-gap position (X) being placed over the center of the oblique cut. The point where the other mark (Y) on the tape falls should be indicated *on the block* by marking the block, either with a grease pencil (the mark then covered with transparent adhesive tape) or by making a light cut in the block edge with a hacksaw. The distance between X and Y on the tape recorder is therefore identical to the distance marked off on the EdiTall block. Thereafter, mark tape to be edited at only the one point (Y), the marking point. With the marked tape in the block, match the two Y marks. Finally, cut at the diagonal cutting slot.

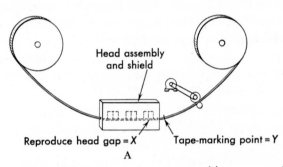

Reproduce head gap = X   Tape-marking point = Y

A

Fig. 10-3A. Diagram showing tape in correct position on recorder and ready to be marked. The distance between the reproduce head gap (X) and the tape-marking point (Y), once established, should not vary.

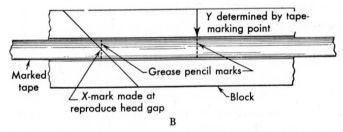

Fig. 10-3B. With X (the mark on the tape) placed at the center of the diagonal cut on the EdiTall block, Y indicates the point at which the EdiTall block should be marked.

This method is actually more accurate than marking the tape at the head, since the tape is marked while under normal tension and is not moved between the time the sound to be cut out is heard and the time the boundaries of the section to be deleted are marked. When we mark tape for editing in this way—using a marking point instead of marking at the reproduce-head gap—we get an additional dividend without paying for it. Sometimes, while editing, we may cut out a word or a phrase, lay the tape on which it is recorded aside, and check the remainder for naturalness. Then we may decide we do not like the result and that the cut-out portion ought to be put back in context. Now, tape has no direction indicator, one end looking the same as the other, and the only way we can find out which way it goes is by splicing the piece back in and playing it. If it has been marked as recommended above, the temporarily removed section of tape will have a grease-pencil mark at its trailing end, thus identifying the direction of tape travel. Thus, considerable time in editing is saved without extra time or effort being needed.

WHERE TO CUT—
RECOGNITION OF SOUND AT LOW SPEEDS

The difference between a top-notch tape editor and a rank amateur can be expressed in a very few words: The former knows *where to cut* and the latter does not. To learn where to cut takes much time and practice. It is impossible to acquire this ability overnight. A working knowledge of sound, phonetics, and music helps, but practice is the key to success in producing well-edited sound. We may begin with practice in the recognition of sound at low speeds.

Sound on tape (or any magnetic medium) is made up of magnetic marks, as we might call them. These marks, let us say, are recorded at a speed of 7 1/2 in. per sec. When we play them back at that speed, the reproduced sound is exactly like the original, allowing for the grade of fidelity of the particular machine used. If sound recorded at one speed is reproduced at a *lower* speed, the frequency decreases and the sound is dragged out in articulation. Thus, if a tone that had a frequency of 1000 cy per sec was recorded at a speed of 30 in. per sec and played back at a speed of 15 in. per sec, the frequency of the tone would be 500 cycles. So on down the scale. At 7 1/2 in. per sec the tone would be 250 cycles and at 3 3/4 in. per sec, 125 cycles. It is obvious, then, that if we are to recognize sounds at very low speeds—for instance, the speeds at which we pull tape through a machine by hand while editing—we shall require considerable practice. Do not lose sight of the fact that you have to recognize the sound before you can decide where to cut it. Shall we emphasize, then, that practice, and still more practice, is indicated? As you will see later, especially in the chapters on radio broadcasting practice and on motion-picture and television techniques, machines have been built with visual indicators of the recorded sound, but nothing yet invented, or likely to be invented, can take the place of the human brain, at least as far as this kind of aural recognition is concerned.

Practice in acquiring the ability to recognize sounds at low speeds should begin with the fricative sounds of *f, v, s,* and *z* and with the hard sounds of *t, b, p, d,* and so on. At very slow speeds, there is great similarity between the sound of *t* and the sound of *s,* for example. The beginning tongue-click constitutes almost the only real difference. After you have gained the ability to recognize all the hard consonant sounds, begin on the vowel and diphthong sounds, those of *a, e, i, o, u,* and their various combinations. Learn to differentiate between sounds almost similar; after a while you will find that recognition of sounds becomes automatic, and you will have very little difficulty in recognizing normal sounds of speech at low editing speed. It helps a great deal if, in practicing, you learn to turn the tape reels by hand at a constant, slow speed while learning.

REVERSE-LISTENING

The process of learning to recognize speech sounds at lower than normal speeds might be expedited if at the same time one were to learn to recognize sound played in reverse at the same low speeds. E. W. Kellogg, writing in the *Journal of the Acoustical Society of America* (vol. 10, pp. 324–326, 1939) pointed out the greater ease of recognition of most phonetic sounds when they were heard in reverse. This phenomenon, reverse recognition, was observed and used by the writer in editing as early as 1947. In 1950, Dr. W. Meyer-Eppler, of the Phonetics Institute of the University of Bonn, Germany, writing in the *Journal of the Acoustical Society of Amer-*

ica (vol. 22, no. 6, 1950) said, "It is a well-known fact that the ear may recognize speech sounds by hearing the *reversed* record, where the context would often mislead it in normal playing, even when we are accustomed to listening phonetically."

This "reverse-listening" technique, if we may call it such, is especially valuable when one is trying to cut within a combination sound or diphthong. In normal listening, at the regular forward speeds as recorded, we are apt to supply the missing sounds out of our own imagination. Although we cannot cut an *imagined* sound, we must, when editing, leave space in which the imagined sound *may* occur. (If this sounds devious to you, just leave it for a while! It will be clear in a few more pages.) During reverse-listening we are forced to listen to actual sound, and we find that we can then separate from each other sounds that could not otherwise be separated by our hearing.

An example of the use of reverse-listening is the following: In 1947 or thereabouts, the writer edited a radio program called "We Went Back" (Columbia Broadcasting System). A number of recordings made on wire and disks by CBS correspondents while they were revisiting various battlefields of World War II were later copied to 7.5-in.-per-sec tape and edited for the program. One of these correspondents crossed from England to France and the Normandy beaches aboard a Channel steamer. As it happened, he accidentally called the "steamer" a "streamer," and the *r* had to be cut out of the word. The operation of cutting sound recorded at 7.5-in.-per-sec is not easy. The *t* sound is very short and not very pronounced; the *r* sound is also short in duration and is not easily recognized at low speed. By reversing the tape's direction, however, it was possible to recognize the *r* much more easily, and this, in turn, enabled the editor to cut it out cleanly.

In practicing with the reverse-listening method, note that sounds like beginning *d, f, k,* and so on lose their hard character and seem to be less definitely voiced than in the normal direction of playback. Good loudspeaker equipment and a quiet editing room are required if you are to hear them clearly.

SPEECH CHARACTERISTICS

MOOD

After you have learned to recognize and edit speech sounds of all kinds and combinations, you are ready to undertake the cutting of connected speech. In this category of editing there are many things to consider, first among them being what we call "mood." One of the most fascinating aspects of editing is that we are dealing, most of the time, with human reactions and sensibilities. We learn to recognize the "mood" of a series of words. We sense sorrow, gladness—all the emotions—expressed in the way words are spoken. True it is that the human voice is the most superb musical instrument ever known. But it is easily possible to ruin a fine expression by careless editing; edited mood must match original mood. In condensing a speech one should not jump from a sentence that is in one mood to another sentence that expresses an entirely different mood. It *must not* be done—even if the two sentences make perfect sense in all other respects. Very few people, as we can hear by their recorded voices, remain in any one mood for any length of time. Moods change, perhaps ever so slightly, but still they change perceptibly, and although the changes are not striking in the unedited speech, they are immediately noticeable in a crudely edited version. Since the primary reason for editing is to improve a recording, the editor should learn to match moods, thus not losing the real meaning and color of the recording.

PACE

Every speaker has his own pace in speaking; it will change according to his mood, but with each mood there will be a corresponding pace. Now, pace concerns the periods between words as well as the words themselves. We must allow for breathing sounds, for "ers" and "ahems" and all the other vocal tricks that everyone plays with his speech apparatus. There is a very simple way to maintain a speaker's pace; it is also a very efficient way to edit speech. *Say* the edited version to yourself *before* you cut the tape; if you can *say* it easily and in good rhythm, you can cut the tape to *sound* the same way. Then, cut from sound to sound. Do *not* cut in the middle of so-called "quiet" tape unless you can't avoid it. For example, suppose we had to edit this sentence: "John, my big brother, is home in bed." We want to cut out the phrase "my big brother." How would you say what remains? Would you say, "John"—pause—"is home in bed," or would you say, "Johnis home in bed"? The normal pace would be, if the word *John* was accented correctly, one with practically no space between the word "John" and the word "is." In some cases, if the "John" was accented too clearly and thus indicated that a word beginning with a consonant was to follow ("my"), it might make a smoother editing job to cut the *i* of "is" and make the sentence "John's home in bed." The final criterion is how the finished sentence sounds. If it sounds natural, then it is right. If it does not sound *perfectly* natural, then it is *completely* wrong.

RHYTHMIC SOUNDS

When there is a rhythmic sound in the background of the material you are editing, you *must* edit to the rhythm of the sound, or the version will not sound right. The ticking of a clock, the clicking of railroad car wheels on rail-ends, or any kind of repetitively patterned sound in the background should be retained in its original rhythm. In some cases this can be done without too much trouble, even if it means transposing the rhythmic sounds from one spot to another in the edited tape. In other cases dubbing is the only way it can be done properly; we shall get a glimpse of this operation shortly.

SPEECH HABITS

You will notice, while using the "say it to yourself" method, that a speaker has speech habits that result in clipping certain sounds at the ends of words, or he may slur certain sounds and not even pronounce others. These speech habits must be retained in editing, or else the person's character will apparently be changed. Very often, especially in the editing of radio program material, an attempt is made to eliminate coughs and "ers" completely. When this is done (very often it cannot be done owing to slurring together of the "er" and the following beginning of a word), the speech acquires a strangely clipped character. Strive for naturalness in editing at all times—mechanical speech is not human, not natural, and certainly not credible.

INFLECTION

Inflection in pronouncing words often gives them definite meaning, and that definite meaning applies only in the context in which the word is used. It is the way in which words are inflected that makes speech musical and worth listening to. Read a speech by some modern orator, let us say Winston Churchill, and then, if you can, listen to a recording of the same speech. What a world of meaning he gives his words—merely by the way he intones and inflects them. The same word at various times may be serious or laugh-provoking, sarcastic or guileless, bitter or gay. Inflection poses a problem in editing that is truly insurmountable; it is difficult to use a heavily inflected word except in its natural context. The only exceptions to this rule—and there are two—are these: A speech may be cut abruptly after a heavily inflected word by: 1. a sound like a cough, 2. applause, or 3. another speaker interrupting at that point. For example, let us take the following sentence: "On Wednesday next the ship will dock." We want to edit it to read, "On Wednesday the ship will dock." The inflection at "day" is up, to lead into "next" naturally. If "next" is cut, two things happen. The "day" of "Wednesday" is left with an unnatural up-inflection, and the sound of "day," as it precedes "next," is different from the sound it would have had if it had preceded "the." Say it to yourself—you will hear the truth in the above statement. People shape their lips in anticipation of pronouncing sounds in certain ways. The more you study speech editing, the more you will appreciate this fact. The safest way, then, to edit speech complicated by inflections is to avoid cutting after an inflection *unless* the next word follows naturally. If it does not follow naturally, interrupt by the insertion of some extraneous sound, such as a cough; then continue with the following word.

CUTTING WITHIN SOUND

Normally, as mentioned above, we cut from the beginning sound of one word to the beginning sound of the next word that we plan to retain. For example, in the sentence, "Editing according to the rules we are following is not difficult," the obvious way to eliminate the qualifying phrase "according to the rules we are following" would be to cut from just before "according" to just before "is." There is another way to edit this sentence, and that is to cut in the middle of the *g* sound in "Editing" to the comparable point in the middle of the *g* of "following." This "cutting within sound" is a refinement in editing speech and sound of all kinds that proves very useful on occasion. This technique is used very frequently—in many cases where a speaker mispronounces a word and corrects himself abruptly. Here the normal manner of editing does not work out well, for when the mispronounced, or garbled, word is cut out, we are left with a heavily accented word but with no indication of *why* it was heavily accented. By cutting within sound we edit from the "good" part of the mispronounced word to the unaccented part of the corrected word. An example showing how this works should make the method clear. "The President returned to Washling— WASHington—by train." We cut from the middle of the *sh* sound in "Washling" to the middle of the *sh* sound in "WASHington." The result is a perfectly natural "Washington" with normal accent. This same method is utilized in music-editing and in assembling program material onto a master tape after re-recording. We shall come to that later.

SPECIAL PROBLEMS IN EDITING

"LEVEL" OR SOUND INTENSITY

We should never lose sight of the fact that those things which change the voice and its meaning—factors like mood, pace, and inflection—are always present at the same time in the same phrase or sentence. We cannot always separate them into separate little compartments labeled "mood" or "pace." Very often, when a speaker accents or inflects, the intensity of sound that his voice projects increases. On the other hand, in order to create an effect, a speaker may drop his voice and change his pace. These changes in "level" or "sound intensity" create problems in editing. We obviously cannot cut from a low-level word to a high-level word; it would sound unnatural and would shock the listeners. There is very little that can be done, merely through cutting, to correct this situation. It calls for re-recording, a process by which levels can be corrected *before* editing so that they will match after editing. However, there are some tricks that can be used where no re-recording facilities are available. They are as follows:

CORRECTION OF LEVEL BY PARTIAL ERASING

In most low-priced recorders and in some of the higher priced ones, there is no control of the erasing current. In other words, either the recording is erased completely or not at all. But if a control were placed in the erase circuit, the amount of erasure could be controlled. Thus, by running a "high-level" tape through the recorder while it is in the "record" position, the input volume control being turned off and thus preventing sound from being recorded, and by varying the "erase" control from "off" to very slightly "on," you can find some point where you can partially erase the tape. The amount of erasing that the tape will require depends upon individual circumstances. In some cases it would be sufficient to by-pass the erase head and run the tape through the record head while the recorder is switched to the record position. As you know, the "record" current partially erases even while it records. Be sure that when you try this trick you have turned off the recording gain-control to avoid new sound being recorded on top of the old.

Partial erasing can also be accomplished by means of a properly spaced series of ordinary, permanent magnets. The amount of separation of the tape from these magnets determines how much erasure takes place, and the distances are very critical. If you try the permanent-magnet dc erase method, it is best to rig up some kind of mechanical system that will move the magnets nearer or farther away from the tape by imperceptible distances. Either method of partial erasure for correcting level discrepancies requires experimentation if you are to determine how much erasure takes place and at what distances from the erase head or magnets. Either method, if carefully followed, will yield very good results.

CORRECTING STUMBLES

Another problem in editing that occasionally crops up is this: The speaker has stumbled and corrects himself in a very loud voice. Even without re-recording the heavily accented correction at the correct

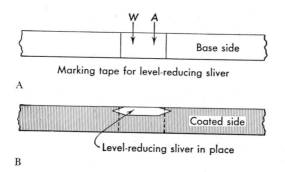

Fig. 10-4. The procedure for reducing the level of sound is simple; above it is illustrated for the reduction of the sound level of "Wa" in "Washington." The base side of the tape should first be properly marked, as shown in A, and a sliver of adhesive tape should then be attached to the other (coated) side of the tape, as shown in B.

level, the sound can be made to seem natural after editing. Here's the example: "The train stopped at Balt—WAshington at three o'clock." Cut before the B of "Balt" to just before the W of "Washington." Splice the tape together, and snap it out of the block. Now play the tape and mark with the grease pencil the boundaries of the high-level "WA" of the word "Washington," as in Fig. 10-4A. Then cut a tiny sliver of No. 41 Scotch Tape, pointed at both ends, just as long as the "WA" space on the tape but only a fraction of the width of the recording tape. Place this sliver of splicing adhesive on the *coated side* of the tape, exactly between the two grease-pencil marks that denote the position of the "WA" sound and close to one edge of the tape (Fig. 10-4B). When this section of the tape is reproduced, the sliver of adhesive tape will separate the recorded tape at the "WA" point from the reproduce head. Such separation will reduce the reproduced sound intensity at that point, diminishing more of the high-frequency than of the low-frequency sound. The *width* of the sliver controls the *amount* by which the reproduced sound is diminished. Obviously, an expedient like this should not be used where high-quality reproduction is desired; but in a pinch, where re-recording facilities are absent, it does the job. Incidentally, after this particular tape has been erased for re-use, do not forget to remove the patch of adhesive, since it might ruin a subsequent recording.

BACKGROUND SOUND

We have now covered some of the bare fundamentals involved in editing speech. It has been assumed that there were no complicating factors except those which were mentioned—those due to pace, mood, inflection, and level. We have taken what the photographers call a "flat" photograph—our sound has only one dimension. But now we are ready to face the facts of everyday editing and add another dimension to our view—the dimension of background sound. Very little sound is recorded in a blankly quiet background—some characteristic sound that tends to *place* the recording is generally present. During recording, the recordist should try to control his background sound, within reason, with a view to later editing. Seldom, however, except in a soundproof room or recording studio, can background be completely controlled. In a home the noise of a passing automobile, a factory whistle, the tick of a clock—a multitude of sounds in all—may be recorded in the background while conversation is being recorded in the foreground. Now, here is the rub. Although background sound is inevitable and enriches the over-all pattern of sound, it *does* complicate editing. Editing a speech that has been recorded with a clock ticking in the background, for instance, requires that in addition to editing the words of the speech (including all that operation implies), one must keep the "ticktock" in perfect time. The ways in which editing against background sound is performed are almost similar to the cutting and editing of music. In order to understand that problem properly we must necessarily find out a little about the limitations of hearing and their use in editing.

THE LIMITATIONS OF HEARING
AND THEIR USE IN EDITING

Alexander Pope, among others, once said that the proper study of mankind was man. Mankind, personified by great investigators like Helmholtz and Savart, gave impetus and direction to research still being carried on into principles of hearing. Boring, Wever, Stevens, Davis—all are great names in the study of hearing, and there are many others who deserve our gratitude for their discoveries. This volume, however, cannot turn from its course into a discussion of the theories of hearing. Our job is not to dwell on theories of audition that cannot affect our work in recording and editing, but to catalogue and dissect the facts concerning *why* we hear things as we do —and then to learn how we may utilize this knowledge in editing magnetic recordings. The primary purpose of this section, then, is to explain the methods that enable us to take advantage of certain limitations in human hearing.

The human ear is an extremely sensitive apparatus. Most of us never can appreciate how sensitive it is, living as we do in noisy environments. At its point of greatest sensitivity, about 3000 cy per sec, it is almost sensitive enough to detect the noises caused by the collision of particles of air as they move around in space, and it declines in sensitivity at both the low- and the high-frequency ends of the audible spectrum. This fact was pointed out by many noted experimenters, especially by Fletcher and Munson.

AVOIDANCE OF HEARING FATIGUE
WHILE EDITING

In editing recordings made against changing background sounds and noises, we have to make sure that we can clearly hear everything recorded. Now, it is a peculiarity of human beings that we apparently use our senses best when we make no conscious effort to do so. We see best when we glance at a thing only casually; we think best when we do not strain to think; and we hear best when we do not try too purposefully to hear. The hearing system gets tired easily during a long spell of editing; once it has become affected by this "hearing fatigue," it can cause us to make errors we would not have made under normal conditions. There are two ways to avoid this incapacitating fatigue: 1. to stop and rest frequently and 2. to adapt the loudspeaker amplifier or recorder to reproduce in a particular way.

A few pages previous to this we described methods of recognizing sounds at low speeds (when moving the tape manually). As you realize, this necessitates that we learn to recognize the differences between separate sounds heard at very low frequencies. Should both the loudspeaker and your hearing be inefficient at low frequencies, as they generally are, you will have to strain to hear or else turn up the volume considerably. Either way, you will become rapidly fatigued. Besides, when the intensity of sound is raised almost to the point of hurting your ears, your recognition of pitch changes. The cure, then, is to incorporate in the playback system of the recorder (it may be a separate amplifier) a low-boost circuit. That is half the battle. We still have to hear high-frequency sounds clearly and without straining in order to be able to tell the difference between a *t* and a *d* or similar sounds. This means that a high-frequency "boost" is also needed and, therefore, should be installed. Thus our loudspeaker and, in turn, our hearing, if the acoustics of the room are not too bad, are furnished with sound that is high at both ends and low in the middle. What we have done, in trying to make hearing less fatiguing for the editor, is to compensate for the deficiencies in our hearing and our loudspeakers. It is best to have the bass- and treble-boost controls variable so that you can maintain the volume at which you find you can hear best for the longest period of time without fatigue setting in. (As an example of how little bass- and treble-boost may be needed, the author used a 3-db boost, approximately, at both 50 cy and 12,000 cy and found that his efficiency improved almost 100 per cent.) Remember that the boost is intended for use only in reducing the incidence of fatigue while editing is actually in process—do not employ it when you are re-recording from one machine to another unless you do so purposely. Remember, also, that excessive bass can induce fatigue as quickly as no bass. If you balance the sound to your comfort, you will be right.

It is difficult to describe the "feeling" of hearing fatigue. Hearing differs considerably from one person to the next; it is an individual sense, and individual reactions differ considerably. When the ear and its neural pathway leading to the brain get "tired," several things happen. Some of the physical components of hearing tighten up, and thus our sense of perception of sound, particularly "pitch," is affected. Low-frequency sounds will then sound flat and strangely distorted; high sounds will appear shrill and ear-piercing; some of the resonant sounds, called "wolf tones," will cause discomfort. Strangest of all, we sometimes do not hear sounds that are present, especially short-duration sounds. What these effects are due to—whether they originate in the physical, neural, or mental part of the hearing system—does not concern us here. If interested, the reader can pursue this subject further. What does concern us is that the editor must be free of fatigue when he edits sound if he is to obtain results that seem natural. While an editor is afflicted with auditory fatigue, his hearing may be working at only 50 per cent efficiency or less; he is in the position of an artist trying to paint a sunset while wearing smoked glasses. How can he tell the "color" of sound with such dulled and distorted perceptions?

Auditory fatigue is of more than ordinary interest to us because it exaggerates the *normal* limitations of hearing. Some of the errors of perception present in high degree during auditory fatigue are also present, but in a lesser degree, during normal unstrained listening. The point to note, therefore, is this: If you know what these quirks of hearing are, you can, by taking advantage of them, do better editing with the expenditure of less energy.

TIME FACTOR IN HEARING

One useful idiosyncrasy of hearing has to do with what we hear as noise and what we hear as a sound that has a musical pitch. If you will take the trouble to observe closely the sounds you hear in everyday life by means of your unaided ears, you will find that every sound in nature, whether commonly classed as noise or not, has a musical pitch. The difference, for our purposes, resolves itself to: What sounds natural?—What does not sound natural? The writer has come to this conclusion: Sounds that rise gradually and fall gradually are not disturbing to us and are "natural" to listen to. Sounds that "chop" on and off disturb our hearing; we hear the beginnings and ends as noises without natural pitch or, if you will, at practically all frequencies in the audible spectrum. For our purposes, therefore, we shall class sounds that have natural beginnings and endings as musical sound; sounds with artificially steep wave fronts and/or endings we shall class as noise. Here is a point to note: It takes a normal human being a definite time in which to recognize a sound as a musical sound. If the time is too short for recognition to take place, he hears a noise instead. If the time is very much shorter, he hears nothing. Therefore, in editing recorded sound on tape (or film) we use a diagonal cut in order to cause sounds to start and stop *gradually*. Actually, at a speed of 15 in. per sec, a 45-degree angle cut makes the splice 1/60 sec "long." Were we to cut *sound* at a 90-degree angle, we would hear noise (at 15-in-per-sec tape speed). In most cases the noise is *not* created by the cut tape passing the reproducing-head gap; it is caused by the inability of the ear to hear a musical sound owing to the confusion set up in the ear by the too-rapid onset or cessation of sound.

It is very difficult, in comparing the theory of hearing regarding this point with personal experience, to come to a definite conclusion as to the minimum length of time absolutely necessary for recognition of sound as musical. Stevens and Davis (in *Hearing*, published by John Wiley & Sons—see bibliography) mention that recognition of pitch at the mid-frequencies can be made in 1/100 sec, with the time increasing at both low and high frequencies. The writer has found that for all cases within his experience the 45-degree angle for quarter-inch tape at a speed of 15 in. per sec is sufficient to avoid this incipient noise trouble. It is not generally safe, however, to use a cut any steeper in its angle. The following experiment makes the point graphically.

If you have an audio-oscillator or tone-generator available (a pitch pipe or any sustained musical sound will do), record 10 sec of its sound. Then cut out, at 90-degree cuts across the tape, two

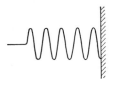

A

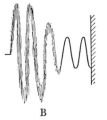

B

Fig. 10-5A. *Imaginary* oscillogram of sound as reproduced from a recorded tape section that was spliced at a 90-degree angle.

Fig. 10-5B. *Imaginary* oscillogram of the transient response of the human auditory system to sound that is being reproduced from a tape section spliced at a 90-degree angle.

sec of this recorded sound. Next splice clean tape onto each end of this two-sec tape. Add another two sec of the sound with cuts made diagonally at 45 degrees. Splice clean tape onto this piece, also. Then play the entire edited recording on your machine. Notice that when the 90-degree splices pass the reproduce head you will hear noise; when the 45-degree splices pass, you will not hear noise.

You might well ask, "Is the noise created at the magnetic gap?" As far as the writer has been able to ascertain, by use of ordinary practical methods, the noise one hears due to 90-degree cuts originates in the hearing system, not in the magnetic reproducing system. If you were to look at a picture, in a cathode-ray tube, of the sound you had edited at a 90-degree angle, you might see something that looked, roughly, like Fig. 10-5A. Described in words, the tone played back begins abruptly, but there are no electrical transients, or "wild waves," in the reproducing system. If, however, you could by some means take a picture of what was going on in your hearing system when you heard this abruptly beginning tone, you might see something like Fig. 10-5B. Transients are excited in the hearing system by the abrupt onset of the tone. These transients are not confined to any particular frequency of sound but cover the whole spectrum indiscriminately. They constitute what we call noise. Whenever possible, tape should be cut at an angle, preferably 45 degrees or less. In some techniques, as we shall see when we read Chapter 13, it may be necessary to cut at almost a 90-degree angle. But there are then extenuating circumstances, chief among which is our less acute perception of sound when it is accompanied by a picture. (However, let us not anticipate the description of a modern technique.)

HEARING PERSISTENCE

The persistence of the sensation of hearing is another of the quirks (or facts, if you prefer) of hearing that has led to the development of a very interesting technique used by the tape editor. Persistence of hearing is something like persistence of vision (which makes moving pictures possible), but it persists nowhere near as long a time. We have just seen that it takes a definite time for us to hear a sound as a musical tone. Now we must learn how to use persistence of hearing or the sensation of hearing that persists in our hearing system after the sound that has stimulated the sensation has died out in physical outer space. We are not interested in finding out whether hearing persistence is due to reverberation within the physical ear, to time effects in the nervous system, or to recognition effects in the brain. We are concerned with: 1. What is it? and 2. How do we make use of it in editing?

Many scientists who concerned themselves with hearing, from Helmholtz to those of the present day, have measured the time of persistence of hearing. They found that it varied appreciably with the intensity of sound attacking the hearing system. You, yourself, have probably experienced extreme persistence of hearing—for instance, when suddenly shocked by an extremely loud burst of sound close by. But persistence in everyday experience is not commonly recognized because it is a normal happening. And just because it is a "natural" experience, we must learn to use it naturally in editing tape.

In normal hearing, at sound intensities commonly encountered, the persistence effect lasts a very short time. The writer's experience indicates that it cannot be depended on for much longer than 0.03 to 0.04 sec. This is perfectly natural and, in fact, desirable; music as we know it could not exist if persistence time were much longer. And how difficult it would be to understand anyone if sounds of his words continued in our hearing and blended together into a Babelic mixture! The Scientist who designed our hearing systems did a far better job than we realize.

Irwin Pollack, in the *Journal of the Acoustical Society of America* for November, 1951, estimated the duration of persistence of all noise frequencies at about 0.055 second. Other estimates have allowed persistence of tones a longer duration; these do not agree with the writer's editing experience, discussed above. For our purposes, then, we shall consider the time duration for persistence to be from 0.03 to 0.06 sec for sounds of normal intensities. If the sound is more intense, longer persistence of the sensation of hearing may be counted on. When the sound becomes so intense that it actually produces hearing shock, it cannot be regarded as causing persistence of hearing but rather as effecting a deterioration of hearing. We are not likely to listen very long to sounds of such intensities. Now that we know how long sound, on the average, persists in our hearing, how shall we use this information? The phenomenon of persistence may regularly be used to speed up the process of editing and to make dubbing and re-recording unnecessary in effecting fairly good blends from one sound sequence to another. In this technique of utilizing persistence one must be imaginative, on the one hand, and true to one's own hearing capabilities, on the other.

If you have recorded a program for your own entertainment at some future time, you may wish to cut out the commercials. There is usually a long round of applause, followed by the commercial, which in turn is followed by the next part of the show. If you cut the tape directly after an isolated handclap and join it to the first word following the commercial, leaving no blank tape between, the applause will seem to blend into the following sound. As a matter of fact, when this operation is properly performed, it will sound as though the applause continues for a split second *underneath* the voice or following sound. This is a "persistence-blend."

Many conditions make it difficult to create a natural persistence-blend. All the factors we talked about before—mood, pace, level, and background—affect the creation of this kind of edited effect. It would not do, obviously, to cut from a laugh to a serious voice, or from an extremely rapid pace to a very slow one of the same or another speaker. Moods must agree. If laughter, for instance, is to be persistence-blended to a following voice, the latter must be in a laughing mood or be saying something amusing. A little practice in making these blends will show you exactly what can be done by use of this technique.

MEMORY OBLITERATION

In the same category as persistence-blending is an editing trick that is useful on occasions. It is useful when there is either no time to dub or no equipment available for dubbing and when there is a difference between background sounds on two sections of tape (or tape "cues") that are to be spliced together. The insertion, between the two parts, of any slightly shocking sound that is in character— a cough, a mike noise, a door slamming—and that has been recorded in the same background as either of the tape segments will cause the listener to forget the slight difference between backgrounds and accept the sequence as perfectly natural. As we noted before, in doing this kind of editing, do not cut in an area of clear background sound, but cut close either to one sequence or the other (Fig. 10-6).

In making use of any of the editing techniques described, do not consider the job well done unless you can listen to the sequence without noticing the splice. It must sound natural—as if it happened just that way. An imaginative editor, for example, in editing heavy applause to a following voice, may cut part-way into the first fol-

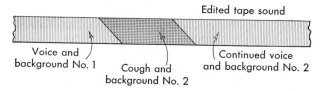

Edited tape sound

Voice and background No. 1

Cough and background No. 2

Continued voice and background No. 2

Fig. 10-6. Attention of a listener to a playback is distracted from a change in the background sound when a different, slightly shocking sound, such as a cough, intervenes between the two different background sounds. Tape is edited in the manner shown above when *unnoticeable* shifts in background sound must be made.

lowing word, on the assumption that if the sequence had actually happened the way it was being edited, part of the first word would have been drowned out by the applause.

"THIRD" SOUNDS

There is a sound—heard occasionally when voice is closely edited —that is hard to analyze. It may be caused in part by the excitation of transient vibrations in the physical ear, in part by persistence, and finally, in part by imperfect recognition. This sound occurs only when editing is close and when one sound immediately follows another, with *not quite enough time between* for normal recognition. This unintelligible sound, which, for want of a better name, we shall call the "third" sound, can always be eliminated by the insertion of a minimum of approximately 1/60 sec of tape from the same background. If, before cutting, you find that you can say the same words in the same length of time as that to which you intend to edit the tape, you will not have to perform this "inserting" operation.

This section has covered most of the main points in tape-editing techniques that, for the most part, can also be employed in magnetic-film cutting. Adeptness in editing, however, cannot be handed to you; it comes only with continued study and long practice.

11

Re-recording and Copying Techniques

"Re-recording" is a term used in recording to indicate the process of copying an original record or records. It does not mean "to record the original sound all over again." During this process the original sound may be changed in many ways or new sounds may be introduced. (This latter process is often termed "dubbing.") Re-recording magnetically is simple, and if done with well-designed recording machines, adds very little to the total distortion. By means of re-recording, many copies (exact duplicates or modified) may easily be made from the original, which loses practically none of its quality by repeated playing.

There are several ways in which a magnetic record may be copied. The most-used method is that of simply recording the output of a playback machine on a recording machine; or, in order to make many copies at once, the master machine may play back to a bank of recording machines. There is also the multiple re-recorder, which does the whole job of producing many copies from an original on a single machine. Then there is the Camras-Herr Printer, and finally, the proposed iron-deposit method of duplication. All are described in this chapter.

It is plain that, in order to re-record, at least two machines are required, one that plays the recording and one that copies it. There is one process that is apparently, but not really, an exception to this rule, the process of "re-record editing."

RE-RECORD EDITING

Re-record editing is rarely used in professional magnetic recording because the process is useful only when the sound track cannot be cut. It is therefore a useful technique only when multiple-track systems are used. It is obvious that in this kind of recording it would be extremely difficult to cut out an error by removing just one track physically, longitudinally, and replacing it with the correct words or sounds recorded on a bit of new track. Therefore, re-record editing is limited in application to the correction of an already recorded signal and is done by recording the corrected original signal again at the proper point. One method is as follows: Play the incorrect portion, timing it exactly in seconds. Then check to make certain that the original speaker or sound source is in exactly the same position, the microphone in the same place, and that all amplifier levels are the same as they were, respectively, during the original recording. Then have the speaker or artists rehearse the portion to be re-recorded, making sure that the time required is the same as it was originally. If all is correct, start the machine on "playback" and, at the end of the "good" part of the recording, signal the speaker or artists to begin, at the same instant switching to "record." When they have finished, switch back to "playback."

This method of re-record editing, to be successful, presupposes that all equipment and audio conditions are the same as when the original recording was made. There are several things to look out for, however, and one of them is a "click" noise that may be heard at the beginning and end of the newly recorded portion, when the machine was switched to "record" and then to "playback." You will recall, from the theory of recording, that recording is performed in a magnetic flux field, which if it rises abruptly, records a "click" on the magnetic medium. Several manufacturers have corrected this fault by designing their recorders so that the recording field rises gradually, sometimes taking 1/4 to 1/2 sec to reach full strength. One pioneer maker routes the biasing current through a vacuum tube that requires almost 1/3 sec to begin conducting. By causing the vacuum-tube filament to begin heating when the record switch is turned on and to cool off when the record switch is turned off, the bias field is made to rise and fall gradually, the gradual slopes eliminating the objectionable clicks. Of course this click may also be eliminated by moving the recording medium away from the recording head before switching to record and moving it back into the recording head's field a fraction of a second after the record head has been energized by the bias current and the audio current. Any method following these two principles will avoid the recording of clicks caused by a sharply rising and falling bias field.

Another trouble to guard against in re-record editing is that arising from the fact that it seems almost impossible for anyone but a trained actor to repeat the same sentence without changing it in some way. Thus the re-recorded part will sound quite different from the original in many instances. In addition to the human factors involved, acoustical response may vary, causing the newly recorded part to sound different from the rest of the recording. It is better, for all these reasons, not to re-record edit unless it is impractical to record the whole thing over again.

RE-RECORDING METHODS

SPEED PROBLEMS

It is not easy to make an *exact* copy of a magnetic recording. Many variables and many possibilities of error are involved. In a typical setup, we have two magnetic recorders, one of which is playing the original record while the other records a copy of it. Whenever it is possible, the record should be played back on the same machine on which it was recorded and the machine supplied by the same electric current as during the recording period. Most machines of the home type use motors that provide fairly constant speed regardless of small changes in the voltage or frequency of the supply current. But professional machines have capstan drives that are driven by synchronous motors. These synchronous motors are designed to work properly as long as the supply is above a certain minimum ac voltage, but any change in the *frequency* of the supply current is reflected in a corresponding change in the speed of the motor. If the motor was built to operate from 117 volts at 60 cy per sec, for instance, it will run at the correct speed *only* if the voltage is near 117 volts or above and the frequency is 60 cy. If the frequency were 57 cy, one would not notice anything wrong while recording but would notice it when reproducing the recording on the same machine, now supplied by 60-cy alternating current. The difference is 60 minus 57, or 3 cy per sec, which means that on 60 cy the speed would be 5 per cent faster. When a recording made at 57 cy is reproduced on 60 cy, therefore, one immediately notices that the sounds are pitched high and that the recording plays back in less time than it should. This recording, obviously, is not usable as it is. It should be reproduced on a machine that can duplicate the exact speed at the time of recording and should be re-recorded at standard speed. For this operation the needed equipment is either a machine incorporating a variable-speed mechanical drive or a variable-oscillator-driven amplifier from which a 57-cy alternating current may be supplied to the synchronous motor. The latter method is in general use now and will be described.

Speed Information. Before we re-record at a changed speed we must know at what speed the original was recorded. There are several ways we can find that out, if the frequency of the current supply was not measured and noted on the recording for the use of the re-recordist. We can frequently find out from the original recordist the exact time of the original recording in minutes and seconds and then adjust the playback time to match. If a piece of music was recorded, we can ask a musician with perfect sense of pitch to listen and adjust the speed so that the pitch is correct. This method may prove inaccurate, however, since the standard of musical pitch varies from country to country and even from one orchestra to another. In the final analysis, the accurate methods of determining at what speed to re-record must be associated with a signal recorded on the medium itself. We can, as suggested previously, record a standard tone on the medium, either that of a pitch pipe, or any other agreed-upon tone, from either physical or electrical sources. The tone, however, should be an easily obtained standard and should not vary appreciably under any condition of use. Tuning forks are good for this purpose, if so made as not to vary in frequency with temperature changes. Electronically generated tones, such as those produced by oscillators, may be used to advantage in those cases where the same standard is available for comparison purposes, both at the place where the recording is made and where it is played back. However, beat oscillators, unless controlled by some standard such as a tuned fork, are susceptible to changes due to humidity.

What all the above resolves into is this: If some kind of time information is recorded on the tape, we can reproduce the recorded signal in the same time that it took to record it. If we do that, the sound will be played back in the same pitch and in the same elapsed time. There are other discrepancies, not so easy to dispose of, that we will come to in a moment, but what concerns us now is the actual method of matching speed.

Methods of Varying Drive Speed. The commonly used way to vary the speed of the synchronous motor, and thus the speed of travel of the recording medium, is to supply the motor with alternating current (from a specially designed power pack) that is variable in frequency. These power packs may be purchased as complete units or made up from several separate units, which are: a sine-wave oscillator, variable manually in frequency over a wide enough range to take care of all contingencies; a power amplifier capable of amplifying the oscillator output sufficiently to supply the capstan motor with the necessary voltage and current; and a dependable frequency meter. When using this kind of power supply, remember that generally it is designed to supply current *only* to the speed-determining motor, which is the capstan-drive motor. The rest of the recorder is supplied from the regular ac source, and only the capstan motor supply is hooked up to the variable-frequency power source.

Other kinds of variable-frequency power supplies have been built and used, such as vibrator-controlled supplies. The main points to remember about supplying current to synchronous motors are that constant torque depends on voltage and speed depends on frequency.

The speed of medium travel in machines that use the ordinary induction type of ac motor for driving the capstan may be controlled to some extent by varying the voltage applied to the capstan-drive motor. Generally speaking, however, these motors are designed to operate properly within narrow voltage limits. If we inserted a variable resistance (power rheostat) in series with the lead to such a motor, we would find that we could obtain a speed variation of only about 10 per cent without having the motor stall.

Mechanical drives that permit variations in speed are not common. The best known is the driving device similar to a variable-speed disk transmission once used in an automobile.

Assuming that a standard tone (for example, a 400-cy tone or a 440-cy pitch-pipe "A" tone) has been recorded on the medium, we now play it back and compare it with the standard tone *at equal loudness*. Do not forget that large differences in loudness give the impression of change of pitch. It is quite easy to match tones by ear alone in this manner, but if there is any doubt, both tones can be fed to one indicating meter and the recorded tone varied by increasing or decreasing the motor speed until the two tones "beat" with each other. This "beating" method will reveal even a slight difference between the two by a rise or fall of the meter indicator. When the meter needle stands still, after rising and falling slowly, the two tones can be assumed to be in step and exactly similar. We may then proceed to re-record.

Correction of Wrong-Speed Recordings. A record made at incorrect speed will sound defective in several respects when it is played back at the correct speed. The most pronounced effect is that of change in level. It must be remembered that, up to a certain point, when speed is increased, the strength of the reproduced signal is increased. At the same time, its frequency also increases. When speed is decreased, similar changes occur—the strength of the signal and its frequency decrease. The change in level can be easily compensated for, but not the change in frequency response. If, for instance, a machine that normally operates at 15 in. per sec recorded a program while running at 10 in. per sec, its recording system, predicated upon the normal speed, would not make up for the great difference in tape speed. When played back, such recording would be found deficient in high frequency response. Obviously, during the re-recording process we would have to correct not only speed but also frequency response. Again, we need several points of reference before we can re-equalize the frequency response during re-recording. One method is to record, at the same signal strength or level, tone on the original tape at frequencies of 100, 400, 2000, and 6000 cy per sec and higher, depending upon the frequency range of the recorders. Then, when reproducing the recording, one could determine how much different from normal any particular frequency was and re-equalize accordingly, using for this purpose a variable equalizer.

METHODS OF CONNECTION FOR RE-RECORDING

Amateurs in re-recording are often perplexed when they try to decide how to feed the output of a machine to the input of the re-recording machine. A few fundamental precepts should be adhered to for best results. We must assume, in the first place, that the two machines are similar in frequency response, or at least that the re-recording machine is capable of recording a true copy from the playback machine. A good copy could not be obtained if the playback machine's response was good all the way from 50 cy per sec to 15,000 cy per sec while the recording machine did not record appreciably above 7500 cy per sec. We must know, before we begin to re-record, what kind of response we may expect from each machine. The easiest way to find this out is to record tone from an audio tone-generator which is variable in frequency over the necessary audio range, keeping the current from the audio-oscillator constant at all frequencies. Then, upon playback to an indicating meter, the response at each frequency can be seen and noted. When you know just what each machine can record and play back, you have taken the first step toward good re-recording.

Matching and Bridging Connections. There are, in general, two ways in which one piece of audio apparatus can be connected to another; one way is to "match" impedances, and the other is to "bridge." To "match" means that the output circuit of the playback machine and the input circuit of the recording machine are exactly the same in impedance. If, for example, the specifications of the playback machine say "output impedance, 500 ohms," the specifications of the input circuit of the re-recording machine would have to read exactly the same for a perfect match to obtain. A perfect match would give the greatest transfer of energy, but, in practice, a perfect match is rare. Generally there is a point of resonance between the output transformer and the input transformer; this will result in accentuation of some frequencies at the expense of others unless an isolation pad of at least 6 db is inserted between the two coils. Practically, also, a great deal of energy is not needed for re-recording, for the power required in re-recording (at the input stage) is very little, much less than the power delivered at the output of the playback machine.

For these reasons "bridging" circuits are used to feed the playback to the re-recording machine. A "bridge" may take several forms; its main characteristic is that it is not capable of resonating at any audible frequency and, therefore, it passes all frequencies in the audio spectrum without discrimination. The "bridge" circuit also provides a convenient loss of energy in itself and may even take the form of a variable resistance or "attenuator," by means of which the energy flowing from one machine to the other may be easily controlled. The ratio of the bridge impedance to that of the output circuit must always be high—the higher the better, provided that enough signal energy to record properly is finally available. Practical bridges vary from 5:1 to 20:1. Remember also that the playback output circuit must always be terminated by a resistance equivalent to its rated impedance (for example, 500 ohms, etc.) before it can be properly bridged. It is this "termination" resistance that prevents the output circuit from resonating and running wild at audio-frequencies, and from thus creating distortion. In emergencies, where proper equipment is not available, a terminated out-

put may be fed into any input circuit that has greater impedance
—never into one of lower impedance.

RE-EQUALIZATION AND FILTERING

In discussing the use of audio equalizers and filters in re-recording, we must always keep in mind the fact that equalization has
already taken place twice in the original record-reproduce cycle.
When the magnetic record was originally made, it was "equalized"
so that all the audio-frequencies it was capable of recording would
be reproduced on an approximate par with each other. In the better machines there is very little difference in level in a reproduced
record between the sounds recorded at 100 cy per sec and those recorded at 10,000 cy and more. The amount of distortion differs appreciably at various frequencies, but we shall discuss that later in
this chapter. As far as level is concerned, modern professional machines are fairly uniform in response over wide frequency ranges.
But it often happens, even with the best of recorders, that troublesome sounds are heard in a recording after it has been made and
after it is no longer possible, for some reason, to record another, and
better, original. There is nothing else to do but to attempt in the
re-recording process to improve on what you have.

Several pieces of apparatus are available by means of which a
record lacking in good frequency response may be improved. This
same equipment also permits the recordist to "tailor" the frequency
response for some particular purpose. In re-recording, equalizers
may be inserted in the circuit between the playback unit and the
re-recording machine. The "roll-off" equalizer permits the recordist
to vary the frequency response of the original recording to suit his
needs. The response may be curved in almost any manner, as the
charts of Fig. 11-1 show.

Another type of equipment, broadly termed the "band-pass
filter," serves to pass on the output of the reproducing machine only
between chosen bands of frequencies. Its controls allow some bands
of sound to pass through undeterred while others are reduced by
varying amounts, depending upon the specifications of the filter

and how it is set. This filter is useful mainly in eliminating low-frequency response that contains too much ac hum and very-high-frequency "hiss" from improperly recorded originals.

"Peaking" filters, which are more or less broadly tuned resonant circuits, reduce response at all frequencies except those throughout

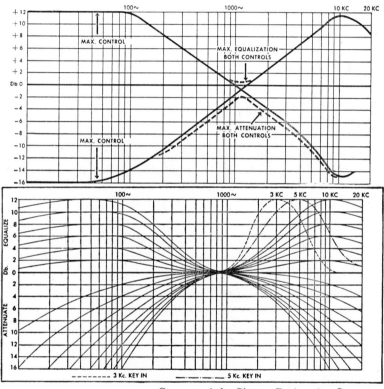

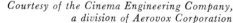

Courtesy of the Cinema Engineering Company,
a division of Aerovox Corporation

Fig. 11-1. Equalization curves obtainable with the 4031-B Program Equalizer.

that band to which the filter is tuned. One or more of these "peaking" filters may be used to good effect in rendering intelligible otherwise unintelligible speech.

The reverse of the peaking filter, an "absorption" or "notching" filter, absorbs one or more particular bands of frequencies and may be made to cut out very narrow bands of sound. Such a filter may be used to remove a jarring single-frequency tone from an otherwise intelligible recording. Singly or in different combinations, equalizers and filters make it possible for the careful recordist to tailor-make his final re-recording.

REVERBERATION EQUIPMENT AND GENERATION

A reverberation chamber has for many years been considered part of the equipment of a first-class sound studio. It is nothing more than a totally enclosed room, with "hard" or reflecting surfaces, in which are placed a microphone and a loudspeaker. The sound to be reverberated is fed to the loudspeaker; the sound coming out of the loudspeaker is picked up by the microphone and mixed with the original sound being sent into the studio's total sound output. The kind of echo, or its character, is determined by the physical construction of the echo room—by the way in which sound is bounced around from wall to ceiling to floor and so forth.

Reverberation time is determined by the distance (which can be increased or decreased as desired) and the complexities of the sound path between the microphone and the loudspeaker. Many kinds of reverberation machines have been constructed in years past in the hope that the sounds repeated would resemble natural reverberation. But it was not until magnetic recording came along that an acceptable medium for the artificial generation of reverberation appeared. For with magnetic recording, whose output is practically free from noise and distortion, sound can be reverberated without the addition of unnatural-sounding by-products, which always tend to brand a sound as false.

Several magnetic reverberation machines have been manufactured over the last 20 years to fill this long-felt need on the part of sound studios, radio broadcasting stations, and others in the sound-producing and -recording field. Probably the first practical recorder manufactured for the purpose of reverberation was produced by the then Brush Development Company in 1938.

Although the designs of these reverberation machines vary, their function is similar. All must first record the sound to be reverberated and then to reproduce it by means of two or more reproducing heads. In one type of machine the reproducing heads can be moved and the reverberation time thus changed; in machines of another design the reproducing heads remain stationary while the signal's re-introduction into the record circuit is adjusted, more or less, electronically. Reverberation machines generally use magnetic 1/4-in. tape, arranged in a continuous loop, as the recording medium, although other materials have been suggested, such as plated drums, disks, and rubber belts impregnated with iron oxide. A description of a typical machine, Audio Instrument Company's Model 42A Reverberation Unit (Fig. 11-2) follows.

This reverberation unit is a tape recording system especially designed to replace an echo chamber in broadcasting and sound recording. The sound (as an electrical signal) is allowed to circulate about in a closed loop formed by the multiple heads of a seven-head unit, in the same way that sound circulates with multiple reflections in a room. The reverberant decay of this circulating signal is analogous to that of sound in a concert hall.

Sound circulates about a concert hall repeatedly, being reflected many times before it dies out. When a note is played on a musical instrument, one part of the sound goes directly to the ear of the listener; some of the remainder strikes the nearest surface and is reflected. The reflected sound and the original sound not yet reflected spread out and strike the next nearest surface, from which they are in turn reflected. These two reflection products spread out still farther and are yet again reflected. At each reflection the sound is attenuated, and after a sufficient number of reflections the sound has become so weak as to be inaudible.

Model 42A uses a process exactly analogous to the one described to generate reverberation, except that the signal is handled electronically and magnetically instead of acoustically.

The incoming signal is divided between two channels for its trip through the reverberation unit (Fig. 11-3). One portion goes through the "direct" channel isolation amplifier to the output, just as some sound travels directly from the instrument to the ear. The balance of the incoming signal passes into the reverberation channel and undergoes "multiple reflection" in circulating about a tape loop system. A controlled amount of this reverberant signal is fed to the output and is mixed with the direct signal. By regulation of the

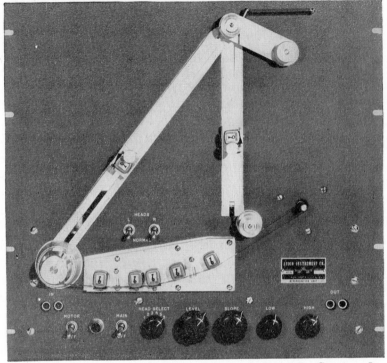

Courtesy of the Audio Instrument Company, Inc.

Fig. 11-2. The Model 42A Reverberation Unit.

proportion of direct to reverberant signal, various effects may be produced.

The mode of generating reverberation is as follows: The signal entering the reverberation channel passes first through high- and low-frequency equalizers, next to the recording head, and then on to the tape loop. The recorded signals are reproduced from the tape a fraction of a second after they are recorded, and a controlled portion of the recorded sound is fed back to the head, to be re-recorded and fed through again. Actually, more than one playback head may be used in order that the signal may be reproduced and re-recorded several times with varying degrees of delay, thus imitating the multiple reflection of sound—with different time intervals—from the several walls of the concert hall. The degree of attenuation

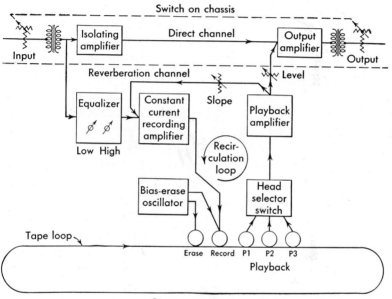

Courtesy of the Audio Instrument Company, Inc.

Fig. 11-3. Functional diagram of a reverberation unit.

during re-recording is adjusted, so that the signal may circulate many times, or only a few, around this reverberation loop before it decays to inaudibility.

By manipulation of two or more playback heads, a smooth, natural reverberation decay may be produced. Alternatively, a single reproducing head may be used to achieve sharp echoes for special effects. High- and low-frequency equalizers modify the signal that feeds the reverberation loop; by their use a wide variety of other effects may be obtained.

USES OF REVERBERATION

For Dramatic Effect. The commonest use of reverberation is for dramatic effect. This effect may be frightful, grand, or barely noticeable, depending upon the original sound and how it is reverberated.

For instance, in most people's minds an oration delivered in a reverberating atmosphere is presumed to have been spoken in a large auditorium. Thus, when we want to *place* a voice in a large auditorium, we use some reverberation. Many large auditoriums today are quite free of reverberation, especially when filled with people, but if we are to produce the right "picture" in the mind of the listener, we must cater to his association of reverberation with large auditoriums. Things, in this physical world, change much more rapidly than do ideas.

For Improving Speech Intelligibility. If two identical sounds of the same intensity, one without reverberation and the other with, were to be reproduced on the same loudspeaker alternately, the reverberated sound would seem to be appreciably louder. Also, due to other conditions that require no exposition here, reverberated sound is more brilliant and intelligible, provided that the period of reverberation is very short. Speech thus treated becomes crisper and more intelligible than before. Consequently, a standard treatment for improving recorded speech that has been too much filtered in overseas transmission, for instance, is to reverberate it slightly during re-recording. In many cases this measure produces an intelligible record out of what otherwise could not be understood. It is up to the recordist to determine the reverberation time to be used. If the speaker talks rapidly, a very short time is all that can be used; if he speaks slowly, a longer time may be used—but only if it improves the distinctness of the speech.

For Matching Sound. Another use for reverberation is to match one sound with another. In many places in the production of radio and television programs, for instance, this must be done. As one example, a talk recorded by a celebrity in California was played back over a public-address system to an audience in New York as part of a memorial dinner. The next day the talk and the sounds of the people who were participating in the dinner and applauding occasionally, were to form part of a broadcast of the affair. Part of the preparation for this program consisted in reverberating the original recorded speech to approximately the same reverberation time as that of the rest of the dinner program (which had been recorded), mixing the speech with the audience's recorded reaction and applause, and re-recording as a unit. In this way, instead of a voice obviously coming out of loudspeakers, the speaker sounded as though he were present at the dinner and no incongruous note was struck.

Although not much in use at present, the techniques of matching sounds, recorded at widely separated places, and integrating them into a program are bound to be taken advantage of more and more in the near future. These methods make it possible for actors in a radio play, for example, to record their speeches at widely separated points. The editor can then match the room tones of the different pieces and edit them together into the finished play.

In Editing and for Eliminating a "Cut" Effect. In order to produce a natural effect in editing sound recorded in a reverberant atmosphere, it is often necessary to use artificial reverberation. We shall make use of two examples, one of speech and the other of music. Suppose that a speech delivered in an auditorium with a reverberation time of 2 sec has been recorded. The inexperienced speaker, in such surroundings, would not notice this reverberation time and would speak more rapidly than he should. The experienced public speaker, in these circumstances, would speak slowly enough for his words not to be garbled by their reverberations. Any portion of the speech that is edited should have *its own* reverberations included by the editor. Thus using this sentence as an example: "Prosperous farms require both convenient markets and good roads," if we analyze the sounds recorded, we shall find that reverberations (or echo) of the preceding word are in the background of the next succeeding word. If we were to cut out the words "both convenient markets and," we would find that we had cut in a way that left the echo of the original word "and" more or less prominent in the background of the word "good." Properly it should not be there, if the edited version is to sound completely natural. The method of making the edited version sound natural is to reverberate the whole speech artificially after the editing has been completed. In this way the original echoes will be submerged by a slightly greater level of artificial echo.

In cutting music, say a chorus played by an orchestra in reverberant surroundings, we are sometimes confronted with a similar situation. Sometimes it may not even be reverberation that causes our difficulty but the natural "overhang" or resonances of the instruments themselves. Ordinarily the editor will cut music either at a rest, when reverberance and overhang have ceased, or on two identical sounds, in precise rhythm. If it is not possible to cut according to one of these two methods, either of two other techniques is possible. One way is to cut *after* the last sound that one wants to include and just *before* the sound that is to be cut out. Then splice blank tape or film to this sequence and re-record it to fresh tape through a reverberation machine, fading in (turning *on* the level control to the proper level) just before the last note. Now this bit of re-recorded reverberated music can be put into its proper place in the whole piece, and in place of the natural reverberations that normally would "hang over" the last edited sound, we have artificial overhang or reverberation, as the case may be. If this technique has been performed correctly, in proper tempo and level, the cut cannot be observed, not even by the musicians who played the piece of music.

The other technique is to make the needed cut, splicing in enough blank tape or film to preserve the tempo, and then to re-record the whole piece of music through the reverberation facilities. When using this method one must be sure to increase the reverberation most at the exact spot where it is needed, else a noticeable difference in reverberance will still be noticed at the cut spot. As mentioned before, a sound that has the property of reverberance seems louder than a sound that does not have reverberation. Therefore, it is well, in this instance at least, to heed the level-indicating meter less and trust more to your hearing, provided that you are certain that your monitoring facilities can reproduce the complete range of frequencies that the recording machines are capable of recording.

BACKGROUND SOUND

We may review here a few of the rules regarding background sound that were given in the chapters on recording and editing: Rapid background changes should be avoided since they are shocking to the listener's sensibilities; rhythmic background sounds, such as the ticking of a clock or the tolling of a bell, should remain in the same rhythm after the editing as before. Other observations of the same general character could be made endlessly, but the reader need only remember that the background should "fit," that it should be completely in character with the main theme of what is occurring and with the place where it is occurring. If such background sound cannot be edited in properly, it must be dubbed in. It is for this purpose that the author advocates recording clean background sound whenever possible, especially when moving the recording locale from place to place. It must be remembered that we become accustomed to hearing a background sound but pay very little attention to it, especially if it is unobtrusive. But let it suddenly be lacking, even for a split second, and we are instantly aware of its absence to the point of being shocked out of following the theme or the main sound—be it voice or music—and are conscious only of the break in background continuity for at least a second or two.

CHARACTER OF BACKGROUND SOUND

Before learning the ways in which this background "adding" or "dubbing" is accomplished, we should become somewhat familiar with the character of background sounds, including what is called "noise" and "silence." We should also learn how the addition of background sounds and noise affect the main sound or "theme."

One kind of background sound could be termed an "obbligato" or, as the dictionary calls it, "a necessary accompaniment." This obbligato background would be present in a recording made in a business office, for example; depending upon the kind of office, it would contain the sounds of business machines, the ringing of telephone bells, subdued conversations, and so on. Also present in a recording of a public concert, it would consist of all the incidental sounds on and off the stage—the rustling of the audience during intermissions, the buzzing of whispering people, all the sounds created by a typical audience. All these obbligatos may be included in one category: They are recognizable sounds and possess a distinct character of their own. They also possess rhythm in some of their aspects, as in the rhythm of an adding machine or the cadence of applause, a rhythm that is not sharply defined nor regular, but that nevertheless has a recurring time period.

The next kind of background sound we call "noise." Just what is "noise"? Dayton Clarence Miller, in *The Science of Musical Sounds* (New York: The Macmillan Company), says on page 22, " . . . noise is a sound of too short duration or too complex structure to be analyzed or understood by the ear." It is not within our province in this book to digress into a discussion of the nature of noise and nature of musical tone. Suffice it for our purposes if we can tell the point of cleavage between noise and sound that has musical pitch. If there is a definite pitch, we may class it as "tone"; if there is none, we may call it "noise." Noise may have all the qualities of sound except pitch. If it had pitch it would not be classified as noise but as musical tone. As D. C. Miller has it (page 25), "Tones are sounds having such continuity and definiteness that their characteristics may be appreciated by the ear, thus rendering them useful for musical purposes; these characteristics are *pitch* or frequency, loudness or intensity, and quality or tone color."

In editing sound we notice the following phenomena: (1) Noise is made conspicuous generally by its sudden disappearance or by a sudden change from one kind of noise background to another. (2) We hear noise if a musical sound, because of poor editing, is played back too rapidly for recognition. Matching noise should always be dubbed in to cover a particularly quiet spot between two sequences that have the same noise background. If noise background changes suddenly from one type to another, the two kinds should be blended by a careful re-recording being made.

There is no such thing, except in the sound laboratory, as an absolutely quiet background. There may be varying degrees of noise and of reverberation, but absolutely quiet backgrounds are rarely encountered. We speak of "room tone" in editing, frequently, and we try, when dubbing in covering sound, to match this room tone or characteristic background. The careful worker, using high-grade equipment and possessing good hearing, will be able to discern the difference between one room tone and another. If we disregard the rules of editing in this respect and cut abruptly from one room tone or background to another, the result is incongruous and shocking to the ear.

MASKING

"Masking" occurs in our hearing when one sound, or tone, makes it difficult for us to hear another sound. It is a phenomenon that has been explored by many workers in the field of hearing, but no definite description of all its effects can be laid down here. We all know that masking affects our hearing—how much, however, must be determined in each individual case by trial and experiment.

In the process of mixing sounds during re-recording and dubbing, we must find out what the resultant sound will be if a number of separate sounds of differing intensities and frequencies are mixed together and recorded. The literature on hearing has not as yet presented us with enough facts about masking to enable us to determine in advance approximately of what the total sound as heard will consist. Therefore, when mixing sound during re-recording or dubbing to match another already recorded, composite sound, we should listen for any suggestion of difference existing between the two, making adjustments of level and quality until the composites match each other exactly. An example will make this a little clearer, perhaps. We have a recording, made on a battlefield in France, of an interview between a foreign correspondent and a French woman. About halfway through the original interview, the correspondent noticed planes passing overhead but continued recording. When the record was edited for use in a radio broadcast, it had to be done in such a way that in the edited version of the interview there was an abrupt transition from airplane-propeller background to clear background. Since, obviously, the airplane noise could not be taken out of the first part, the only possible procedure was to add, by dubbing it in, propeller sound to the clear background of the second part. Luckily, enough airplane sound had been recorded during a pause in the interview to make an authentic dub possible. Otherwise it might have been necessary to use a different airplane sound, recorded elsewhere, for the dubbing. The approximate level of the noise could be judged by noticing the indications of the output meter between the peaks of the voices of the correspondent and his interviewee. When the airplane sound was dubbed in at this level, the effect was just the same as in the original recording. The voices had the slightly "warbled" quality peculiar to the situation; their pitches had not changed, and the airplane sound, as recorded behind the first part of the interview, was in perfect rhythm with the original.

PITCH CHANGED BY MASKING

One of the effects noticed in dubbing and re-recording sound magnetically is the change in pitch in sound "A" that takes place as sound "A" is influenced by sound "B." This effect might be due to a number of causes, possibly mostly subjective. Perceived pitch might change because of "beats" between nearly identical frequencies of sound as heard because of masking of some frequencies by others, or possibly because of intermodulation effects in the magnetic recording medium. The exact cause is not known by the writer at this time, but experience has shown that changes in pitch do take place when separate sounds are mixed together to make a composite sound. This effect is most pronounced in the dubbing in of a noise or room-tone background to a bass voice; the voice then goes up in pitch perceptibly. A recording of a man's voice, made in a "dead" or nonreverberant location, may be made to sound more "alive" or reverberant, simply by re-recording it with a slight noise background or room tone. Of course, to make the voice itself reverberant requires that it be re-recorded through an echo chamber or magnetic reverberation machine.

The quality of re-recording depends in the final analysis upon the ability of the recordist to match sounds and to create new composite sound structures out of the basic ingredients. Many standard accessories are available to perform this work, some of which have been detailed here. Effects can be created by the use of seemingly incongruous articles, like electric fans, tubs of water, and all the other "effects" for creating and distorting sound that are now commonly used in sound recording. The artistry of the final re-recording will reflect the artistry of the recordist.

DUBBING METHODS

Producing a composite recording, made out of several separate recordings dubbed in at specific times and at predetermined levels of sound, is an undertaking requiring considerable know-how and experience. As we have just seen, many factors concerning the sound quality must be considered; as we shall see now, we have also to think of time and level. "Dubbing in" sound requires a minimum of three sound-producing and -recording devices, as noted previously. Since we are interested in magnetic recording, let these three devices be magnetic recorders, although two of them may well be disk playback machines, film sound reproducers, or microphone and preamplifier combinations. We have our apparatus so hooked up that we can produce any effect needed for the particular re-recording we are making (Fig. 11-4).

CUEING METHODS

The important things for us to know now are: When, and how, do we "cue in" a desired sound? When and how do we "cue" it out? What intensity should the sound have? There are several ways in which these operations can be performed; each requires a "cue," either a visible or an audible point at which the sound is to be "dubbed in." Usually, since we are working in sound, the cues are sounds and generally consist of words. The machine containing the sound to be dubbed in is in readiness; it is set so that its output level at a certain position of the potentiometer controlling its level (in the mixing unit) is known, but the machine is not turned on. For example, door-opening and traffic noises are to be dubbed into a

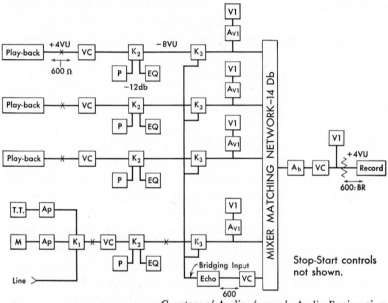

Courtesy of Audio, *formerly* Audio Engineering

Fig. 11-4. Diagram of a re-recording hookup. (From Joel Tall, "The Art of Tape Recording," *Audio Engineering,* June 1950)

dialogue already recorded and edited. The place where the noise is to be inserted is at the end of the cue sentence, "Open the door, Frank." The re-recordist has "cued" the dubbing machine to begin to play back the sound in exactly one second after he starts the machine. (Most machines reach normal speed within one second.) He knows, because he has played back the recorded dialogue, that the cue sentence is exactly one second long, from "Open" to "Frank." He can, if he wishes, have the recorded door-opening "click" come immediately after the word "Frank," but his better judgment, or the judgment of the director of the program, indicates an elapsed time between "Frank" and the door-click of half a second, or what is commonly called a "beat." Therefore the cue word at which the dubbing machine should be started should precede the end of the cue sentence by half a second. With the dubbing machine set for a one-second start, the first sound will be played back exactly half a second after the word "Frank." As the dubbing machine is started, the potentiometer controlling its output level in the mixer is brought up slowly or rapidly, depending upon the degree of "fade-in" wanted. At the proper cue in the dialogue, the potentiometer is turned to "off," and the sound has been "faded-out." Then the dubbing machine is stopped and set for the next cue.

Visible Cueing. Another cueing method uses visible markings on the dialogue or main piece. With magnetic tape it is easy to affix white or colored adhesive tape to the reverse or base side of the tape at positions indicating starting points for cueing-in the dubbing machine or machines. This method is not much used because of the possibility of confusing "start" and "stop" marks with the ordinary splicing adhesive tape used in editing.

Time Cues. Cueing solely on a time basis can be very accurate. After the main show or program into which the material is to be dubbed is timed accurately in minutes, seconds, and possibly half-seconds, a time-cue sheet is made out. The dubbing material is then cued in and out at the respective times noted on the cue sheet.

Another means of accomplishing the same purpose can be used. In this method the tapes are prepared before dubbing begins, "blank" tape being inserted between the dubs; such tape pieces are exactly equal in length to those of corresponding tape sections on the main reel between dubs. If all the machines, which are started at exactly the same time, run in exact synchronization with each other, each tape piece will be dubbed right on time. This method requires considerable preparatory work and is not used to any great extent in ordinary sound-dubbing. It is, however, used in the re-recording of motion-picture sound where sprocketed film makes synchronization relatively easy.

Automatic Cueing. Automatic cueing methods in which the dubbing machines were started and stopped by relays actuated by a metallic paint or metal-foil electrical contact on the master tape or by supersonic tone bursts recorded at the cue point on the master tape have been suggested and even used in isolated instances. It remains the opinion of most recordists, however, that better work can be done by the old-fashioned audible cue method (the first one outlined in this section), which permits individual timing of each dub as the show progresses and allows the recordist a little leeway in expression. The writer prefers to perform all dubs individually; after all the individual dubs have been recorded on the third machine, they are edited into the master tape.

DUBBING FROM LOOPS

It is a common technique, when some sound is to be dubbed in as a background for a sizable portion of a recording, to make use of the "endless" loop method on the dubbing machine, by which a few seconds of sound are repeated for as long as necessary to provide background sound. Be careful in using this method to avoid repetitive patterns where they are not wanted. For instance, if a "ticktock" of a clock is wanted, the repetitive pattern should be exactly right and sound natural, but *no other* extraneous sound should be repeated over and over again in the same dubbed-in section. Should crowd noise be dubbed in by this method, there might be distinguishable repetitive sound that would make the dub sound mechanical, like a phonograph record caught in a groove.

RE-RECORDED EFFECTS

Many effects otherwise difficult to achieve may be obtained by re-recording. For instance, a crowd effect may be achieved by means of recording a few people talking, applauding, and so forth and then re-recording as many times as necessary to get the effect of a great crowd of people. The trick consists in staggering the re-recordings of the sound, each time copying both the previously re-recorded copy and the original record on the third machine. The final result may then be still further improved by re-recording it through a reverbera- tion room or magnetic reverberation unit. Also, the original sound may be filtered each time it is re-recorded in order to vary the ap- parent pitch of the individual voices. Any wanted crowd effect can be obtained in this way.

It is recommended that the serious worker build up a library of sounds. Re-recording will enable him to secure a "stock" of effects for use in programs or tape shows for home entertainment. Do not neglect to catalog the sounds by an accurate description.

A novel use of re-recording is that of the multiple-voice song or instrumental piece. The technique is repetitive, as in the creation of crowd effects, with the important difference that in this case there must be precise synchronization of each new recording with the previous re-recordings.

For example, let us say we are making up a multiple-voice and instrumental piece, which the artist sings successively in several voices or pitches, accompanying himself. The first part has already been recorded on machine "A." We play back the first part, re- recording it on machine "B" and at the same time recording the artist's second part on recorder "B" in precise synchronization. We now have two parts recorded. We take the tape reel off machine "B" and load the reel for its playback on machine "A." Then we record the third part on machine "B" while we are also re-recording on the same tape on machine "B" the other two parts from machine "A." And so on until the re-recording is completed.

DISTORTION IN RE-RECORDING

You will probably have observed, by the time you read this, that in order to dub a number of different sounds into the same sequence, either of the following has to be true: (1) A separate playback machine of some kind must be available for each separate sound to be dubbed or (2) the material will have to be dubbed, redubbed, and re-redubbed if all wanted sounds are to be incorporated. The latter procedure is ordinarily followed in the majority of sound recording studios whereas the former, possibly, applies only to motion-picture production studios.

It is axiomatic in audio work that distortions are generally additive, the total distortion resulting from addition of the individual distortions of each amplifier or audio process. This rule is just as true in magnetic recording, judging by practical results, as in any other audio work. (Also, in re-recording, the total amount of distortion is increased each time by the machine's flutter.)

REVERSE RE-RECORDING

Since distortion increases with each re-recording, the more we dub and redub and re-record, the more distorted the final record becomes. Most persons can tolerate heavy distortions without discomfort (from 3.5 to 5.0 per cent, it is said); however, we are obviously not utilizing all the low-distortion capabilities of magnetic recording when we produce a heavily distorted record. Therefore any method we can use to reduce distortion of any kind in the final recording is welcome. Such a method is employed and is termed "reverse re-recording." A method of reverse re-recording on disks was patented by Lincoln Thompson in 1949, and his disclosures led to further research in the matter.

Dr. W. Meyer-Eppler, of the University of Bonn, Germany, writing in the *Journal of the Acoustical Society of America* (vol. 22, no. 6, November, 1950, pp. 804–806) on "Reversed Speech and Repetition Systems as Means of Phonetic Research," made a significant observation on re-recording speech and music on magnetic tape recorders in the reverse direction to that of the original recording. He noted that "observers with good musical training stated that tapes rerecorded in reverse were far more brilliant, precise and clear than usual rerecordings." He demonstrated the distortion-removing effect of reverse re-recording by recording a number of pulses of very short duration and photographing their wave shapes as observed after (1) original recording, (2) normal re-recording, and (3) reversed re-recording. (The results are shown in Fig. 11-5.) The following is quoted from the *Journal:* "Figure *a* illustrates the pulse shape recorded on the original tape. This becomes less symmetrical by re-recording in the usual direction, see Figure *b*. The improvement from re-recording in the reversed direction becomes evident in Figure *c*—the pulse is symmetrical or at least nearly symmetrical. (The systems used for recording and re-recording had not quite the same properties.) There can be no doubt that the reproduction quality shown in Figure *c* is considerably higher than in Figure *b*. . . . " (Observe that the pulse shown at *c* is exactly opposite in phase to the pulse in the original recording at *a*.) The present writer

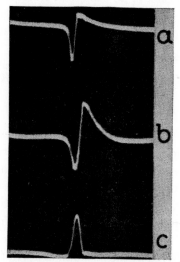

Fig. 11-5. Transient response of re-recorded tape. Oscillograms show pulse shapes: a, as recorded on the original tape; b, of the normally re-recorded copy; and c, after reverse re-recording has been completed. (From Dr. W. Meyer-Eppler, "Reversed Speech and Repetition Systems as Means of Phonetic Research," *J. Acoust. Soc. Am.,* vol. 22, no. 6, Nov. 1950)

*Courtesy of Dr. W. Meyer-Eppler
and of* J. Acoust. Soc. Am.

has observed that reverse-re-recorded material sounds much "cleaner" and quieter and has much more "presence" (the quality of sound that imparts the feeling that the sound is intimate) than sound re-recorded in the usual manner. This method of re-recording is to be preferred wherever good audio quality is desired.

There are two ways to reverse-re-record. One requires the use of machines that record and reproduce at the same speed in either direction. Using a recorder like this, one need only copy the record, playing it back in the reverse direction to that in which it was recorded. In the other method, it is best to use regular two-sided reels on both the supply and take-up turntables. After the program has been recorded, do not rewind, but simply transpose the reels, playing the record back in reverse to the other machine for copying. After the copy has been recorded, the take-up reel will serve as the reverse re-recording, ready for playback from the supply position.

There is another use to which reverse re-recording may be put. Sometimes, in an original recording of loud sounds, it will have been almost impossible to control the volume of sound recorded, say of a gunshot or an explosion. In reverse-re-recording it is possible to control volume, either manually or by means of an automatic compressor amplifier, without adding to the already present distortion.

MULTIPLE RE-RECORDING

SEPARATE RECORDERS

Multiple re-recording may be accomplished in several ways, but the basic technique is exactly the same as simple single-copy re-recording. Instead of playing back a master tape to one machine, one may re-record it simultaneously on several separate machines or, what amounts to the same thing, on several recording reels and equipments operating as a multiple unit.

An example of multiple re-recording by use of many machines is offered by the installation at Audio and Video Products Corporation in New York. Here many identical recorders record the output of the master machine at high speed, in reverse. All the machines are identically equalized, and the bias frequency is high enough to permit the speed of operation to be doubled or even quadrupled without affecting adversely the frequency response of the copies. The reverse re-recording serves two purposes: (1) As we have observed, it produces the best possible quality in the copy. (2) As soon as a copy has been recorded it may be packed, ready for shipping; it need not be rewound since it is now ready for playback.

The installation of the Audio and Video Products Corporation is so arranged that reels may be easily threaded. Control of all machines is brought to a central position, from which all can be started and stopped simultaneously. Ampex recorders are used exclusively.

MULTIPLE RE-RECORDING MACHINES

Several-unit multiple re-recorders have been built during the last few years. The Marchant machine, developed by Dr. Reynolds Marchant of the Minnesota Mining and Manufacturing Company several years ago, was the first commercial unit of this kind (Fig.

Courtesy of the Minnesota Mining
& Manufacturing Company

Fig. 11-6. The Marchant multiple recorder, built for research purposes. (Shown in use at the L. S. Toogood Company, Chicago)

11-6). Others have since been designed and manufactured, including a recent well-engineered machine from the laboratories of Rawdon Smith Associates in Washington, D.C., and another by the Tokyo Telecommunications Engineering Company, Ltd.

DUPLICATION BY CONTACT PRINTING

In 1949 a method for duplicating magnetic recordings by contact printing was worked out by Marvin Camras of the Armour Research Foundation and Robert Herr of the Minnesota Mining and Manufacturing Company's staff of physicists. Although this method of copying has not yet found wide use in the field of sound, owing to serious shortcomings in the duplicated print, it points the way to certain applications that may in time prove it to be very useful. For one thing, contact printing of high quality would not add to the original flutter content.

Many other devices and arrangements for duplicating magnetic recordings have been proposed; most of them make use of re-recording. The most novel departure from all the foregoing methods is seen in U.S. Patent No. 2,559,505. This patent (given to James Hillier, assignor to Radio Corporation of America) proposes that the master recording be a variable-density photographic record, that a halftone engraved plate be made from this, and that this plate be then used to print the variable-density recording upon a nonmagnetic base with magnetizable ink. This ink deposit may then be magnetized uniformly, by direct current, to produce a magnetic record.

12

Radio Broadcasting Practice

The radio broadcasting industry was one of the first to take advantage of the economies obtainable through the use of magnetic tape. At this writing it is estimated that more than half of all radio programs are tape-recorded in whole or in part. With the techniques now rapidly being evolved it is quite possible that, within a few years, all broadcasting, with the exception of spot news, will be tape-recorded.

The two great primary advantages of magnetic tape recording are: (1) easy editing and (2) facility of erasure and re-use. Other minor advantages are almost limitless. Tape recording can be accurately timed, eliminating the need for "cutting" or "stretching" a program while it is on the air. It is possible to record foreign news programs at times when overseas transmission and reception are excellent, for broadcast at a later time when direct broadcast from overseas might be extremely poor. It makes possible the recording of on-the-spot news of all kinds at minimum expense. By tape recording, programs can be assembled from parts recorded in different sections of the country or of the world, making it unnecessary for actors in great demand to travel thousands of miles to appear on a live program. Economies can be effected by recording a series of dramatic programs at one session, thus reducing production costs considerably. Tape recording can result in the reduction of rehearsal time, since the program can be edited and timed without holding a cast, orchestra, and superfluous operating personnel.

The disadvantages of tape recording are few and comparatively unimportant. Actors and musicians, knowing that tape can be edited, tend to become careless and to produce poorer work. Taped programs, unless prepared for network broadcast in a certain way,

Courtesy of The British Broadcasting Corporation

Fig. 12-1. Tape recorders made by Electric and Musical Industries (E.M.I.) in use at a London studio.

are difficult to cut, or shorten, in an emergency, for instance, when a program's start is delayed for a special news flash. Another disadvantage—compared to live programs—is that any recording, no matter how well done, adds more distortion, and although this distortion is generally below the level at which it is recognizable, it will still adversely affect network program fidelity. But by far the greatest hazard connected with tape broadcasting lies in the possibility that improper practice may offset some of its advantages.

Previous to 1948 professional magnetic tape machines were not commercially available in the United States. Some broadcasters used wire recorders for field recording, making use of machines such as the General Electric Model 50 and the Peirce Wire Recorder. In 1946 and 1947 the Brush BK 401, although designed for home use, was made to perform heroically in a great many studios across the country. Provided in the course of the next few years with a volume-indicating meter and with slight improvements, it did yeoman duty. In 1948 the Ampex 200 became commercially available. Originally designed for operation at 30 in. per sec, many of the 200's are still in use at 30-in. speed, but others have been converted to operate at either 30 or 15 in. per sec. In Germany at that time (1948), new dual Magnetophon units were being installed in a number of studios. The British Broadcasting Corporation first used machines of its own design and later, machines manufactured by Electric and Musical Industries (Fig. 12-1). In Japan, broadcast stations were using tape equipment made by the Tokyo Telecommunications Engineering Company. By 1952 a number of professional-grade machines were available to broadcasters in the United States and abroad, most of which conformed to the tentative standards set up by the National Association of Radio and Television Broadcasters in this country.

EQUIPMENT

Standard machines are now available in several different forms: mounted in portable cases, on panels for mounting in racks, and in consoles. For most purposes the horizontally mounted machines are easier to use. If machines are to be employed for editing as well as for recording and reproduction, it is less fatiguing to the operator if the machine design is such that he can be seated comfortably. If the machines are used solely for recording and playback, they are often mounted vertically in racks, permitting easy accessibility for maintenance and conserving studio space.

Most professional recorders are designed to record either from line level or from the output of a microphone amplifier. Some have variable input and output controls mounted upon the top plate of the recorder, and others have these controls mounted in the record and playback amplifiers for permanent level adjustment, depending upon external mixing and gaining. Several models in different makes are available with a low-level microphone amplifier and built-in control (see Fig. 12-2). Sufficient choice exists for any kind of studio use. The output of most machines is sufficient for normal line level ($+4$ to $+10$ volume units).

It is important, if tape is to be used economically, that the installation be designed for the use expected to be made of it. In many in-

Courtesy of Berlant Instruments, Inc.

Fig. 12-2.   The Concertone BRX-1 recorder.

stances a broadcast station will have very little use for studio machines but will need portable recorders for field use. In such cases the studio and field recorders may be the same machines. The studio can be so arranged that the field type of portable machine may be easily slipped into a frame and plugged into input and output circuits. In instances where the major function of a tape studio consists of rebroadcasting programs recorded from a line, console or rack-mounted machines are more practical.

Tape recorders, as far as audio external to the machine is concerned, are handled in the same way as any audio equipment is;

any approved method of wiring may be used. There are a few points to be considered in the installation of recorders, however, and to these special care must be given.

Average professional machines draw about 400 watts at 115 to 125 volts alternating current. Some will not operate properly if the voltage supply is less than 115 volts. If possible, their supply current should be wired separately from that supplying the low-level amplifiers in the studio. If an ac eraser is used in the studio, remember that its surge current may exceed 15 amperes at the instant it is turned on, and that it therefore requires a separate 20-ampere line for its power to prevent the voltage in other current supplies from dropping. Be certain that the erase unit is mounted far enough away from the recording machines to ensure that program tapes will not be erased accidentally or otherwise affected. It should not be closer than four feet to any recorded tape (or even unrecorded tape, for that matter), or to the recording machines.

The ac polarity should be the same for all equipment employed in recording or playback so that the ac grounding will be uniform. This uniformity will remove one source of hum and noise.

When a number of recorders are installed in one room and used independently at times, you may find that stopping and starting one machine while another is recording or playing back may produce an audible "click" in the output of the second machine. This trouble may be aggravated by poor grounding. The clicks are caused in some cases by arcing switch and relay contacts and may be cut out by by-passing the arc to ground by means of a condenser or by additionally inserting a small choke in series with the offending part.

Modern recorders contain circuits for eliminating radio-frequency pickup, but in isolated cases strong signals may get through and be recorded. The results are increased noise and hum, and when the signal is strong enough and carries audio, the radio program is recorded as an undesired obbligato to the regular program coming over the line. Radio-frequency interference should not be picked up if the incoming line is balanced to ground or is fed into the recorder through a grounded coil. If it is picked up in spite of these precautions, it may be trapped out, preferably by a "brute force" trap. If the radio-frequency interference is so close that it cannot be trapped out successfully, the studio may be shielded by any approved method. This may take the form of metallic paint or metal screening. Generally speaking, the closer to the actual ground that a studio is located, the less radio-frequency interference will there be.

Telephone companies will, on request, provide facilities for recording from the telephone line for broadcast. These facilities consist of a special ac operated amplifier, containing level-equalizing pads, and a switch for feeding the output of the amplifier to the recorder input. This amplifier, in addition to equalizing the voice levels somewhat, contains a tone generator that produces a 1400-cy note every 15 sec, which is recorded along with the telephoned voices. Many broadcasters now make use of this facility for recording from the telephone line spot news reports that otherwise could not be obtained.

Very little lightweight tape-recording equipment has been designed specifically for broadcast field use. Where a dependable source of alternating current is available, any of the portable machines may be employed (Fig. 12-3). If two technicians perform the recording chore, separate mixing equipment should be taken along so that the recordist may concentrate on monitoring the recorded output. When one technician is expected to mix and also record, it is preferable to use a recorder with self-contained mixer or microphone control. Then the recordist will have all his equipment under his immediate surveillance, and there will be less chance of error or poor recording. Field work of a nonrepeatable nature should be recorded in duplicate on two machines.

The situation as of this writing in respect to hand-portable recorders is quite different from that of just a few years ago. The writer remembers very well a hurried procession of men bearing equipment to record a senator's comments in a Pullman car leaving New York after the Democratic Convention in 1948. First came a reporter carting a case containing tape and a microphone; next the present writer, stumbling along the aisle with a Brush BK 401 pounding his legs. Then a now-famous news analyst carrying a vibrator supply, and last another reporter weighed down with two storage batteries. In the 15 minutes or so that it took that train to travel from Pennsylvania Station in New York to Newark, New Jersey, all that equipment had been set up in the car vestibule, the senator had recorded his talk, and the equipment had been disconnected. At Newark it was hurriedly pushed out the car door and

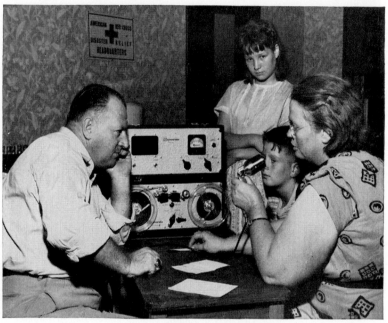

Courtesy of The American National Red Cross

Fig. 12-3. Russ Jones, as Assistant Director of Public Information for the Southeastern Area of The American National Red Cross, makes a tape recording as Mrs. William Clark tells of her rescue efforts in Ottawa, Kansas. The machine is a Magnecorder.

then was repacked on the station platform for the ride in a taxi back to the broadcasting studio for airing.

Shortly after that time William V. Stancil provided broadcasters with a dry-cell-operated recorder that performed very well. Weighing 20 pounds then (and less than 15 pounds now), the Stancil-Hoffman Minitape Recorder made "magnetic reporting" far easier to accomplish than it had ever been before (Fig. 12-14). The cur-

Courtesy of Lowell Thomas and of Lowell Thomas, Jr.

Fig. 12-4. Lowell Thomas and Lowell Thomas, Jr. shown while recording material in Tibet for subsequent broadcast over the Columbia Broadcasting System. The recorder shown is one of the first Minitapes produced. (From, and copyrighted 1950 by, Lowell Thomas, Jr., *Out of This World,* New York: The Greystone Press, page 55)

rent model uses, as power sources, a 6-volt miniature storage battery to energize the electric-drive motor and dry-cell batteries for operating the bias oscillator and amplifier. Other recorders of the same general type are now being manufactured. The small storage batteries are rechargeable, of course, but this caution should be observed: Either remove the battery from the recorder case while it is charging or leave the case open, to permit the battery "gas" to escape. If precaution is not taken the battery gas may cause corrosion and subsequent damage to the recorder.

Spring-driven lightweight tape recorders have been manufactured for several years all over the world. Outstanding machines are the Wirek "Reporter," made by Wirek Electronics, Ltd. in England, and the "Magnemite," manufactured by Amplifier Corporation of America in New York. The Wirek is shoe-box size and operates at 7.5 in. per sec; the dry-cell component consists of two 67.5-volt "B" batteries and two standard flashlight cells. The only operating control is a start-stop switch. One winding of the spring will drive the tape for about 8 minutes.

The Magnemite is made in several models for operation at 15.0, 7.5, 3.75, and 1.875 in. per sec. For broadcast use, machines operating at either of the two highest speeds, 15.0 and 7.5 in. per sec, are recommended. At 15 in. per sec the dynamic range is 50 db, with a usable frequency response of 50 to 15,000 cy per sec. The total flutter at this speed is slightly more than 0.2 per cent. (The above specifications meet primary NARTB standards.) The Magnemite was developed to meet the requirements of recordists who need completely hand-portable equipment for operation away from sources of power. Dr. Peter Paul Kellogg of Cornell University was in a large degree responsible for the development of the Magnemite and uses it in recording natural sounds. (See Chapter 7.) Several other makes of spring-driven recorders are made in the United States, Japan, Germany, England, and Switzerland.

Although wire recorders, as a rule, are not now used in broadcasting, the "Miniphone," a German-made miniature wire machine, has been utilized for voice recording. It can be slipped into a pocket, and a microphone, simulating a watch, is strapped to the wrist for completely secret recording.

Most of the machines now on the market are both recorders and reproducers. As this is being written, several manufacturers are making playback machines which cost considerably less than complete recorders. At the present time several kinds of tape drives are available that derive their motive power from phonograph turntables, using existing amplifiers for tape playback.

In 1948 Richard S. O'Brien of the General Engineering Department of Columbia Broadcasting System in New York designed an editing machine called the "Edispot." The experimental model consisted of a tape drive that could be operated from very low speed, barely moving, to a speed of approximately 35 in. per sec. Timers, driven by the tape, indicated in minutes and seconds the length of tape, thus permitting any particular spot in a recorded reel to be reached quickly. The reproducing head was mounted on the periphery of a revolvable drum, and after the part to be edited was reached, the main drive was stopped and the revolving drum-mounted head then scanned approximately a foot of the recorded tape. In this way the editor was able to hear, repeatedly, the small section that he wished to edit. By throwing a toggle switch to "Blank," the reproducing head was shorted at the tape-marking point. Thus, every time the drum revolved it reproduced sound only after the head had passed the tape-marking point. In order to determine the exact point at which to cut the tape, then, one had only to move the tape manually, in either one direction or the other, until the sound that was to remain in the edited tape was heard and nothing else. If, from the words "tape editing machine," we wanted to cut the word "editing," we would mark the tape at the end of "tape" and at the end of "editing." By the blanking-out method this can be very easily accomplished. The Edispot was never manufactured, probably because it was designed for possible use in editing tape with a speed of 7.5 in. per sec, which became a secondary standard in broadcasting. For tape running at 15 in. per sec, special editing machines are not normally required. If tape recorded at 7.5 in. per sec requires close editing, it is faster to re-record it to 15 in. per sec, edit, and re-record again to 7.5 in. per sec, if that secondary speed is required.

Several years ago RCA-Victor engineers designed a multiple-turntable editing console, with a built-in tape-cutting and splice-trimming device (Fig. 12-5). The sloping top surface of the console has four variable-speed turntables arranged in such a way that they can be used as three pairs, each pair of turntables having its own drive, with all controls recessed below the work-surface. This arrangement makes it possible to edit two reels of tape at the same time, splicing selected portions, as desired, from both supply reels to one take-up reel. The tape drive speeds are controlled by finger-pressure on a button control that is located on the top of the associated turntable spindle. High speed forward and reverse, standard

Courtesy of the Radio Corporation of America

Fig. 12-5. A multiple-turntable tape-editing machine, made by, and in use at the New York studios of, RCA-Victor. Stan Schmidt is seen threading tape into the take-up reel preparatory to editing, and Al Pulley is shown in the background.

speed, and extremely low speed for spotting wanted sections are thus easily obtained. Braking is almost instantaneous; the brake-actuating control is placed next to the associated playback-head. The tape is held down for cutting by means of suction applied through tiny holes in the bottom of the splicing-block groove. Suctional pull is supplied from a built-in vacuum pump. After being spliced, the tape is moved along the block to a trimming section where accurately positioned blades trim off the excess splicing tape in the approved undercutting manner.

PROGRAM PRODUCTION

The methods of producing tape-recorded programs vary according to the kind of program that is to be produced. Some programs may be produced exactly as are live shows, but others require an entirely different procedure. Common sense and experience govern the procedure in every case.

A "delayed broadcast" or "repeat broadcast" is simply a recording of a radio program, recorded from a network feed, that is to be reproduced at a later time. This kind of program requires no special treatment except care in recording and simple timing on the part of production personnel. In rare instances the original program may "run over" a few seconds; time can be cut by editing out a sentence or two that will not disturb the plot or by cutting a few bars of a musical bridge. The director should be prepared to pick cuts that will not damage the content of the program.

In recording a "script" show, or radio program that is read by actors, the director should be prepared to stop recording within the first 5 minutes or so if there is excessive "fluffing" on the part of the actors or musicians. It costs less to start fresh, except after the program has been recorded almost entirely, than to edit out the "fluff." The rehearsal should be accurately timed and recorded. If it turns out to be okay, that is all that need be done; the program is ready for air. If the rehearsal time is wrong, or if there are too many stumbles, the tape should be erased, and the show should be recorded again after cuts or additions have been made in the script. Actors should be warned before beginning to record the program that, in case of a fluff, they should stop for a few seconds, and then begin afresh at the beginning of the sentence in which the fluff occurred. The rapid correction of a mistake in reading script always results in accentuation of the corrected word, and, of course, is difficult to edit properly. Timing may follow any practical method but the beginning or end of each minute should be indicated.

There is very little more that need be said about the simple recorded program. After it has been recorded, any errors or fluffs should be edited as indicated (the program need not be retimed after editing unless the production man is unsure of his timings), and the program should then be re-recorded to a freshly erased tape, which should be the copy of the program that is aired. The edited copy should be the alternate or "safety" tape, to be switched to air only if there is failure of the "air" tape or of the machine on which it is reproduced.

TAPE COUNTERS

Incidentally, much time can be saved in checking the total running time of a taped program by the use of a footage counter, so constructed that it will measure accurately in minutes and seconds while the tape is running at high speed forward or in reverse. Such a counter should have a minimum of slippage and inertia and should produce total timings with an accuracy of approximately three seconds in half an hour.

TIMING MARKERS

Timing markers that are available for affixing to the standard NARTB reel show how much tape, in minutes and seconds, is stored on the reel. The first of these markers was devised, in the form of a decalcomania, by Richard S. O'Brien, Columbia Broadcasting System, in 1947 (Fig. 12-6). Another made by Ampex for NARTB standard reels is shown in Fig. 12-7.

TIMING BACKWARDS

It is possible to "backtime" directly on most tape machines, whether the capstan-drive motor is reversible or not, merely by looping the tape over the capstan drive in the reverse direction to the normal one.

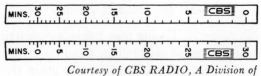

Fig. 12-6. The tape-timing marker designed in 1947 by Richard S. O'Brien of Columbia Broadcasting System. This type of marker was affixed, in the form of a decalcomania, to the reels then in general use. The recording speed was 7.5 in. per sec.

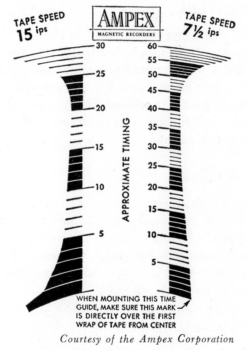

Fig. 12-7. Tape-timing marker.

Recorded program reels should be labeled with all the information needed for airing, bookkeeping, and cataloging, according to NARTB standards. A copy of these Standards may be obtained from the National Association of Radio and Television Broadcasters, Washington, D.C.

In all cases the total time of the program should be the time from the beginning of the program to the last spoken word. In some cases the last spoken word will be a "cue," such as "Network" in "The Columbia Radio Network," or "Drake" in "This is Galen Drake." The music, if any, after the last word spoken, should be timed separately and noted as "theme—25 seconds," or by some such notation, on the label. If the "break away" cue or "network" cue is not recorded on the tape and is made "live" at the proper time, it should be mixed *over the theme* so that it appears as an integral part of the program and not as an afterthought.

PRODUCTION OF PROGRAMS WITH "INSERTS"

Programs that are recorded with provision for the insertion of either live or other recorded material from disks are not as popular as they were several years ago. A discussion of the production methods used in making up these programs is instructive, however, since the same methods are used in preparing some documentary tapes.

There are two ways in which to prepare a program of this nature. One way is to "cue" the master tape, either visually or aurally, so that it is stopped at the proper point, after the cue. Then comes the insert, from a disk, live voice, or from another tape machine. At the proper "cue" at the end of the insert the master tape is restarted, and the program continues.

The other way is to record the master tape continuously, the inserted material not being recorded but only listened to on a monitor speaker. Thus the master tape will not be stopped and started when on the air, but its silent portions will be exactly the length of time that it takes to air the respective inserts.

Both the foregoing methods require exact production timing and no errors while recording or airing. An error in cueing a disk while on the air and when the continuous tape is in use, for instance, might result in a jumble of cross talk, with both tape and disk going to air simultaneously. The "stop and start" method, with visual cues and audible cues, requires a high grade of coördination between production and engineering personnel.

The method of cueing most popular in this kind of "stop-start" broadcast requires the use of "leader" tape, a paper or plastic tape that has no magnetic coating and that is white in color or marked in some way to indicate its nature. *Just enough* tape should be spliced in at the "cue" point to permit the machine to be stopped

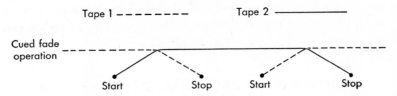

Fig. 12-8. Diagram of cross-fading, showing method of avoiding "stop-start" sounds. Tapes 1 and 2 are faded in and out, as shown by the diagonal lines above.

and restarted without the necessity of "cueing up" the tape to the starting point. All that this means is that the operator should put in just the amount of leader tape that will permit him to stop after the cue and be in exactly the right place to start again on the next cue. In most cases one second is sufficient, although some operators of tape machines prefer two or more seconds of leader. (A standard of 3/4 sec is suggested.)

It is important when timing the main show and the inserts separately to figure on the reaction times for switching. When added together these sometimes amount to 20 or 30 secs. An average operator will react within half a second to an aural or visual cue; some operators are much faster in reacting — as fast, in some instances, as 1/20 sec.

In order to avoid jerky and discontinuous operation in putting a "stop start" program on the air, it is best to provide fade material at the beginning and the end of each segment, or cue, and to start and stop each cue in the background of the next. Graphically, such an operation might look like that indicated in Fig. 12-8. The mixer engineer should know the exact length of time for each fade from one part of the program to the next. The production timer, in this case, should note how much time is telescoped or cross-faded or overlapped, whatever you wish to call this operation. An intricate show of this nature may require several rehearsals before it turns out right in all respects. It is much better practice, instead of airing a program of this type directly, to record it on tape and air the completed result. This procedure permits errors in cueing or mixing to be corrected in re-recording and takes most advantage of the use of tape recording.

PRODUCTION OF DOCUMENTARY PROGRAMS

The documentary form of tape program is representative of the highest type of artistic radio production. The production routine is the most involved of all, since more ingredients enter into its proper production than into that of any other kind of radio program, with the possible exception of the audience participation program. The idea or theme of the program is discussed by a team composed of the writer, the producer, the director, the engineers, and production personnel. In cases where music is involved, the musical director and the composer of special music are also present. After the idea of the show is thoroughly understood by everyone on the team, the recording places and times are arranged, and the people involved are approached and interviewed.

Sound effects and background sounds are recorded separately at each interview or recording location. All reels are labeled, and an exact production log is made, if possible, while recording. The log and notes regarding the quality of the recording should accompany the reels of tape. After all recording has been completed, it is best to obtain transcripts of all interviews. Then the material is played back and notes are taken of material wanted, where it occurred in the reel, what kind of background sound was present, and how long the "spots" are. After all the recorded material has been heard, the wanted portions may be cut out and transferred to another reel or re-recorded to a blank reel in the order in which they are to be used. It is best to re-record, for two reasons: First, re-recording makes it possible to correct, before editing, differences in level and quality that might make editing difficult, and second, re-recording leaves the original intact for use as a safety copy and for reference or as a source of background sound for dubbing.

After editing has been completed, the recorded material that forms the show proper should be cued with leader tape so that cues can be easily noted visually. Sound effects, as well as backgrounds,

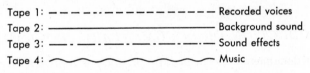

Fig. 12-9. One method for notation of sound components.

should also be cued on tape. In general, tape documentaries for radio broadcast may consist of three reels being played back, each on cue, while the total sound, including narration and live music, if any, is recorded after mixing. The parts may be shown graphically (see Fig. 12-9). All the background sound may be put on one reel and timed against the main reel of the show so that the *proper* background sound is always available to the mixer at the right time. For example, let us say we have a recorded speech on tape 1 that lasts 20 sec, and that near the end of the speech we continue with tape 2, giving background sound for 5 sec, which then blends with music for 10 sec. Then the music takes over for 20 sec, fading into background sound for another sequence on tape 1. In order to keep the background-sound reel running, without cueing it in or out, we could have sufficient sound on tape 2 to play continuously throughout the show and could change the character of the sound played back only when, according to the script, it is not being heard. Preparation of such a reel takes editing time, and many production people prefer to "cue" all the tapes, including the sound, starting and stopping them on exact cues. The sample script will make this point clear (Fig. 12-10).

[If sufficient background sound has not been recorded for a scene, a tape loop of such sound may be used, provided it is not recognizably repetitive. Any capstan-operated machine will drive a continuous loop of tape at the correct speed, providing a constant source of background sound. (A sound-effects machine containing many continuous loops of recorded tape has been developed in this manner and should be extremely useful.)]

It has become the practice to pre-record a documentary program instead of airing it directly, mixing all the components during recording. Today's documentary is an artistic structure composed of many different sounds and effects, which may take an appreciable length of time to put together in such fashion that they appear to be a homogeneous whole.

A top-drawer documentary of this type was "Time and Her Life," aired by station WHAS in Louisville, Kentucky, on December 15, 1948 (Fig. 12-11). In the words of Dorcas Ruthenberg, Director of Public Affairs Programming for WHAS, who produced the program (about cancer),

It recorded the experiences of a housewife step by step from the time she discovered a lump in her breast, her reaction, the reaction of her husband, the visit to the physician, questionnaire, examination and consultation at the cancer clinic, explanation of the diagnosis, her preparation for an operation, relations in the cancer ward, the operation, convalescence, follow-up, X-ray treatment and prognosis.

Each of these episodes, plus numerous sound effects which included everything from the patient's dog to the freezing of the tissues was recorded. . . . When they brought Mrs. B, the first patient, into the operating room, she was practically unconscious from sedatives. They lifted her off the stretcher onto the operating table—she had her hands crossed on her breast—her lips moved and the anaesthetist leaned over to catch what she was saying. I supposed she was murmuring a prayer but what she really said, according to the anaesthetist, was "Will I be able to hear the transcription?"

TAPE CUE #8   Dibelius: Well, you may say the reason is tuberculosis,
                           but in the depths of the thing it was under-
                           nourishment going on from one year to the other.
                           The number of calories may be not so bad. It
                           is possible to live on very poor rations,
                           certainly, but to live on these poor rations
                           year by year and year by year and because of the
                           time, in the long run, it is not enough, you
                           see. And this is the reason our death rate is
                           so high.

DALY: And you learn from Bishop Dibelius that in Berlin there is an

         unfavorable balance between the death rate and the birth rate.

TAPE CUE #9   Dibelius: I only know that during the last year in
                           Berlin 24,000 childrens were born and 105,000
                           people died. That means that 81,000 people
                           more died than children were born.

DALY: And the sins of the father are visited on the children who are

         born today. They must pay for Hitler's follies. On this point,

         a government worker in Essen--Mary Doppelfeld--says.

TAPE CUE #10   Doppelfeld: We talk so much about guilt, but really the
                           children are not guilty and we must do
                           everything to help them and to bring back
                           better life conditions for the kids. Our
                           most urgent problem for the children is food.
                           There is not enough.

DALY: There is not enough, food, ~~teachers, schools. Without books~~
         but what of other things in a
         child's world, are they learning self respect, to be
         ~~and shivering in poorly equipped schools that operate in shifts,~~
         trustworthy helpfull loyal friendly courteous
         ~~Frau Doppelfeld believes children have little incentive to~~
         ~~attend...~~ *kind--and are they learning the 3 R's*   *come in on "3"*

TAPE CUE #11   Doppelfeld: Even the young ones are not attending school
                           regularly. Most mothers complain the kids
                           haven't any shoes, and without shoes they
                           do not come to school. (X) They're sent
                           on the black market intentionally to barter
                           either some towels for the mother or perhaps
                           father has an old pair of shoes left for them,
                           somewhere in a corner, and they try to bring
                           home whatever they can.

Courtesy of CBS RADIO, A Division of Columbia
Broadcasting System, Inc.

Fig. 12-10. Part of the production script of the radio documentary, *Germany—An Inside Story.*

DALY: And they often bring home more <u>misery</u>, according to Mary

Doppelfeld....

TAPE CUE #12   Doppelfeld: They are not learning good things now but
only how to avoid things, how to avoid
certain laws and try and find something--
first it's food for their families, later
on it's cigarettes for themselves and so
they are step by step becoming, perhaps,
<u>clever criminals. That is what we fear so
much.</u>

DALY: Crime begets crime and the black market is a breeding ground.

In Hamburg Lenore Fitze reveals to Allan Jackson the depths of

black market degradation...

TAPE CUE #13   Fitze: During the last winter, even children playing
in the streets were robbed of their clothes.
They were left naked....

Jackson: They were left naked, without any clothing,
because people had taken the clothing to sell
in the black market?

Fitze: Yes.

Jackson: Do you think there will be more of that this
winter?

Fitze: I'm afraid that conditions will be even worse
in that respect in this winter.   *improve!*

DALY: The German black market is a vicious evil that is being perpetuated

even by those who fear and despise it--perpetuated by the

scarcity of food. Trade Unionist Wilhelm Durr is a typical case....

TAPE CUE #14   Durr: I can't live with 200 gram butter for a month,
and what shall I do? I must buy it on the
black market. And if I buy one pound in a
month, (X) then I must pay 220 mark and that is
set for what the employee shall have for a month.
Jackson: And what is the employee's monthly wage? (X)
Durr: The same
Jackson: Two hundred and twenty mark.
Durr: <u>Yes.</u>

237

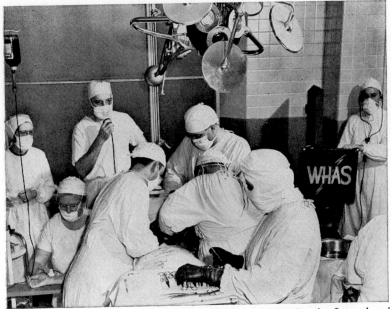

Courtesy of The Courier-Journal and
The Louisville Times

Fig. 12-11. The operation scene from the documentary radio program, *Time and Her Life,* is here being recorded on a Magnecorder. The doctor in the rear who is holding a microphone is the narrator. To the extreme left is the producer of the program, Dorcas Ruthenberg of Station WHAS in Louisville, Kentucky.

AUDIENCE PARTICIPATION PROGRAMS

Audience participation programs pose some problems that are not present in other types of radio shows. For several reasons, these programs are often recorded and edited before being broadcast, the main reason being that the director is thus enabled to cut out questionable material that might be objectionable when broadcast. This procedure also makes it possible to present to the radio audience a more entertaining show than would otherwise be possible.

The program is generally recorded overlength by approximately one third. Thus, 45 minutes of original recording will provide the raw material for a 30-minute program. Some audience participation programs make use of prepared material and scripts; others do not, but the production routine is similar. A log should be made during the recording, and the total time of various sequences or spots, and the running time should be noted. Thus, when editing, the editing personnel can tell exactly where in the reel each spot occurs. Descriptive notes, indicating the "show" quality of the spots, should also be jotted down on this log, to facilitate the editing process. During the same time the show is being recorded on "air" tape it should also be recorded on monitoring tape or disks, and if the expense is warranted, a transcript should be made by a typist.

Before attempting to edit a program of this nature, the director should check, by means of the second tape or phonograph disks, his various ideas of rearranging the original sequences. He can also determine, at this time, how the various sequences will fit together when edited and can time the roughly edited (in his mind) program. Let us say that a show, as originally recorded, consisted of ten spots, each of which is timed. There is room in the air show for only six spots, and they must be rearranged in position in the show for the best effect dramatically. The director can decide where, approximately, one sequence should end, on the edited tape, and the other begin. He should be able, then, to write down fairly definite directions for editing, so that rearrangement and editing of the program consumes the minimum time. A program produced in this manner should time possibly 30 sec over air time, and it should be possible to edit out this 30 sec in the last editing or "tightening" of the program.

A transcript of the program, if available, facilitates editing production a great deal, since the instructions for rearrangement of the show and editing can then be noted on the transcript, which should be time-marked from the log.

In general an audience participation program should require very little dubbing, since it is easily possible to cut from one audience reaction—laughter, applause, and so forth—to another. If dubbing is necessary, it should be indicated by the director plainly so that a minimum of time is consumed in the preparatory processes. Thus: "Sequence 3: After applause has continued for

8 sec, cross-fade to sequence 4 beginning with words 'and now, folks,' keeping applause in at decreasing level up to 'tomorrow,' when it should be faded out." It is then the engineer's concern to determine, by trial, just how the dubbing is to be made. Some prefer to use leader tape with which to isolate these dubbing sequences, but others prefer not to prepare them in this manner. The rapidity of the fade can be determined by trial but should appear natural when completed. Referring to the example mentioned, for instance, if the applause is so long that it does not come to an approximate end when it is faded out—that is, the isolated "clap-clap" stage— enough should be cut out of the middle of it prior to dubbing to achieve such an ending.

Good production of taped programs depends, in the last analysis, on the showmanship of the director and is not any different, actually, from the production of live programs. Methods of timing and techniques used to produce desired effects may differ a great deal, depending on the director's conception of ways in which to get the desired reaction with the material he has to work with.

AIRING OF RECORDED PROGRAMS

Before we leave this discussion of completely recorded programs, we should note again one disadvantage connected with their use on networks. They cannot be cut easily or edited just before airing to make way for an emergency news broadcast and, consequently, may have to be totally scrapped or postponed in such a contingency. It seems to the writer that the format of these script programs might be so arranged that there would be a one-minute "pad" (material that might easily be eliminated without seriously affecting the program) at the beginning of the show. Thus, in an emergency that would subtract exactly one minute (the usual case), the show could be started at the prearranged "late starting" point and finish exactly on time. Such a general routining of taped script shows would remove one of the hazards contingent to their use on networks.

It might be mentioned again that, in airing any taped program, the "air" tape should be started on time or on cue, and the engineer should listen for the first word or sound to come back on the "cue monitor," which is fed from the audio going to the transmitter. When he has heard the first word or sound on the monitor, he should start the "safety tape." The "lag" of the safety may vary from one to two seconds. In this way a possible delay or error in switching can be corrected. Do not, in any case, start both tapes simultaneously; after the program is on the air the safety tape may be synchronized exactly with the air tape.

REFERENCE RECORDING

Most radio broadcasting stations record for reference purposes all program material transmitted. Tape recorders may well be used for this purpose, assuming several machines to be available that will record continuously and automatically on several channels with a minimum of maintenance. Enough tape is stored at the transmitter to permit the record to be kept (intact) for the number of days required. When it is no longer needed for reference, the tape is erased and re-used.

SHIPPING AND STORAGE

Ideally, recorded tape reels should be enclosed in airtight metal containers for shipping, especially if the tape will be in atmospheres that are exceedingly dry or moist for long periods of time. We must remember that ordinary plastic tape, in order to remain in good condition, requires an atmosphere of about 40- to 50-per cent humidity at a temperature of 60 to 80° F.

The same conditions that apply to shipment apply to storage of both new and recorded tape (see Chapter 9 on spurious printing). Tape will not record or reproduce properly if it is curled by stretching or drying out. Neither can good-quality sound be recorded on tape that has been spliced improperly.

The additional time required to splice accurately is more than compensated for by the time saved in eliminating the inspection of erased tape for bad splices before erasure and re-use. In the chapter on editing details of splicing tape accurately and for permanence are given. If storage conditions are proper, the tape will not expand or contract in storage, the splices will not pull apart, and rounds of tape will not stick together. If the recorders are maintained properly, the tape will not become curled or stretched. In other words, if tape is to be used economically, every operative procedure must be carried out properly, and proper facilities must be provided for the right kind of care of both machines and medium.

Enough time has now elapsed in tape recording experience for it to be safely stated that taped program material, properly stored, can be kept in a library for re-use with little deterioration (see Chapter 9 on spurious printing). The program reels should be kept in sealed cans or in a properly air-conditioned room, and a timed script (or at least a timed description of the recording) should be kept within the container. The outside of the container should be marked with date of broadcast, title, and other necessary and pertinent information. In this way re-use of a complete program or of a portion of it will be expedited.

13

Motion-Picture and Television Techniques

Most of the techniques explained in this chapter may be employed in the production of motion-picture and television film. The factor common to both types of film is synchronization of pictures (action) and sound.

It was in Elstree, England, in 1929 that one of the first attempts was made to synchronize magnetically recorded sound with motion pictures. Mr. Louis Blattner, a motion-picture producer, made use of what he called the "Blattnerphone," an adaptation of one of Dr. Stille's solid-steel-tape recorders. Although acclaimed by the press as a revolutionary achievement, magnetic recording did not at that time take hold in motion-picture production for several reasons. Direct-current bias recording was too noisy; the steel tape reels were awkward to use because of their size; and synchronization of sound and picture was difficult because of the extremely high speeds at which the steel tape had to move in order to provide even fair quality of sound. Accordingly, phonograph records remained the best sound source and continued in use, despite the resulting occasional erratic synchronization. Very shortly thereafter, in the 1930's, rapid strides in the development of optical sound-recording methods on sprocketed film caused magnetic recording to be practically forgotten as far as the motion-picture industry was concerned.

243

[In optical recording of sound a source of light is focused through a lens system upon the sound-track area of sensitized photographic film. Between the source of light and the film is placed either a "light valve," for variable density sound recording, or a mirror oscillograph, for variable area recording. The action of the light valve or oscillograph serves to convert varying frequencies and intensities of sound into corresponding frequencies and intensities of light, respectively. The patterns of light to which the photographic film's sound track is thus exposed are almost exact translations of the sound patterns. After the exposed film is developed and a photographic print has been made, the printed sound track may be reproduced by a process that reverses the original method of recording. That is, a light beam is focused through the sound track area onto a photoelectric cell (a special kind of vacuum tube that is sensitive to light). The varying frequencies and intensities of light reaching the photoelectric cell cause it to pass tiny electric currents in corresponding ratios of frequency and intensity. These currents are then amplified and may actuate sound reproducers.]

Interest in the use of magnetic recording for motion-picture sound was renewed after World War II. Doctors Braunmühl and Weber, by the application of supersonic bias, had succeeded in recording sound throughout a wide range on coated tape at a speed of 30 in. per sec; when reproduced, this sound in quality was equal to, or better than, any other recorded sound at that time. Marvin Camras, at the Armour Research Foundation in Chicago, had also perfected a method of using supersonic bias in recording on wire. Machines employing his method of recording on wire were used by the Allies during World War II but found no permanent place in motion-picture production.

Developmental work by Holmes and Clark (of Stromberg-Carlson), by Bell Telephone Laboratories, by Brush Electronics Company, by Heller Magnograph Company, and by many others gave impetus and direction to the work done on methods of magnetic recording on film in this country.

During November, 1946, Marvin Camras demonstrated a magnetic film recorder in the United States. Some film producers began to use a home type of tape recorder, not to record sound for use in exhibiting the finished picture but for "protection" and use in rehearsal and as memoranda. Since 1945, German film studios have recorded all original sound on magnetic tape (using AEG and Opta tape recorders), re-recording the good takes to optical film for further processing. Since 1948, when the first commercial film recorder adapted to use magnetically coated film was demonstrated at the Sixty-Third Semiannual Convention of the Society of Motion Picture and Television Engineers in Santa Monica, California, improvements in application of magnetic recording to motion-picture production have steadily emerged. New machines have been designed and manufactured; new methods have been perfected; and new standards have been adopted to assure high quality and uniformity in this highly developed industry.

OPTICAL VERSUS MAGNETIC SOUND

The reasons for the increasing use of magnetic recording of sound in television and in the motion-picture industry are mainly economic. The quality of reproduction of good 35-mm optical sound does not differ greatly from that of good magnetic sound recorded on sprocketed film. But magnetic sound is much more economical to use, mainly because the magnetically coated film can be erased and reused many times. Other factors favoring the employment of the magnetic method are:

1. Takes can be heard and compared immediately after recording.
2. The cost of magnetic film is less than that of optical sound film.
3. Portability is greater because equipment is lighter.
4. Less power is needed to operate the equipment. •
5. The cost of processing work prints may be eliminated.

All in all, the cost of recording and processing sound magnetically has been estimated to be but a fraction of the cost of comparable work with optically recorded sound. A suggestion for still further reduction in cost deals with halving the speed in order to save film, that is, that split 35-mm (17.5-mm) sound film be operated at half the standard speed of 18 in. per sec. Costs could also be reduced by use of 1/4-in. tape as the sound-recording medium. But both methods introduce complications into the process of synchronization. Use of sprocketed film at the standard speed of 18 in. per sec for either 35-mm or 17.5-mm (split 35-mm) film is the simplest means of maintaining synchronization. For many years people engaged in production of picture-sound film have been accustomed to techniques based upon the use of sprocketed film and cannot be expected to develop dexterity overnight when using new techniques. Whether sprocketed film (recorded at normal speed or at half speed) or tape is employed depends upon the techniques involved and the cost of processing time.

Production of motion pictures for exhibition differs from production of taped-sound television film. For that reason we shall treat the operations separately, first discussing the synchronized-film techniques used with sprocketed film.

SYNCHRONOUS FILM TECHNIQUES

PROBLEM OF INTERMITTENT MOTION

It may be advisable to recall the principles underlying talking-moving pictures. In the first place, the pictures do not move; they only *seem* to move. A series of stationary pictures is taken, the number of "frames," or pictures, per sec depending upon the quality of the work. For professional work with 35-mm film the standard is 24 pictures per sec; this is the lowest speed of frame-change at which "flicker," which causes discomfort to viewers, disappears entirely. As moving pictures are projected onto a screen, each succeeding picture is seen before the impression of the last one (after-image) has completely died away in the viewer's "mind's eye." Thus there is apparent continuity of movement when a given object in one stationary picture is in a position not too different from the one it had in the preceding frame. In the recording of images on film and projection of them in a series that will convey an impression of movement, the film frames are pulled down into position (in camera and projector), one after another, and allowed to remain stationary only long enough to be exposed and projected, respectively. It is apparent, then, that film which is to give the viewer the sense of continued motion must travel in regular but intermittent fashion. The film is exposed or projected only when it is "framed" and at rest. While the frame is in motion—being pulled down into place in the camera—the light aperture of the camera is closed, thus preventing light from reaching the film. While the completed film is being projected, light, in almost the same way, is not permitted to pass through the film until each frame is stationary.

But this intermittent motion, which is a necessity (except in cameras for special purposes) in photographing and projecting images in action, cannot be tolerated in the recording and the reproducing of sound. An individual's perception of sound differs from his visual perception, both in respect to recognition time and time required for the "dying away" of the impression. A person looking at pictures changed only 16 times a second will gain an acceptable illusion of motion, but considerable flicker will be apparent to him. Unfortunately, a comparable statement cannot be made for what he hears. A discontinuity of sound, even that evident at such a high rate as 50 times a second (sound interrupted that frequently), can be perceived. Therefore, when picture and sound are both recorded on one film by the same camera or are both projected from the same projector, the sound must be treated as a continuously moving medium, but the picture must be accurately and regularly placed in a light-beam-and-lens path exactly so many times a second. (We are here considering only single-system recording, in which picture and sound are on the same film. In double-system, the sound is recorded on a separate film and in a separate machine, its transport action being continuous and not intermittent; projection of the completed picture is generally made from a single composite film.)

In other words, the *picture* frames *must be continually jerked* into position while at the same time the *sound* accompanying the picture must be *free of all jerky motion*. This apparent impasse is solved by the simple expedient of separating sound and picture for the same frame by varying distances, the exact distance depending upon the film being used.

In the case of all film on which both picture and sound are recorded, or from which picture and sound are projected, the recorded sound *always leads* the picture frame with which it synchronizes. The separation of the picture frame from the sound with which it is synchronized is approximately 26 frames if 16-mm film is used, and 19 frames if 35-mm film is used. Such displacement is necessary, of course, only in single-system recording or projection, that is, when the sound and picture are recorded on, or are projected from, the same film.

The length of film provided by the longitudinal separation of sound from picture is passed around a motion-dampener that effectively removes almost all the intermittent motion before the sound is recorded or reproduced. Because the film is transported by means of sprocket teeth that engage in sprocket holes punched near the edge of the film (in 35-mm and some 16-mm film, *both* edges are sprocketed), there can be no change in the distance between the film frame at the sound-head and the frame at the lens-aperture points at any time. In this way perfect synchronization can be maintained at all times between picture and sound. The sprocket system does contribute some noise and sound-head-contact troubles in magnetic recording, but, in general, it is the simplest method yet available for synchronization of recorded action and sound.

PROBLEM OF MAGNETIC FILM HEAD-CONTACT

In all magnetic recording of sound—except in the Boundary-Displacement Method of Engineering Research Associates, Inc. and similar noncontact methods mentioned in the following chapter on information recording—good contact of the magnetic coating with the magnetic heads is indispensable if reproduction, especially at the higher frequencies, is to be of acceptable quality. Sprocketed film is not as good a medium in respect to proper contact as magnetic tape, for several reasons. In the first place, film is necessarily much thicker than tape; punching of sprocket holes needed in the edges requires that the material be strong enough to withstand tearing or breaking at the sprocket holes under normal conditions of use. Since film, because it is so much thicker than tape, has less flexibility, it does not accommodate itself to the contour of the faces of the magnetic heads so readily. At high frequencies there may be considerable loss of magnetic energy when film is used.

Another condition resulting in varying degrees of contact, the variations being heard as a modulation of the sound, is caused by

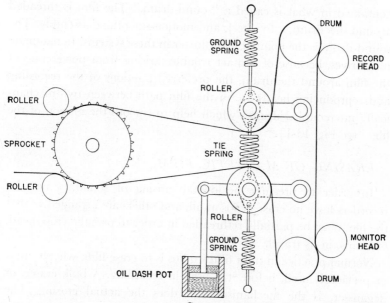

Courtesy of Carl E. Hittle and J. SMPTE

Fig. 13-1. Schematic diagram of the mechanical filter assembly of a film-drive. (From "Twin-Drum Film-Drive Filter System for Magnetic Recorder-Reproducer," *J. SMPTE,* vol. 58, April 1952, page 326)

deformation (during the manufacturing process) of the film near the sprocket holes. Since there are four holes to each frame of film, sprocket-hole modulation has a frequency of 96 cy per sec (4 times 24 frames per sec). Even near the center of the film some of this type of modulation may occur, because the film will bend more easily in the sprocket-hole areas than in those where the film is solid throughout its width. This phenomenon has been called "polygoning," since the bending of the film at the sprocket holes produces a polygonal figure as the film travels over the sprocket wheels and damping drums. Polygoning does not cause quite as much difficulty in optically recorded sound film as in magnetically recorded sound film, since the optical sound track—recorded and reproduced by means of light—does not require that contact of the film be as intimate as does recording made by means of a magnetic head.

In optical-film-drive systems the sound-translating mechanism is contained in what is called a "sound-drum." The film is threaded around this drum, a flywheel, and motion-smoothing assembly. The sound-drum is the point of least flutter in these systems. In magnetic film drives, because of contact troubles arising from polygoning of the film around the drum, the preferred positions of the recording and reproducing heads are in the film path between two mechanically intercoupled drums, which help to smooth the motion of the film (see Fig. 13-1).*

ERASING OF MAGNETIC FILM

In order to preclude accidental erasing of sound, some film recorders have no erase heads at all, and others are arranged so that the film must be partially rethreaded in order to pass the erase head, or heads, in its travel.

Normal practice in most film studios is to erase film, whether new or previously used, before it is used in recording. A bulk eraser, or degausser, is the mechanism that does the actual erasing. The degausser when turned on energizes large electromagnets so displaced from each other that they create two or three very strong 60-cy-per-sec magnetic fields. A roll of film is brought within these fields and revolved very slowly on the surface of the degausser, perhaps for 10 or 20 sec before it is removed from the eraser. Turning

* "The mechanical filter system consists of two drum shaft assemblies having identical flywheels as inertia elements. Both drums are film-pulled. Two sprung tensioning rollers with damping applied to one tension roller comprise the other elements of the filter system, the damping being obtained by means of a fluid silicone-oil type of dashpot connected to one roller arm by a mechanical linkage. The entire system is near critically damped with a resonant frequency of approximately 1 1/2 cycles per second." (From K. Singer and J. L. Pettus, "Building Block Approach to Magnetic Recording Equipment Design," *J. SMPTE*, vol. 59, Oct. 1952, p. 326)

over the roll and duplicating the procedure results in a slightly better erase. It is *very important* to keep the *roll* of magnetic film *moving* while it is in the magnetic fields and to remove it from the fields entirely before the eraser is switched off. Improperly erased film or tape creates noisy spots or "bumps" which will result in the sound recorded at those points being distorted.

MEDIA

Several kinds of magnetic film are now available, all of them made of regulation safety film stock. Film may be obtained in 35-mm, 17.5-mm (split 35-mm with sprocket perforations on only one edge), 16-mm, and 8-mm sizes, this last size being employed only in amateur movie cameras and projectors. The film may have a magnetic coating covering the film completely from one edge to the other, or the magnetic coating may be applied in longitudinal stripes. The studios, as a rule, make use of fully coated 17.5-mm film for original recording, although multi-striped 35-mm film, with coating stripes 0.200 in. wide, separated by 0.150 in. of clear base, is coming into use. On single-system 16-mm film, used for news pick-ups, industrial filmings, and television, sound is recorded on a magnetic stripe opposite the perforated side. Magnetic striping is impervious to normal photographic processing and is not harmed by quite high temperatures of developing baths.

MICROPHONE TECHNIQUES

Microphone placement and handling in motion-picture production differ considerably from those in radio broadcasting or even those in live telecasts. Since radio broadcasting is not a visual medium, the microphone can be placed in the position from which the best pickup is obtained; a microphone, if moved during a broadcast, may be carried by the broadcaster.

During the filming of motion pictures, on the other hand, there is considerable moving around of the actors, and microphones should not ordinarily be seen in the picture. Usually the microphone is mounted on a boom (a traveling crane), which can easily and noiselessly be extended or contracted, being manipulated by its operator in a way that will assure good recording of the desired sound even though the mike itself is out of the camera's range. It has been remarked that good mike-boom operators are born, not made. However that may be, the truth is that a great deal of the success of a picture depends upon the show-sense and know-how of the boom operator. He and the sound-mixer operate as a team. Generally speaking, the boom mike, or mikes, can be used to advantage in most setups. In some cases, however, in static scenes where camera shots make it necessary, microphones may be hidden in fixtures that are part of the set and remain stationary. The goal in boom mike pickup is the best possible quality of sound that can be *consistently* obtained throughout the scene or take. During rehearsal the boom operator takes note of necessary changes both in microphone placement and in the distance of the microphone from the action taking place; he does not try to get an extra good "presence" in one part if, in another part of the same scene, equally good presence cannot be obtained. Although much can be done during re-recording to improve the sound, too radical a change in presence during the same scene should be avoided.

PRE-SCORING AND POST-RECORDING

Usually, only scenes containing dialogue are recorded and photographed simultaneously. In takes of vocal music sound is recorded in advance of "shooting";* the singers then listen to the recorded music as it is played back, "mouthing" the words in synchronization with the sound as the action is being photographed. Pre-scoring of this nature, by use of magnetic recording, has made it much easier to shoot, and to obtain satisfactory recorded sound during, scenes involving motion. In the production of musical "horse-operas," for instance, when the star is galloping along and singing, it is easier and faster to play his pre-scored music back to him from a magnetic film than from an optical film or a disk. Pre-scoring may also be used on those occasions when an actor does not have sufficient time to

---

* Filming the action.

memorize a long scene or when the scene necessitates motion that cannot be followed by a microphone.

Post-recording occurs after the picture is shot, when the actor or actors, while watching a scene being projected, speak the corresponding lines in "synchronization" with the action. During this process the spoken lines are recorded, and the recorded sound is later synchronized with the pictures.

MULTIPLE-CHANNEL SCORING

In motion-picture production multiple-channel scoring is often used. When by this process vocalists, chorus, and orchestra are simultaneously recording, a separate track is used for recording the sound made by each group. Of the several reasons for separate tracks, the main one is to obtain the best possible pickup of each section. Multiple-channel scoring makes it possible to combine the three tracks to best advantage during re-recording. Modern film recorders are able to record three or more separate tracks simultaneously on 35-mm magnetic film.

DEVELOPMENT OF MAGNETIC-FILM RECORDERS

During the late 1940's optical-film recorders were adapted for magnetic use simply by removal of the optical sound-head, substitution of a magnetic head, and the making of some changes in the amplifiers. As mentioned before, this expedient provided a fair quality of sound, but the percentage of flutter from all sources was too high. Design engineers then began to use double-flywheel systems, with the record and reproduce heads in the film path between the two flywheels. At the present time most magnetic-film recorders are of this dual-flywheel type.

An early example of a recording system that employed the dual flywheel is the recorder developed by Loren L. Ryder and his staff at Paramount Pictures in Hollywood. Mr. Ryder was one of the pioneers in recording sound magnetically for motion pictures. Presuming that he was called upon to define an ideal magnetic recording system for film, he wrote "the definition would call for all of the mechanical procedures to be automatic, all manual operation to be simple and foolproof, all magnetic film to be available for re-use, production equipment to be light in weight and the release quality to retain the quality heard at the microphone."* The equipment he produced in 1949 came very close to achieving these objectives. A complete single channel or recording unit (including a mixer unit, power unit, and recorder), loaded with film and ready for use, weighed less than 100 pounds. Ryder's description says in part:

The production recording channel is, in effect, a sound storage unit. Except for microphone placement and mixing, it is completely automatic and requires no attention. The plan of operation at Paramount is to service, load and unload all units at the recording plant prior to each day's work. Two complete channels are sent with each production. In operation the recording units are exchanged rather than reloaded. When shooting at the studios, the used recording unit is replaced with a freshly loaded recorder from the Recording Building. Trouble shooting on production is eliminated. The complete channel is exchanged in case of trouble or suspicion of trouble.

All recording amplification, including the preamplification, is enclosed in the mixer unit. The input to the two dials accommodates either dynamic or ribbon microphones. The mixer unit output is fed to the recording machine. Playback monitoring is available to the mixer by pressing a button. The mixer unit also includes an announce microphone with control button, a dialogue-or-music equalization control and a rotary control switch. The switch positions are: "off," "A supply on," "A and B supply on" with 6 db attenuation in the volume indicator meter and "B voltage" measurement on the indicator meter. A special feature of this mixer is that two such units can be clipped together to form a four-dial mixer.

The power supply is from dry batteries when shooting on location and from a power unit for studio use. The power supply is plugged into the cable between the mixer unit and recorder, thus reducing the number of cables to the mixer unit. Tap switches are located in the battery box for maintaining proper voltage as measured at the mixer unit. A set of batteries lasts four to six days of production shooting.

The recording machine uses the Alexis Badmaieff two-flywheel sys-

* Loren L. Ryder, "Motion-Picture Studio Use of Magnetic Recording," *J. SMPTE,* vol. 55, Dec. 1950, pp. 605–612.

tem of film stabilization and movement. This provides low flutter and extremely good contact as the film complies with the recording and playback heads. The recorder case also includes the bias oscillator, pre-equalizer and playback amplifier, all powered and under the control switch of the mixer. The playback amplifier filament supply is wired through the playback control switch so that the filaments are only fired up when the mixer is listening to playback monitoring. The recording machine is driven by a 1/50-horsepower synchronous motor, either 110-v, ac, single phase, or 220-v, three phase. At Paramount 220-v, three-phase motors are used. For studio operation the recording machine gains its motor power in return wires from the camera. Under this arrangement the recording machine starts and stops under the control of the cameraman. The camera is synchronously driven from the 220-v, three-phase studio supply. DC, ac, or multi-duty type motors are used on the cameras when shooting on location. The ac windings from the [camera] motor, which are normally used for interlocking, are in this case used as a power supply for driving the recorder. On location, the same as at the studio, the equipment is started and stopped by the cameraman. . . . The recording machine loaded with 2500 feet of magnetic film [17 1/2 mm] weighs less than 50 pounds. The feed reel is on the hinged front cover and can be operated either open or closed. . . . There are no switches or operating controls either in or on the recording unit.*

The Tempelhof Film Studio's methods of recording sound magnetically differ in several respects from techniques encountered elsewhere. Beginning in 1950 this German studio processed all sound magnetically up to and including the stage of final edited copy for re-recording to the optical (photographic) negative. Magnetic recording is done originally on 17.5-mm film, and safety copies are recorded on tape. In case of damage to a portion of the 17.5-mm film record, that portion is re-recorded to magnetic film from the tape. The tape remains uncut and is erased and re-used after the picture has been finished. As Dr. ing. Martin Ulner, of the Tempelhof Film Studio, reported:†

---

* *Ibid.*

† Martin Ulner, "A German Magnetic Sound Recording System in Motion Pictures," *J. SMPTE*, vol. 56, April 1951, pp. 411–423.

For feature pictures the print-takes [which average one-fifth of the total footage recorded] . . . are rerecorded again, this time on 17.5 mm. magnetic film. . . . For advertising, documentary and cultural films, and for dubbing of foreign films, it has been found that only a single recording was needed. One magnetic film is sufficient for the working print, for the editing, for the review and for the final rerecording print.

THE PHOTOMAGNETIC RECORDING METHOD

A method of dual recording on the same film, one track magnetic and the other (on the opposite side of the film) optical, was devised in 1952 by J. G. Frayne, of Westrex Corporation, and John P. Livadary, of Columbia Pictures. Named the "Photomagnetic" method, its use proved to be a distinct aid to film editors accustomed to optical editing. The only drawback to its use was voiced by a film editor who commented that he objected slightly "to reducing the transparent area adjacent to the normal photographic sound track by the application of the magnetic stripe." This reduced his field of vision "while running the sound and action film superimposed and made it difficult to follow some of the action on the fringe of the picture frame."

The Photomagnetic method is reportedly economical to use and less disruptive of editing personnel's habits than is a complete changeover to magnetic equipment from optical. It does not require that projection-room equipment be modified in order to make possible the reproduction of magnetic film. Of significance is the fact that the high quality of magnetic recording is retained through all processing, up to the final print. Many films with sound tracks magnetically recorded are now being released for exhibition.

WESTREX TRIPLE-TRACK RECORDER

The purpose of another development by the Westrex Corporation, its triple-track recorder, Model RA-1506-A, was the saving to be effected in space and manpower required. This is the machine that can be used as a multichannel recorder in the multiple-scoring operations mentioned previously. It may also be used to advantage in re-recording and in providing compact storage for recorded sound. Sound—entirely unrelated or consisting of three tracks, in synchronism, of the same production—may be stored on the three separate tracks, each 0.200 in. wide.

A novel feature of this recorder is the fact that crosstalk between tracks has been reduced almost to the point of nonexistence. An invention of C. C. Davis of Westrex, this method of radically reducing crosstalk consists of "small magnetic paths introduced diagonally between one-half of each magnetic head and the corresponding opposite half of the adjacent head, and of such proportions and phase relationships as to cancel effectively the crosstalk leakage from one head to the other. These substantially decouple the two heads electrically or magnetically and are referred to as decouplers."*

It is to be noted that crosstalk, or leakage of sound waves from one track to an adjacent track, varies both with the physical wave length of a sound and with the characteristic curve of hearing. As mentioned previously in Chapter 9 on spurious printing, the recorded sound "leaks" through the thickness of tape, the largest leaks being at low frequencies with their longer wave lengths, but these are not as noticeable to a listener as those at the frequencies where the ear is most sensitive, namely from 1000 to 3000 cy per sec.

Other developments and refinements in the design of magnetic-film recorders that tend to make the work of the recordist and editor easier include a freewheeling-sprocket and drive-motor assembly and also a rewind footage counter, both being included in RCA-Victor's various models of recorders. The so-called "freewheeling sprocket" may be manually disengaged from the film-drive shaft in order to bring synchronization marks up to a reference point, such as the reproduce-head gap; this operation may be performed without the interlock of the driving motor being disengaged. The footage counter, another innovation, may relieve the operator of considerable listening fatigue.

* C. C. Davis, J. G. Frayne, and E. W. Templin, "Multichannel Magnetic Film Recording and Reproducing Unit," *J. SMPTE,* vol. 58, Feb. 1952, pp. 105–118.

MOTORS USED

No description of the methods used in the recording of magnetic film would be complete without some mention of the motors available for driving the film-transport mechanism. In many modern recorders provision is made for operation from 110-volt single-phase or 220-volt three-phase alternating current, or from battery-pack supplies whose voltage may vary from 24 to 96. When batteries are used, provision is made to supply the filaments of the tubes directly from the batteries, in some cases, while a dynamotor (or generator) driven by the battery supply furnishes plate voltage for the amplifiers. When the drive motors of the recorder are battery-operated, a motor-control rheostat and a frequency meter are made available so that recording speed equivalent to 60-cy operation may be maintained.

SYNCHRONIZATION METHODS IN DOUBLE-SYSTEM RECORDING AND EDITING

When action is photographed on one film and the sound is recorded on another, an exact means must be used for marking both films so that they may be started and played back in synchronization. A favorite method is that in which the camera photographs a production assistant clapping two sticks (clapsticks) together; the resultant sound is recorded simultaneously on the sound film, whether it be optical or magnetic.

Loren L. Ryder describes the synchronization process, as follows:

Synchronization can be by clapstick or . . . a magnetic "bloop" signal is recorded on the magnetic film along with completion of automatic slating in the camera. The take numbers are announced by the mixer [and recorded on the magnetic film] during the five second period while the equipment is coming up to speed and stabilizing. Each roll of magnetic film is marked with the production number and [also] given a sequential number. All rolls of magnetic film at the Paramount plant have a master punch synchronizing mark at the head end of the roll. The sound mixer's log lists all takes in sequence and indicates the roll numbers and also the printed takes. The take footage information can be obtained from the cameraman at the end of the day, if desired. . . .

As fast as complete rolls of magnetic film are received at the Recording Building, the print takes are transferred to direct positive photographic "electro-prints" which are developed and used for editing. The transfer reproducer has the Alexis Badmaieff movement mounted on a panel. . . . This reproducer is equipped with a . . . counter and is capable of fast winding, both forward and backward. The roll of magnetic film is threaded on this machine, starting at the [master] punch synchronization mark, with the counter at zero. The operator fast-winds down through the roll, monitoring and checking his log until the synchronization click for the first print take is located. The click is stopped under the reproduce head and a pencil mark is made between the sprocket holes on the magnetic surface of the film. The footage information is recorded on the log as an expedient for reprinting.*

VISIBLE REGISTRATION OF SOUND

Loren L. Ryder has also developed a special machine that provides a visible signal of the modulation recorded on magnetic film, this signal making it easier for film-cutters, accustomed to photographic sound, to cut magnetic sound. Similar mechanisms have also been developed both in Germany and in England. O. K. Kolb (of British Acoustic Films, Ltd., London, England) described an ingenious method for giving a visible indication of the sound recorded magnetically. This method uses "a dry chemical process in which a stylus made of a special metal reacts with a chemical compound,"† thereby coating the film. The chemical compound consists of zinc oxide mixed with a nitrocellulose lacquer. The recording stylus is made of bronze or brass, and the chemical reaction between the coating and the metal stylus results in the modulation-trace. The process has the advantage that "it is entirely dry and can be carried out at almost any speed."

* Ryder, *op. cit.*
† O. K. Kolb, "Magnetic Sound Film Developments in Great Britain," *J. SMPTE,* vol. 55, Nov. 1950, pp. 496–508.

In Germany, Dr. ing. Martin Ulner, of the Tempelhof Film Studio in Berlin, devised a method of visible registration for magnetic-film editing, quite similar to those of American and British design (Fig. 13-2). Dr. Ulner wrote:

This apparatus consists of a driving mechanism (1), a reproducing head (2), the recording mechanism, a special amplifier (3), and the

Courtesy of Martin Ulner and J. SMPTE

Fig. 13-2. A machine by means of which visible representations of sound can be added to tape. (From Martin Ulner, "A German Magnetic Sound Recording System in Motion Pictures," *J. SMPTE*, vol. 56, April 1951, page 417)

drying chamber (4). The speed with which the film is transported is about one third the normal film speed. On a certain spot the reproducing head picks up the recorded signal and the induced voltage is fed to the amplifier, is amplified and rectified so that the output voltage of the amplifier shows only the envelope of the signal voltage. A peculiarity is that low signals produce a relatively higher output than loud ones. This permits even low signals to be easily recognized.

The output voltage of the amplier is fed to a dynamic system, the moving coil of which carries a special pen. This pen is normally supplied with black drawing ink through a rubber tube (5) from a reservoir (6). The ink supply for the pen is regulated by the tap (7) which is situated between the reservoir and the pen. The pen can easily be removed for cleaning purposes. Between the writing point and the take up spindle the film passes through the drying chamber which consists of heating tubes [8].*

MAGNETIC FILM EDITING IN GERMANY

Dr. Ulner continues his description of German film methods:

. . . the sound waves are registered visibly on the recorded magnetic film which is then forwarded to the editing room. . . . [There] the magnetic film is cut and synchronized to the picture film and [made] ready for daily running (review). After the first assembly of a dialogue reel comes the second cutting, after which it is ready for rerecording on the final negative. As already stated, in [language] dubbing of foreign films the first magnetic film serves for the rerecording. Other magnetic film rolls contain the music and the sound effects. Optical sound reels, for example, library music and sound effects, can of course be mixed in. . . .

Only German editing tables . . . of the horizontal type are employed here [at Tempelhof]. These contain four drums for picture and sound, normal and fast, forward and backward running, and continuous (nonintermittent) picture projection. There is a scale which shows the number of frames out of synchronism between picture and sound. Small projection is on a picture screen. . . .

All editing tables in the studio are supplied with additional magnetic pickups. The photoelectric cell for the optical pickup remains, and the amplifiers have been altered so that it is possible to hear photographic and magnetic film at the same time, *i.e.*, the amplifier has two inputs and the necessary equalizing for magnetic sound reproduction. In order to drive split [17.5 mm] magnetic film, the only mechanical additions necessary on this table are a few guide rollers. Fig. [13-3] shows this table with the additions necessary for magnetic film; R.H. is the magnetic reproducing head, G.R. the additional guide rollers. Attached to the extreme right side of a few of these tables is a separate

* Ulner, *op. cit.*

reproducing head which is connected to the amplifier; the magnetic film can be drawn by hand over this head, thus giving an additional aid for the cutting process.

At a few tables a "rotating reproducing head" [the revolving Tonschreiber head] has been fixed experimentally. This was originally a military invention which made it possible to hear words, syllables and

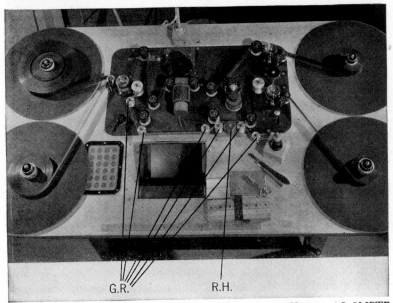

G.R.   R.H.

Fig. 13-3. This editing table contains a mechanism for the magnetic pickup of sound. (From Ulner, *op. cit.*)

even letters slowly, but at the correct frequency even when the tape is stationary. . . .

Further aids to the cutter are the so-called click pencil and the hand eraser. The click pencil is a colored grease pencil containing an iron oxide powder for markings on the magnetic film. Such a pencil marking on the film produces a "click" sound when passing over the reproducing head and enables the cutter to make markings [for identification or synchronization] which can easily be wiped off when no longer needed. The hand eraser is an ordinary magnetic erasing head built into a "handle-shaped" fitting. This head is fed with strong high-frequency current which permits the erasure of unwanted noises, bloops, etc., on the magnetic film, and can, with practice, be used to swell or restrict the sound volume of music. . . . other advantages for the cutter . . . [in the use of magnetic film as opposed to optical film] are that joints and scratches cannot be heard, and dust and fingerprints do not affect the film. All tools used by the cutters and their assistants must be demagnetized regularly before commencement of work. The same applies to the metal parts of the cutting desk, recorders, reproducers and projectors. This has become a general routine in the studio.*

CUTTING AND SPLICING METHODS

Film-cutting methods have not been changed much, basically, by the advent of magnetic film. The two films, the action film and the sound film, are drawn through their respective heads (the action film past the optical viewing gate and the sound film past the magnetic reproducing head) by a variable-speed motor drive in synchronism, and the picture is viewed while the accompanying sound is heard. (Note that double-system films are not displaced, in editing, as they are when the finished film is projected.) Ordinarily, the sound is cut to synchronize with the picture. Any action accompanied by sound must be in exact synchronism if an illusion of reality is to be maintained. In addition to hoof beats, drum beats, and other special sounds, this includes dialogue, especially. A good editor takes into consideration the natural laws of the varying speeds of sound and light and will not attempt to synchronize the flash and sound of a distant explosion. As in any art, proficiency in film cutting cannot be learned from a book but only by actual practice and experience.

Magnetic film is usually spliced by means of a cemented lap-joint, as is optical film† (Fig. 13-4), although heat-weld splicers are now available. (Transparent film-splicing adhesive plastic is also on the

* Ulner, *op. cit.*

† Detailed information on this subject may be found in the booklet, "The Handling, Repair, and Storage of 16-mm. Films," copyright 1944 by the Eastman Kodak Company, and which is available upon request from the Sales Service Division, Eastman Kodak Company, Rochester 4, New York.

Fig. 1—If a small section of motion-picture film were to be magnified to great size, we should see that the film is made up of more than one layer. In the above illustration the thickness of the various layers is exaggerated.

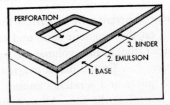

Fig. 2—1. The flexible film base provides a durable support. 2. The emulsion coating consists chiefly of gelatin, in which is suspended the silver or dye image. 3. A thin layer, or binder, between the base and emulsion binds them tightly together.

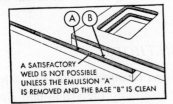

Fig. 3—It is impossible to cement the base side of one piece of film to the emulsion of another. The emulsion and binder must first be completely removed so that the two film base surfaces can come in direct contact with each other.

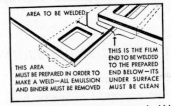

Fig. 4—The emulsion and binder coatings should be moistened with water. This softens the emulsion slightly so that it can be removed easily. The moistened surface should be dry before the film cement is applied.

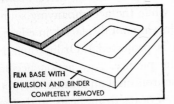

Fig. 5—To make a welded splice, the two top layers —emulsion and binder—should be completely removed. The base side of the other film may have oil on it, picked up from projection. This must be removed before a good weld can be made.

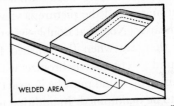

Fig. 6—A good motion-picture film splice is actually a weld. When a perfect splice is made, one side of the film base is dissolved into the base of the other film. With most splicing apparatus this requires from 10 to 20 seconds.

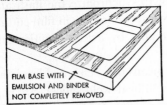

Fig. 7—If any emulsion or binder remains on the base in the area where the splice is to be made, a good weld will not result and the splice may not hold. Small specks of emulsion or binder can be removed by a fine abrasive.

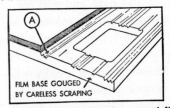

Fig. 8—Scratching or gouging the prepared film base near the emulsion edge should be avoided. Such scratches (A) weaken the weld and may cause the film to break at this point. Fine abrasive scratches are not serious.

Courtesy of, and copyright 1944 by, the Eastman Kodak Company

Fig. 13-4. Directions for splicing Ciné-Kodak film.

market.) A standard splicer may be used, provided that it is kept in a demagnetized condition, but use of a splicer made of beryllium copper or some other hard nonmagnetic metal would be preferable. If lap-splices are not made so that the edge of the top lap, on the magnetic side of the film, faces the direction opposite to that of film travel during reproduction (Fig. 13-4), the impact of this edge against the magnetic head may create a "click." After the splice is dry (drying requires a few seconds), the sound track at the splice

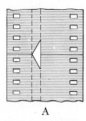   

A   B

Courtesy of O. K. Kolb and J. SMPTE

Fig. 13-5A. Separate lengths of film after being spliced. The joint may be cemented in normal fashion.

Fig. 13-5B. Lengths of magnetic sound film joined for re-use. The joint may be lapped and cemented, or it may be spliced by the application of adhesive tape on the noncoated side.

(Both illustrations are taken from O. K. Kolb, "Magnetic Sound Film Developments in Great Britain," *J. SMPTE,* vol. 55, Nov. 1950, page 506)

should be "blooped," a result achieved by punching out of the track a diamond-shaped hole or a long triangular hole (Fig. 13-5A). Alternatively, a diamond-shaped "bloop" patch may be affixed on the coated side of the track at the splice; this bloop is made of an adhesive tape or paper that is thick enough to separate the sound track from the magnetic head at the location of the splice.

After the edited magnetic film has been re-recorded and is no longer wanted, all bloops and patches should be cut out, and the sections of film should be spliced together, preferably on the diagonal, as shown in Fig. 13-5B. Make sure that the splice is secure; if it is made on a splicer that is standard for the type of film being cut, the sprocket perforations will be lined up properly. The grease-pencil marks and other marks on the film should be washed off with a solvent that will not harm the film or the coating lacquer. Ordinary carbon tetrachloride is good for this purpose, provided that the room in which the work is done is well ventilated. Be certain that only the same type of magnetic film, with the same kind of oxide coating, is patched together in a roll for erasure and re-use. If you are not certain as to the kind of oxide coating, record and play back a constant-frequency tone on both pieces, and compare the outputs. For all ordinary purposes, coatings putting out the same intensity of tone after recording are similar enough to use together in a roll. After erasure, the film should be stored properly.

TRANSFER, RE-RECORDING, AND DUBBING

As we begin to discuss re-recording and dubbing processes (end-papers) we come to understand why different sounds—such as music, sound effects, dialogue, and the like—are recorded on separate tracks or, most commonly, on separate magnetic films. In the first place, sound from different sources must be separated if it is to be editable. In the second place, the quality and sound intensity, or level, of each sound track may then be blended to suit the action film and to agree with the mood of the particular scene. The re-recording mixer (Fig. 13-6) has at his finger tips the controls for varying the level of each sound track separately. He may change the quality of sound called "presence" by varying the equalizer controls, and he is also able to add reverberation to any of the tracks at will. Other reasons for recording separate tracks are:

1. To permit the re-use of sound effects and music with other pictures, if desired
2. To permit foreign-language dubbing of dialogue

Re-record Mixing. The reader may find it advantageous at this point to study the endpapers. At this stage—re-record mixing—each of the separate reels of recorded magnetic film (dialogue, sound effects, and music) has been so edited that, when it is reproduced, its contribution to the total sound will be heard at exactly the right instant and in synchronization with the respective frames on the picture work print. The total playing time of film on each reel is the same; at those places where there is to be no music in the finished film, for instance, the music reel will contribute no sound, blank (leader) film having been spliced into the reel at the corresponding locations. During rehearsal the mixing engineer may test

Courtesy of the Westrex Corporation

Fig. 13-6. Recorded sound is being mixed at the RA-1407 re-recording console in the Hollywood studios of Metro-Goldwyn-Mayer.

each reel of sound separately by running it off in synchronism with the picture work print. At the same time he can write out his work, or cue, sheet—a most important guide. On it he indicates, in terms of film footage or time, the exact places at which to expect each particular track's sound to begin and end; in addition, he notes the proper settings of the mixer-console controls throughout the entire footage and thus prepares a guide which makes it possible for each section of sound on each track to be reproduced with the level and quality of sound required. Many feature pictures require two or three re-recording mixer operators to perform this exacting operation.

After the cue sheets are written out, the reels of film are run back to their synchronization "start" marks, and the sound mixing is rehearsed as many times as necessary. After the final rehearsal, the sound reproducers, or dummies, and the picture-work-print projector are run back once more to the start marks of the different tracks and interlocked, as usual; when the reproducers and the projector are interlocked, they operate as a unit. The output of the mixer console is then recorded magnetically on a single track, or, for stereophonic systems, on a film with three or more tracks.

Language Dubbing. The process of substituting words in another language for the words spoken by the actors in the original picture is called language dubbing. Successful dubbing requires expert translators who are able to write speeches for the actors that:

1. Are exactly as long as the original speeches
2. Contain pauses of equal length
3. Permit the same facial expressions
4. Permit, as much as possible, the same lip movements

After the actors have been given their speeches, they watch the original film run off, listening to the dialogue as it was originally recorded. This process is repeated several times. Any necessary changes are made in the translations, and each actor, since he will be watching the picture while he is speaking during the actual dubbing, memorizes his speeches.

Dubbing of language is ordinarily done in short takes or scenes each one about 30 ft long. The scenes are successively projected on a screen while the original dialogue is played back from an endless loop film sound reproducer. Only the picture is run off while the actors record their lines in lip-synchronism. If necessary, one or more scenes are then cut to synchronize. The whole "dub" is then assembled, re-recorded, and mixed with the original sound and music tracks, as described above.

MAGNETIC TO OPTICAL TRANSFER

After completion of re-recording to the final magnetic film, a transfer is made of this magnetic film, which is recorded optically while it is reproduced. Ordinarily, during this last re-record cycle, all sound above 8000 cy per sec is eliminated for two reasons:

1. Most theater systems do not reproduce sound with good fidelity at frequencies above 8000 cy per sec.
2. It has been found, on repeated tests, that the quality of sound does not suffer by being restricted to the range of 40 to 8000 cy per sec.

The optical recording, when developed, serves as the optical sound negative. From the optical and picture negatives release prints are made for distribution and exhibition.

MAGNETIC SOUND ON RELEASE PRINTS

To date, no magnetic process for recording sound on prints for exhibition has approached optical printing methods both in excellence of quality and in economy of reproduction *in quantities*. It is probably true, however, that in the future a method of magnetic printing will be developed to surpass the optical method in both respects. Projectors in theaters can easily be converted for use of magnetic sound or optical sound recordings interchangeably and with quick and easy switch-over, just as most projectors in use at the movie-production centers were converted long since. At present some stereophonic sound (multiple track) recordings have been supplied on magnetic film.

16-MM FILM METHODS

Sixteen-millimeter film, normally not used in production of motion-picture features, generally is restricted to diverse applications in news filming, industry, education, advertising, and television. The basic double-system methods described heretofore may be applied to 16-mm film. More frequently, however, this smaller film, running at a speed of 36 ft per min, is used in a single-film system. The sound and the picture are recorded at the same time, the sound being recorded ahead of the picture by 26 frames in order to allow sufficient film for the intermittent "film-picture" motion to be smoothed out.

Previous to the use of magnetic recordings, the single-system sound-and-picture film presented a problem almost impossible to overcome. Because the sound was optically recorded, extremely fine development for top-quality results was required. A different kind of development was usually required for the picture negative. Presence of both action and sound on the same film frequently resulted in inferior work, owing to the necessity of having to compromise in the matter of developing techniques used. With magnetic recording this situation has been altered for the better.

Film for use in 16-mm cameras may now be obtained with a magnetic stripe or track along one edge. To balance the film—so that it does not wind crookedly—another much narrower stripe of magnetic material is placed along the film near the other edge. The magnetic track is, as pointed out previously, impervious to temperatures of photographic solutions as high as 125° F, approximately. Picture and magnetic sound of very good quality may now be recorded on the film, the actual quality depending upon the equipment itself and the techniques employed.

SINGLE-SYSTEM EDITING

Single-system editing requires a slightly different technique from that used with double-system editing, in which the picture and sound are recorded on separate films. In the double system, it is possible for an editor, by listening to the sound and viewing the related action from both films at the *same frame number* on a dual Moviola, to edit the picture and sound simultaneously. In this case the picture and its accompanying sound are on separate films; *during editing the sound does not lead the picture* but is synchronized with it, the two films being matched frame to frame. With picture and sound originally recorded on one film (single system), it is impossible to cut sound *accurately* without cutting the picture at a wrong place *unless* action and sound are to be cut at the same frame, which is not too likely in view of the fact that sound leads the picture.*

Obviously, in order to facilitate editing, the single system has to be converted to the double system. Here is a proven technique: After the film negative has been developed, re-record the magnetic sound from the negative to a separate 16-mm magnetic sound film. The separate magnetic sound film and picture film print may then be placed in a double-system device for viewing and listening (dual Moviola) which runs both in exact synchronism; both films may be cut at the same point, no displacement being necessary. In other words, the single system is converted to the double system for editing. After editing has been completed, the original sound on the picture film negative is erased.

From this point on, depending upon the ultimate use, several procedures are possible. The edited picture negative may be printed on positive film that contains a magnetic sound track on which the edited sound may be recorded and from which it is projected magnetically. If many prints are needed, composite prints may be made in the same way as in the 35-mm method outlined. For television projection, no positive is essential; edited sound that is recorded on the original negative's erased magnetic sound track may be used just as it is. When it is known in advance that only one print is needed and no editing will be required, the picture and sound may be shot on direct-reversal magnetic-edged film, which upon development is a positive film complete with magnetic sound track.

16- AND 8-MM FILM FOR AMATEUR USE

Many amateurs in the fields of sound and action recording on film do work worthy of professionals. The rank and file, however, are satisfied with shooting the picture, editing, and merely adding

---

* Of course, unwanted single-system magnetic sound can be erased by a magnetic pencil eraser, just as optical sound can be obliterated by being painted out with India ink.

a sound narrative, possibly with sound effects. The Bell and Howell Filmosound 202 Projector is a 16-mm projector made for either magnetic or optical sound reproduction at either 16 or 24 frames per second. The projector is furnished with an optical and also a magnetic system. The mirror for the optical system and the erase and record heads for the magnetic system are all situated within the sound-drum. This rotary assembly may be turned to

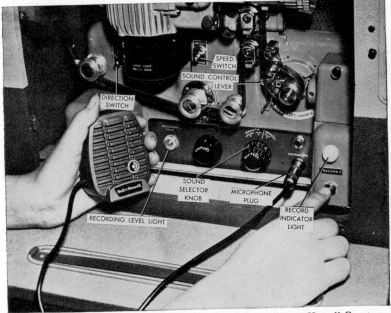

Courtesy of Bell & Howell Company

Fig. 13-7. Close-up view of the microphone and of the principal operating controls of the Filmosound 202, a 16-mm optical-magnetic recording projector.

bring either system into functioning position. The record head becomes the reproduce head when the projector is set up to play back only. Since there is a microphone jack and a phonograph jack input, the user—while recording his descriptive narration of a scene that is being projected—can also mix in music and sound effects from a disk reproducer, tape machine, or other high-level audio source. A neon light serves as the level indicator, helping the user to avoid extreme overmodulation. (See Fig. 13-7.)

The Bell and Howell "Soundstripe" is usually applied to the base side of the film, on the unperforated edge of 16-mm single-perforated film; it may however be put on the emulsion side, if desired, but this is not recommended. The regular "Soundstripe" is approximately 0.200 in. wide, but a magnetic track half this width may be put on old optically recorded film (single-perforated) without destroying the optical sound track. In this case, either sound track may be used when the picture is being projected.

8-MM PROJECTORS

Amateurs who have 8-mm cameras are now also able to utilize magnetic recording. Projectors whose magnetic heads record and

Courtesy of The Calvin Company, Inc.

Fig. 13-8. On the Movie Sound 8 optical-magnetic 8-mm film-projector, sound can be recorded on, and reproduced from, a magnetic stripe. Film speed is 24 frames per second.

reproduce sound on a narrow magnetic stripe are available. Établissements Emel, in Paris, has developed an 8-mm projector that at 16-frames-per-sec speed produces quite good audio response from the very narrow magnetic track used. The Movie Sound 8, made in the United States, is an excellent 8-mm projector (See Fig. 13-8).

FACTORS AFFECTING CHOICE OF MEDIUM

SYNCHRONIZED TAPE TECHNIQUES

In any discussion of magnetic media for sound and action synchronization the question arises, Which medium—film or tape—is preferable in any given situation? Below are some observations that bear on this problem:

1. COST OF RECORDER

Tape recorders providing equivalent quality in reproduction are cheaper.

2. COST OF MEDIUM

Tape is much less expensive, even compared to three-track film.

3. STORAGE SPACE

Approximately equivalent, if triple-track film is used for storage.

4. SPURIOUS PRINTING

Possible on tape, not likely on film. Crosstalk may occur if multitrack film recorder is poorly designed.

5. FLUTTER

Varies with sound frequency and depends upon whether film is single or multiple track, upon the speed of the tape, and upon design, construction, and maintenance in both cases. There is no distinct preference here.

6. NOISE

Tape normally better, if properly maintained.

7. MOBILITY

Depends upon the situation in which recording is to be done.

8. RANGE OF FREQUENCY	Tape better, if machines are properly designed, because of better media contact.
9. EASE OF SYNCHRONIZATION	Film preferred. Synchronization is positive, and the sound film may be run at the same number of frames per second, and inches per second, as the picture film. Tape standards were arbitrarily set at 15, 30, 7.5 in. per sec, and so on. Tape and film are difficult to match linearly for cutting-in a take. However, sprocketed 18-in.-per-sec tape may alter this situation entirely.

UTILITY OF TAPE IN FILM PRODUCTION

Before the description of tape-to-film synchronization methods (to which this section is to be mostly devoted), is begun, some of the utilitarian aspects of tape in both film and television production may be noted. In the first place, safety recordings on tape are sometimes made simultaneously with the original magnetic-film recording, being stored at least until the production is finished. Tape may also be used for recording actors' cues, lighting instructions, cues to propmen for shifting scenery and furniture—in short, as a convenient memorandum recorder. Actors may use tape recorders in order to perfect delivery of a speech while listening to the playback. In other words, the use of tape can confer definite advantages, including saving of rehearsal time during production.

The use of tape provides a comparatively cheap method of recording sound in film productions if exact synchronism is not needed, for instance, narration in documentary films, background sound, and sound effects. The employment of tape recording in television production was a natural consequence of the availability of the machines, since it was a radio-station owner and operator who usually operated the television station. One of the first jobs tape performed in television was recording the sound for a Kinescope re-broadcast.* If the optical 16-mm sound track, after development, was of too poor quality, the taped sound was played back instead. This operation, for best results, requires tape-to-film synchronization, which was not available in the United States until almost 1950.

With sprocketed film for both sound and picture, interlock or synchronous operation guarantees frame-by-frame identity of both media. With the use of tape, however, we face a different situation. Tape is thin, tape drives may slip or creep on occasion, and the tape itself may stretch, more or less, depending upon humidity and the pull exerted by the drive. Tape may run too slowly if the heads become too dirty or if the guides accumulate dirt or wax deposits. Therefore, in tape-film synchronization the tape must be forced by various means to change speed automatically, always keeping step with the picture. This change of speed, when required, must be gradual enough to be unnoticeable, yet rapid enough to maintain lip-synchronism.

SYNCHRONIZED TAPE-FILM SYSTEMS

THE RANGERTONE SYSTEM

The Rangertone system of tape-film synchronization, developed by Colonel R. H. Ranger, was the first practical system developed to solve the problem. Recognizing the need for what he termed "magnetic sprocket holes" to keep the tape in exact step with the film, Colonel Ranger designed an ingenious system of synchronization. Roughly, as we have read previously, his method is based upon recording, simultaneously with the sound, a 60-cy control signal on the same tape; during reproduction this signal keeps the film and the tape in synchronism.

The Rangerette. The Rangerette, a small, light (30 pounds), and portable tape machine, is designed to provide synchronous recording from storage batteries. It is basically a 110-volt ac unit requiring 70 watts of power, which may be supplied by a vibrator power supply operating from a 12-volt battery. In field operation a

---

* A Kinescope is a film made by photographing the monitor in the television studio.

five-segment commutator called a "Syncrotac" is put on the camera's frame shaft, which is turning at 1440 rev per min (rpm) when the camera is making its normal 24 pictures per sec. The five contacts per revolution give 120 cy per sec, and this electrical output is used to keep a vibrator in step at half this rate, or 60 cy per sec. It is this same vibrator that converts the direct current from the 12-volt battery to 115 volts, 60 cy per sec, which drives the synchronous motor of the Rangerette and supplies the synchronizing signal on the tape. The vibrator readily follows changes in camera speeds, which may range from 90 ft per min up to 92 or down to 86 ft per min; this is about as far as the speed variation should be allowed to go, because beyond these points the pitch variation on playback becomes apparent. The cameraman, however, rarely permits his camera to run at other than the standard speed of 90 ft per min.

The Rangerette tape drive is of tight-loop design. It is equipped with a sync record and a sound-record head; the latter also serves as playback head. It is equipped with a motion balancer that enables this lightweight machine to achieve very good stability of motion.

The Rangertone Synchronizer. The Synchronizer is a unit that works from the tape control-track to furnish "lock-in" synchronization on playback. It provides the dual characteristics of fully automatic position and velocity control. What this means, essentially, is that the Synchronizer corrects both tape speed and the tape's position relative to the film frame. It is not enough to control the tape's speed so that it is exactly 15 in per sec. It is necessary to make certain that the tape corrects for any frame loss or gain occurring during the correcting period, thus maintaining over-all synchronism to less than one frame at any time. Synchronizer frame-to-sound alignment is accurate within 1/10 frame.

THE FAIRCHILD PIC-SYNC SYSTEM

The Fairchild Pic-Sync System of synchronizing tape and film makes use of the following integrated parts:

1. The Fairchild Synchroll Drive
2. The "follow-up" servomotor

3. Magnetic marking of the tape, during recording, at 14 kilocycles
4. An automatic framing attachment, consisting of several units
5. An inked number-marking system for marking the tape in visible frame numbers and footage numbers corresponding, if desired, with those on the film

The Fairchild System, to begin with, marks the magnetic tape by recording on it, through the regular recording system and head, a 14,000-cy-per-sec tone which is modulated by the 60-cy supply current, thus establishing a reference point. The frequency of the supply current, whether 60 cy per sec exactly or varying between 58 and 62 cy per sec, as it may, will be recorded on the tape. When the tape is played back, the audio response is limited in frequency to 13 kilocycles, the 14-kilocycle marking carrier being chopped out of the audible sound and used only for activating the synchronizing system. Since all professional tape recorders operating at 15-in.-per-sec speed will record at least up to 15,000 cy per sec, the Fairchild System of recording with a synchronizing signal at 14 kilocycles can be utilized without the installation of additional magnetic heads. The 14-kilocycle signal is generated in a separate, modulated oscillator, which is operated by 110-volt alternating current and is fed to the tape through a simple bridging unit that is connected in the channel feeding the recorder. In order to play back the sound on this tape in synchronism with the film that was shot while the sound was being recorded, a Pic-Sync reproducing machine must be used.

To understand how this 60-cy modulated 14,000-cy signal controls tape speed accurately on playback, we shall have to study the operation of the Synchroll Drive. The clearest exposition of it is given by the inventors,* whom we quote in part:

The development of the Synchroll was predicated upon the reasoning that in a sound system we require the drive to perform two entirely different functions. First, it must provide, over rather short intervals of time, extremely constant speed. Second, the playback time of the recorded program must, to a very high degree of accuracy, equal the time of recording over, say, a half-hour interval. In the past, most

* D. G. C. Hare and W. D. Fling, "Picture-Synchronous Magnetic Tape Recording," *J. SMPTE,* vol. 54, May 1950, pp. 554–566.

drive systems have tried to achieve these two somewhat dissimilar objectives with a single means, or, more frequently, have ignored one in favor of the other. For example, the puck or friction roll drive when properly constructed is capable of having very precise short-term speed control. But all puck or other friction drives either slip or creep to a greater or lesser degree; and, what is worse, this slip or creep may be . . . quite variable. The same remarks, of course, apply to belt drives. Gear drives, on the other hand, if the main drive is synchronous, will provide an absolutely synchronous drive system, but the difficulties of

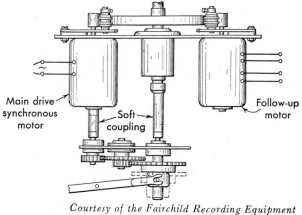

Courtesy of the Fairchild Recording Equipment Corporation

Fig. 13-9. Elements of the Synchroll drive.

getting the tooth ripple out of the gear drive are all too well known. . . . We can, of course, eliminate this gear ripple if we use a sufficiently soft coupling, but as soon as we do this we have a system which is also soft, and which not only takes a long time to settle down but which, when disturbed by a sudden change of load will give rise to a very disturbing wow.

The elements of the [Synchroll] drive are shown [see Fig. 13-9]. Disregarding the right-hand motor for the moment, we have on the upper end of the [main drive] motor shaft a conventional puck drive. The bottom of the motor shaft is coupled to a gear train which, in turn, is coupled to the flywheel shaft. Both the motor and flywheel shafts are isolated from the gear train with soft couplings. If, for the moment, we consider the puck drive separately, we have a drive system which has a characteristic rigidity or stiffness but which, in common with all friction drives, tends to slip or creep. . . . We deliberately choose the diameters of the motor pulley and the flywheel such that their arithmetical ratio is a percent or two lower than that of the gear train. Thus, if the puck did not slip it would drive the capstan a percent or two faster than would the gears. The gears coupled to the capstan through the flexible shaft can then be considered as a load which causes the puck to slip just this percentage. . . . The soft couplings between the gear drive and the motor and capstan effectively filter out any gear ripple, while the stiff coupling of the puck effectively eliminates the hunt and softness due to this flexible coupling.

This type of drive can be looked at in two ways. It can either be considered as a puck drive with a follow-up, or rating, system which keeps it synchronous, or it can be considered as a gear drive with a very high amount of damping supplied by the puck. For the Pic-Sync operation we consider the drive from the first of these two viewpoints. [The first is a puck drive with a follow-up system which keeps it synchronous.] In this operation the gear drive is disengaged, although the main [drive] motor is still coupled to the flywheel through the puck. The follow-up motor, which is the servo motor shown in the block diagram . . . is also coupled to this [same] flywheel through a puck.*

We return for a moment to our earlier discussion describing the Synchroll drive system. By means of a 60-cy modulated 14-kilocycle tone a signal is recorded on the tape to be synchronized with a film. The necessary speed correction is determined by the phase relationship between the control-frequency track and the line frequency at the time of playback.

In playback we amplify the control track signal along with the program in the first two stages of the playback amplifier. In [some models of the] Fairchild Recorder a playback volume control is placed in the front panel which makes for convenience in separating the control signal and the program. This is done by means of a rejection filter tuned to 14 kc [kilocycles] and placed in series with the line to the pad. Ahead of this rejection filter the control track frequency is bridged out through a tuned network, after which it is amplified, further filtered,

---

* Hare and Fling, *op. cit.*

demodulated and limited. Following this limiting it goes to a power amplifier which feeds one phase [winding] of a two-phase servomotor at a level of about 15 w [watts]. On this phase, then, we have the control signal which was originally the line frequency at the time of recording. The other phase of this motor is supplied directly from the line. . . .

The phase-torque characteristic of this motor then provides a varying load on the main drive motor, in some cases assisting and in others retarding. Since this is what is commonly known as a "closed loop" system, there is no need for a gear coupling to the capstan. As the tape comes up to speed, the control signal appears on one winding of the follow-up motor, and the phase of the current in this winding will be varying slowly with respect to that of the line phase. The system is so connected that, as the phase varies, the torque of the follow-up motor changes the speed of the tape in such a fashion as to oppose the change in phase. Given enough power the follow-up motor will hold the [tape] speed at a point such that the frequency of the control signal is equal to that of the line frequency. . . . If the [film] projector is driven by a synchronous motor, the program on the tape will be in exact synchronism with the picture. . . .

. . . additional input to the Pic-Sync power amplifier . . . allows the control phase of the motor to be fed directly from the line in such a way as manually to adjust the speed of the recorder. This is normally not used in Pic-Sync operation but is introduced merely as a convenience for the purpose of changing the time of playing back an uncontrolled program. It could, of course, be used for a manual framing device if desired.*

Automatic Framing Attachment. This part of the Fairchild system of synchronizing tape with film and its operation are illustrated in Fig. 13-10 and discussed below.† In order to use tape in synchronism with film run from a projector, some means is required to "frame" both picture and sound at the beginning of both tracks. Since the time required for the separate machines to come up to playing speeds is different, and since it may change from time to time, depending upon various conditions of service and use, the

* *Ibid.*

† The discussion of the Framing Attachment and of its operation is based on and in part quoted from material prepared and distributed by the Fairchild Recording Equipment Corporation.

means for synchronization must be positive. According to the Fairchild Recording Equipment Corporation, the attachment:

. . . involves the comparison of the projector sprocket rotation with the capstan rotation of the tape (Fig. 13-10). In this system, the information regarding the sprocket rotation is transmitted to the tape recorder by means of a pair of very small self-synchronous motors, one of which is fastened to the sprocket of the projector and the other to one side of a differential in the tape reproducer. The other side of this differential is connected through a gear train of proper ratio to the capstan drive shaft. The output of this differential then will be a meas-

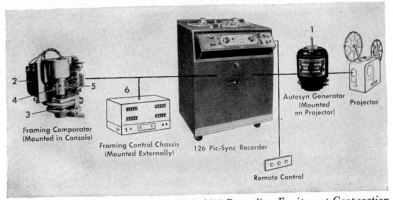

Courtesy of the Fairchild Recording Equipment Corporation

Fig. 13-10. Sequential steps in the Auto-Frame System.

ure of the difference of rotation between capstan and the projector drive sprocket. If we choose the gear ratio such that one revolution of the capstan corresponds to the same number of frames of program material as does one revolution of the drive sprocket, the output shaft of the differential will remain stationary for synchronous operation. Any rotation of this output shaft is an indication of a framing error, and we cause it to correct the speed of the tape reproducer in such a direction as to reduce this error to zero.

This device is arranged so that when the framing error has been corrected and the control track takes over the control of the speed of the tape reproducer, the error-storing mechanism is disengaged from the differential and not re-engaged until the machine is turned off.

This eliminates the necessity of manually resetting to zero at the start of a new program and it also makes it possible, when using tape that has been recorded under suitable conditions, to start and stop the projector several times during the program with a negligible framing error.*

Operation of Auto-Frame System. Film and tape are initially positioned according to start marks, established originally by "clapstick" or similar technique. Starting power is applied by remote control to the projector and tape recorder. The sprocket revolutions of the projector are transmitted to the pic-sync machine by the autosyn generator (1) and motor (2). The compact autosyn generator is easily coupled to any make of projector. Sprocket motion is compared with the capstan's revolutions (through appropriate gearing) in the mechanical differential (3). When film and tape are moving at unchanging relative speeds, there is no motion of the output shaft of differential (3). If, however, the tape recorder is operating ahead of or behind the projector, the output shaft of differential (3) revolves, turning the error storage drum (4) and closing one or the other of the switches (5).

Closure of switch (5) causes the tape machine to speed up or slow down by the amount necessary to correct the framing error. The Pic-Sync machine will even stop completely if the projector lags badly. As the framing error is reduced, the error drum (4) rotates toward its neutral position (neither of switches (5) closed). When the framing error is reduced to zero, error drum (4) is in its neutral position, and normal pic-sync control takes over. Framing control chassis (6) contains relays which handle motor currents. Lights on the panel indicate zero when framing error is absent. The Auto-Frame is then inactive until the Pic-Sync Recorder and Projector are stopped. Any number of starts and stops can be made, but the autoframe will always re-establish exact framing with respect to start marks.

Inked Numbering Device. For facility in editing, the Fairchild System includes, as noted in the list of parts used in the Fairchild Pic-Sync System, an automatic numbering device that prints pic-

* *Ibid.*

ture-frame numbers and film-footage numbers on the tape in quick-drying ink.

TELEVISION TAPE-FILM PRODUCTION

A method of producing an integrated television program for which the original sound may have been recorded either optically or on magnetic film or tape but for which the final track that will be "aired" is all on tape will next be discussed. This method allows the telecasting of live action and sound interspersed with filmed action and recorded sound, regardless of the medium on which the sound was recorded originally—but the sound must have been in synchronization originally with the picture. (This production method was essentially the one used in producing the Edward R. Murrow "See It Now" program on CBS Television, and was evolved by W. D. Fling, formerly of the Fairchild Recording Company, and E. Gille, CBS engineer.)

The equipment needed for recording sound on tape and filming action, in synchronization, is:

1. A synchronous motor-driven camera
2. Either a Fairchild Pic-Sync Tape Recorder or a Pic-Sync Control-Track Generator that feeds a tape recorder which meets NARTB recording standards at 15-in.-per-sec tape speed. (The essential requirements are that tape speed be exactly 15 in. per sec and that the 14,000-cy control track be clearly recorded.)

For original Pic-Sync sound and filmed action, the beforementioned clap-stick start and stop must be photographed and recorded for subsequent ease of editing and synchronization of the action film and the sound tape. The tape should be marked with footage numbers which begin at the clap-stick cue sound and indicate exactly the equivalent tape footage that corresponds with film footage, from the "clap-sticks together" picture frame to the last frame. The frame lines of the film and the sound peaks of the synchronizing control track may also be marked on the base side of the tape in quick-drying ink.

Editing of film and tape can then be easily accomplished. It is necessary only to note the footage mark at which the film is to be cut, using a film footage counter if needed, and then to cut the tape at the corresponding foot and frame marks on the back of the tape. Caution must be exercised in cutting the film *before* and *after* the frames to be joined so that no counted frames are lost. No sound for any frame is lost on the tape, since the tape is butt-spliced, not over-lapped, as is the custom in splicing film. If heat-weld butt-splicing is used in film cutting, there is no need to observe the above caution.

If the tape has not been marked with foot and frame information, simple editing can still be accomplished by measuring from cue sounds or marks in the ratio of 18 in. of film (for 35-mm) to 15 in. of tape. This relationship will remain correct only if the tape record-ers used for recording and editing operate at 15 in. per sec and if the tape has not shrunk or stretched since recording took place. This method of measuring, however, should not be depended upon to be accurate for more than 10 to 15 sec of material; errors in synchro-nization may appear as the results of error in tape-recorder speed or tape stretch. The purpose of the control track on playback, in picture-synchronous operation, is to correct continuously for these errors, which it will readily do provided that they come within the operating limitations of the Pic-Sync machine.

Playback of tape and film prepared in the foregoing manner is normally accomplished by any standard professional tape machine equipped with the Fairchild Framing Control coupled to a synchronous-motor-driven projector. The function of the framing control is to permit both machines to start, attain synchronism, and then continue in direct synchronous interlock on the common alter-nating-current supply. Since the "clap sticks together" picture frame on the film and its corresponding sound on the tape are the common starting cue, the projector is threaded with the "clap sticks-together" frame in the picture gate, and the tape is threaded on the playback machine with the clap-stick sound point over the reproduce-head gap. The capstan of the tape drive is then moved manually, either forward or backward, in the direction indicated by the indicator lights on the framing control. These lights indicate either "tape ahead" or "film ahead" and will both be lit when there is no error between tape and film.

With the starting marks for both film and tape cued together in this way, both machines are in the ready-to-start position. After starting together, they will come up to synchronism within 2 to 3 sec* and will continue in synchronism until stopped. If they are stopped and then restarted within the same sequence of shot and action, the framing control will again cause them to come into direct synchronism and to continue in synchronism during the remainder of the program material.

Thus far we have described the method of handling action and sound telecast from the media on which they were recorded, that is, film (action) and tape (sound) recorded in synchronism. Now we will discuss methods of transferring optically or magnetically filmed sound to tape, for editing before being aired from a synchronized tape machine. This explanation of film-to-tape production techniques presumes that the reader has acquainted himself with procedures of film editing. He must understand the details of synchronous editing of picture and sound on film, the use of the dual footage counter, and the precautions concerning sound-track lead (displacement ahead of picture) in double-system editing. The standard 19-frame sound-track lead (35-mm) in double-system editing must be preserved on the film, obviously, but need not be preserved on the synchronous tape to which the film sound is to be transferred. It must be understood that in all cases in the following description, in transference of sound from 35-mm track to tape, the sound in synchronism with the picture is actually 19 frames in advance of the picture it goes with (16-mm lead of sound to picture is 26 frames). Therefore, advance of all cue marks on the sound track to correspond with cued picture frames will not be mentioned again in the following description. The reader should also understand that if synchronism between sound and picture is accidentally lost in the editing of film, it must be restored before the sound is transferred to sync-track tape.

* More time is required for the projector to come up to speed than for the tape machine to reach its speed.

The required equipment for sound scoring with synchronous tape is:

1. The necessary 35-mm or 16-mm synchronous-motor-driven film projectors and any other interlocked sound reproducers that are needed to play back the sound to be scored.
2. A Fairchild Pic-Sync Recorder and a 14-kilocycle control-track generator, or their equivalent (tape recorder and control-track generator of professional grade).

Aurally identifiable marks on the recorded tape both at the beginning and end of the action sequence are required both for playback and editing purposes. In CBS television practice these cue marks are recorded on the tape in the following manner.

Standard threading of film when the Pic-Sync System is used for playback calls for frame 4 of the Academy leader* to be located in the picture aperture of the projector and for the corresponding "frame 4" aural cue mark on the tape to be located directly over the playback-head gap of the tape playback machine. (This is true when Fairchild Pic-Sync machines with the Framing Control are employed; other machines may require more cueing latitude.) The following procedure permits in-step transfer from synchronized optical film sound to synchronized tape sound.

On the black Academy leader film, the 8th and 4th foot frames are marked in the sound-track area by scratching off the black emulsion as shown in Figs. 13-11 and 13-12. Light from the projector exciter lamp passing through these cleared spots on the film sound track causes audible "pops" to be recorded on the tape; these pops thereafter accurately identify the 8th and 4th foot frames of the film leader on the tape. This audible marking is performed at both ends of a film sequence. By the use of this method several action sequences can be spliced together, picture synchronous stops still being allowed in the Academy leader portion between "takes" or sequences. The ability to stop and start in synchronism provided by this method permits the insertion of either live or recorded action

---

* A numbered series of frames on film. An Academy leader is numbered in descending numerical order and an Academy trailer in ascending order.

and sound from another source or from another set of projector and synchronized-tape machines.

The film and tape are each spliced in sequence in the order and manner shown in the outline for Takes 1 and 2. (See page 290.)

The final product of this cutting method will be a series of takes; between each two adjoining takes there will be 12 ft of leader in the film, with the film's 8th and 4th foot frames identified on the tape

Scratch across sound track
at inner edge of sprocket holes

Scratch across sound track
as shown

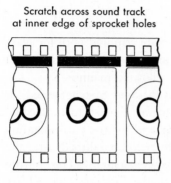

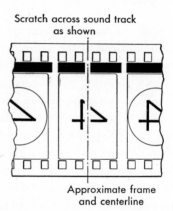

Approximate frame
and centerline

Fig. 13-11. Two pops, which serve as an audible cue during playback, are recorded in the form of two scrape marks made across the solid black strip that represents the film sound track. A "foot" frame is identifiable by the absence of a circle around the number. Note the scrape marks before and after the eighth foot frame above.

Fig. 13-12. The three scrape marks made across the sound track in the fourth foot frame of the film shown above will be heard during playback as three pops; they will serve as a cue.

by the corresponding aural cues. Synchronism will be maintained throughout if the procedures described have been followed exactly.

In preparation of film for CBS Television, 4 ft of trailer that follow the end of any film take are left black. This expedient permits the video switcher to cross-fade to other video material without the danger of fading on the normal Academy trailer numbers.

Television program production, especially of news telecasts, occasionally requires last-minute insertion of program material into a show that is ready for re-recording or in the last stages of preparation and without the use of Academy leaders and trailers. In cases like this, the main portion of the program is prepared as described above except for the parts immediately before and after the take to

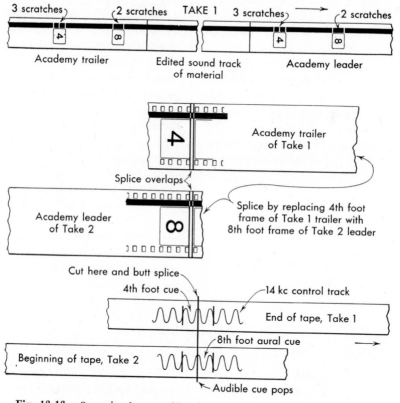

Fig. 13-13. Steps in the assembly of takes into a continuous film. Audible pops serve as guides for the insertion of live program material between adjoining takes.

be inserted at the very last moment possible. In an emergency a show may have to be cut into two or three segments, one being prepared while the preceding section is on the air.

For purposes of illustration (Fig. 13-14) let us call the first part of the recorded telecast Take 1, the take to be inserted Take 2, and

TAKE 1

FILM (Edited Sound Track)	TAPE
Academy leader with 8th and 4th foot frames prepared as above, followed by action (picture) portion of TAKE 1. The black trailer that ends the take is cut in the 4th foot frame. This cut 4th foot frame will be replaced by the 8th foot frame of the leader preceding TAKE 2 (see Fig. 13-13). Remember that no frames must be lost in making this splice, since the overlap for splicing will come from the excess of one of the 4th foot frames.	Control-track tape with aural cue marks at 8th and 4th frames, followed by sound portion of TAKE 1. The tape is cut perpendicularly at the closest peak to the pop in the 4th-foot-frame's aurally marked area at the end of TAKE 1; the tape should be cut accurately on the nearest sound peak of the 14-kc control track, which can be heard at very low speed. This tape end should then be spliced to the tape on which the pops from the corresponding 8th foot frame of TAKE 2 leader have been recorded. Tape should be cut and spliced so that the control track remains undisturbed (Fig. 13-13). (Leave a length of tape equivalent to 12 ft of film between takes.)

TAKE 2

FILM	TAPE
Cut Academy leader one frame ahead of 8th foot frame and, in splicing to the end of TAKE 1 trailer, substitute the 8th foot frame of the TAKE 2 leader for the 4th foot frame of the TAKE 1 trailer (this permits overlap splice without loss of synchronism). See Fig. 13-13.	Find the 8th foot aural-cue pops of TAKE 2 and match them to the remainder of the 4th foot aural-cue pops at the end of the TAKE 1 trailer. Use a butt- (perpendicularly cut, not diagonal) splice, making sure to cut on the control-track peak. What remains on the tape should be one set of three pops. See Fig. 13-13.

the remainder of the program Take 3. At the end of Take 1 about 6 to 12 in. of excess picture and its associated film sound are retained for the purpose of putting a sound cue on that part of the sound track used in the frame immediately following the end of Take 1. This cue frame is prepared as though it were an 8th foot frame of an Academy trailer (see Fig. 13-11). The remainder of the excess film is then spliced to a correspondingly short piece of excess film immediately preceding Take 3. The frame immediately preceding the desired opening frame of Take 3 is also marked, as shown

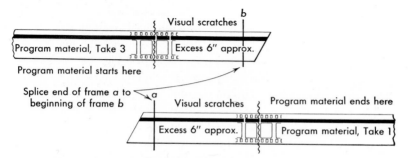

Fig. 13-14. Film marked to show places at which splices should be made during the preparation of the body of the program. (Leaders and trailers are omitted here.)

in Fig. 13-11. Takes 1 and 3 may then be re-recorded to synchronized tape.

The separate preparation of Take 2 prior to re-recording it to tape requires that cue marks be made in the sound-track area on the frame immediately preceding and also on the one immediately following the program material (Fig. 13-14). Take 2 can then be spliced in at any time. Both its picture and tape portions are inserted between the cued frames in Takes 1 and 3. The excess film and tape portions (*excluding* the cued frames) of Tape 2 are discarded.

LOW-COST METHODS OF SYNCHRONIZATION

SANO METHOD

The synchronization of taped sound with action film is a problem by no means confined to the professional motion-picture and television producers. Amateurs have for some years concerned themselves with this problem, and some of them have devised rather clever means of solving it. One of these amateurs, K. Sano, constructed an ingenious synchronizing mechanism for this purpose. His method (the following description of which has been translated by this writer from Sano's article "Synchronisation Precise," published in *Photo-Service* by Gevaert, in Belgium, in March, 1950) may be easily copied by any amateur who could make the needed mechanical parts.

The process explained below permits precise synchronization between magnetic tape and motion-picture film. Principally it consists in the use of (a) visible guiding marks printed or otherwise marked at fixed intervals on the base side of the tape [see Fig. 13-15]; (b) a means permitting the control of the exact location of these marks with respect to corresponding points on the film; and (c) an apparatus able to change the position of the marks on the tape in order to synchronize with the film. This last-mentioned apparatus should permit the operator to re-establish synchronization if it has been lost by unequal speeds of the projector or of the tape recorder, by slipping or stretching of the tape, or by any other like cause. The means used to control the relative position of the guiding marks should permit the operator also to determine in which direction the guiding marks should be moved in order to re-establish synchronization.

This general description [of K. Sano's method] requires a few explanations. First let us examine what is understood by the phrase "corresponding points."

When a film is projected, specific sounds or elements of sounds should synchronize with specific action in the picture. This synchronization ought to be particularly precise in the case of visible lip movement. For example, if one hears the sound "ah," the mouth should be seen open; for a "p" sound, the lips should be seen pressed together. A stroke on a gong and the corresponding sound, the [sight and] sound of a boat horn operated by steam—these are characteristic examples. It is a question of associating visual and auditory images. These images should be evoked simultaneously or the projection fails in realism and sometimes becomes laughable. (This sort of lack of co-ordination can, in special cases, be intentionally produced in order to obtain a special effect.) The "corresponding points" mentioned above

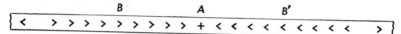

Fig. 13-15. Tape markings used in K. Sano's method of synchronizing tape and film.

Fig. 13-16. Tape recorder on which the synchronizing apparatus (flexible drive shaft from projector not shown) is mounted.

A

Fig. 13-17A. Top view of the synchronizing mechanism.

B

Fig. 13-17B. The flexible shaft that gears the film projector to the synchronization mechanism.

Fig. 13-18. A stationary appearance of the cross in the center of the mirror, which must be viewed from the correct angle, indicates that synchronization is perfect.

All illustrations on this page courtesy of K. Sano and of Gevaert Photo-Producten N.V.

(All illustrations on this page from K. Sano, "Synchronisation Precise," *Photo-Service,* published by Gevaert Photo-Production N.V., Antwerp, Belgium, no. 17, Mars–Avril 1950)

293

are the points on the film and the tape which should synchronize. It is obvious that if visual and auditory images are maintained in synchronism, our goal is attained. The speed at which the film or the magnetic tape is unrolled, considered separately, does not make any difference.

In practice it is difficult to operate two separate machines in synchronization for a long period if they are not rigidly interconnected. It is possible to attach the projector to the sound-reproducing mechanism by a transmission suitable for speed adaptation. This solution, even though theoretically obtainable, presents very great practical difficulties; besides, one cannot be at all certain of perfect synchronization, either with a single sound reproducer or, above all, when the projection must be made with other machines than that used for recording the sound originally. Therefore one cannot expect, without special means, to operate an ordinary projector and a sound reproducing apparatus in synchronism. At the start of the projection the synchronization is good, but after a few minutes an appreciable difference will appear.

Consider the way in which the magnetic tape is marked with guiding marks at fixed distances from each other. It is necessary during the course of the sound recording to fix the positions of these guiding marks with respect to the picture film. (This method is based on the assumption that the tape-recorder speed is more constant than that of the film projector; if this were not the case the quality of the recorded sound would be problematical, since the human ear can easily detect a speed variation of 6.3 per cent.)

We will utilize a means which permits us, after the filming of each multiple of twenty frames (as an example) to see successive marks on the magnetic tape at a given point of the recording machine, and thus it suffices, on projection, to see that these successive marks always appear after twenty frames in the same position as the first of these marks.

One can envisage different means based on stroboscopic lighting, on the principle of revolving mirrors, and others. The essential point is that they be operated by the power drum of the projector. The present method is based upon the use of a revolving mirror.

The back of the tape is marked at regular distances with crosses [see A in Fig. 13-15] preceded and followed by arrows [B and B'] placed in a predetermined manner. The tape recorder [Fig. 13-16] is furnished with the following apparatus: A circle of tape, preferably positioned in front of the take-up reel, is formed around a transparent cylindrical ring [C in Fig. 13-17A]. The circumference of the ring is equal to the distance between two successive crosses on the tape (238 mm for a tape speed of 7.5 in. per sec). The ring can turn freely upon its axis; therefore it turns easily with the motion of the tape around it. The tape is held in place around this transparent ring by the two guides D–1 and D–2. On the inside of the ring, at its center, is fixed a small revolving mirror E on a centered axle. The axle is moved by gears F and G, which are driven by a flexible shaft from the projector. [See Fig. 13-17B.]

These elements are so designed that when there is synchronization the axle of the mirror revolves at one half the angular speed and in the same direction as the transparent ring and in this manner the cross always appears at the initial position. [See Fig. 13-18.]

The coupling between the projector and the mirror being constant, one can calculate the angular speed of the mirror in number of frames per unit of time; that is to say, each frame of film corresponds to a given position of the mirror.

This method is most adaptable to post-synchronization. At recording one should place a cross which corresponds to the start of the recording on the magnetic head gap. Then the mirror should be turned so that a cross is seen in its center. Then the film should be placed in the projector with the first frame facing the lens. The projector and recorder are started simultaneously, taking care that the guide marks are always seen in the center of the mirror. The same procedure is followed when playing back the sound during projection of the film.

Tape and film can go out of synchronization owing to several causes which have already been stressed. If the film is ahead of the tape, the cross will be seen in the mirror displaced toward the left; if behind, the cross will be seen to the right. It is a simple matter, then, with most projectors, to increase or decrease the film speed in order to get back into synchronization (the mirror must be viewed from the *same angle* at all times). If one stops watching the mirror, it is possible that the cross may disappear entirely from the mirror. At that juncture one realizes the utilitarian purpose of the arrows, which will then indicate in which direction the cross has been displaced.*

* Trans. from K. Sano, "Synchronisation Precise," *Photo-Service,* Antwerp: Gevaert Photo-Producten N.V., no. 17, mars–avril 1950, pp. 18–19.

SYNCHROTAPE

The Revere Camera Company, in cooperation with the Minnesota Mining and Manufacturing Company, has devised a method somewhat similar to the above for synchronizing taped sound and film action. This system requires the use of "Synchrotape," a specially made tape bearing printed vertical lines on the base side of the tape. It is designed so that most 8- and 16-mm amateur film projectors, running at a speed of 18 frames per sec, can be made to synchronize with the tape-recorded sound running at 3 3/4 in. per sec. A small deflector is fitted over the projector lens barrel and is adjusted so that "between frame" pulsating light falls upon the tape as it emerges from the head assembly. In operation the stroboscopic effect of the beam causes the lines on the tape base to appear stationary when the film and tape are running in synchronism. The two are brought into synchronism by varying the speed of the projector motor as necessary.

VIDEO TAPE RECORDING

For many years one of the objectives of researchers in magnetic recording has been the recording of scenes on magnetic tape. Dr. Stille was reported to have been working on this problem in 1929, and there is no doubt that others were doing the same before that time. But the results of any experimentation, which in the United States was undertaken by several groups, were not made public until 1952. In that year, on November 11, John T. Mullin and Wayne R. Johnson, researchers in the laboratories of Bing Crosby Enterprises, Incorporated, in Beverly Hills, California, demonstrated their first video tape recorder. Scenes picked up by a television camera were recorded on tape and then reproduced, from the tape, on a television receiver's screen. About one year later, RCA researchers headed by Dr. Harry F. Olson demonstrated video tape recording, both in black-and-white and in color, at the RCA Laboratories in Princeton, New Jersey. (See Fig. 13-19.)

Both systems are basically similar, in that television cameras are employed to pick up a scene, which, after it has been transformed into electronic signals, is recorded on tape. The video tape may then be reproduced directly on a cathode-ray screen, directly telecast, or stored for subsequent reproduction.

Courtesy of the Radio Corporation of America

Fig. 13-19. Video tape recording unit. Research engineer Joseph Zenel displays an experimental recording-head unit. (From a publicity release of December 1, 1953, from the David Sarnoff Research Center)

The technique of recording scenes magnetically, now termed video recording, is somewhat analogous to the manner in which we ourselves sense things. We receive stimuli through our senses from many sources—sounds, odors, scenes. All stimuli reach the brain via the nervous system and are then interpreted and "registered" in the memory. Our responses to physical phenomena are at least in part affected by individual peculiarities of interpretation of sensory stimuli. This fact accounts for one person's interpretation and memory of an occurrence usually being different from another person's interpretation and memory of the same occurrence. Thus people hear sounds that do not actually exist; some people enjoy odors that may be offensive to others; two people standing side by side while witnessing an accident report it differently; and many of us, with varying degrees of pleasure, spend hours viewing television screens whose brightness might, within a few minutes, temporarily blind others whose tolerance of light is lower. In these and other ways, we respond to stimuli in accordance with our own peculiarities of interpretation.

In similar fashion the video recorder responds in accordance with its ability to "interpret." It does not record light or the absence of light; it records on tape only certain "information" about the reflection of light from objects. Its operation may be said to be similar to man's perception and interpretation of a sensory stimulus, but video operation is much cruder than is the highly developed and intricate human process which roughly corresponds. Information about light reflection that is recorded on the tape controls a source of light during playback; by means of this light source the pattern of light reflection as originally recorded is reproduced during playback.

Video tape recording operates on the scanning principle, the same principle that is used in simpler form in facsimile recording.* Recording of video signals, however, is a much more complicated process. In both, however, light patterns are transformed into electrical impulses which can be transmitted and used to reconstitute a replica of the original.

If we wish to record video information on an ordinary tape recorder in the way that we record comparatively slow-motion phenomena (mechanical motion, sound, and low-frequency sonics), we must increase tape speed considerably. Disregarding other factors for the moment, we may say that the wavelength recordable depends upon the speed with which the tape is drawn past the re-

* See facsimile systems, page 422.

cording head gap-edge. A very high speed of tape makes it possible to record video information (at 4,000,000-cy-per-sec and higher speed). But such a high speed introduces tape-handling and tape-storage problems that are formidable. At a speed of 2000 in. per sec, for example, only 9 sec of video information could be recorded on a reel of tape 14 in. in diameter. If video information is to be recorded economically, tape speed must of necessity be reduced.

The early Crosby system divided the incoming very-high-frequency video signal into ten separate signals, each of these signals then being recorded on a separate track on the tape. An eleventh track, recorded simultaneously, recorded the information necessary for synchronizing the picture information vertically and horizontally. A twelfth track recorded the accompanying sound. Because the Crosby video tape recorder broke up the video signal before it was recorded, more picture information could be accommodated within a given unit of space on the tape, and therefore the tape could be run at a speed of 100 in. per sec and still give fairly good picture definition on reproduction. It was possible to record 15 min on a 17-in.-diameter reel of either 1/2- or 3/4-in. tape, the wider tape being required for the necessary additional tracks of color information.

The RCA video tape recorder does not divide the incoming video signal but relies on higher tape speed and specially designed heads. For black-and-white recording, 1/4-in. tape with two tracks is employed, one for both the video and synchronizing signals and one for the sound. For color recording, five tracks are recorded on 1/2-in. tape, one track for each of the primary color signals representing red, green, and blue, the fourth track for the synchronizing signal, and the fifth for recording of the sound. The five signals are obtained from the output of a color television receiver. During reproduction the tape feeds each of the three primary-color signals directly to its corresponding electron gun of an RCA tricolor kinescope; the other two tracks are used to provide the information needed to synchronize scanning and to provide synchronous sound. (Fig. 13-20.) On the RCA color recorder, which contains specially designed stationary heads, color video signals can be recorded and reproduced at a tape speed of 240 in. per sec.

Neither the Crosby system nor the RCA system, however, has been adopted by television broadcasters, although RCA color video-tape recorders are in experimental operation at NBC laboratories in New York and Hollywood. Evidently neither of these ingeniously designed systems adequately met the requirements of television

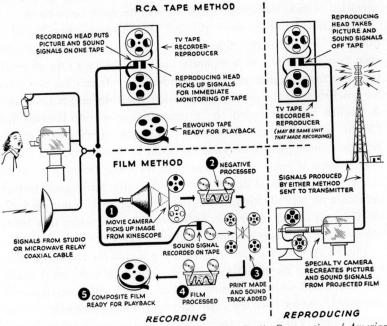

Fig. 13-20. Steps in the recording and reproduction of a television program by means of RCA video tape are compared diagrammatically to steps in the method now used with film in a broadcasting station. (From a publicity release of December 1, 1953, from the David Sarnoff Research Center)

broadcasters. In April, 1956, the Ampex Corporation demonstrated its video recorder to broadcasters in Chicago. Subsequently, several machines were sold to broadcasters who had witnessed the demonstration.

Designers of the Ampex Video recorder circumvented the problem of high tape speed in an ingenious manner. Information is recorded upon a magnetic tape 2 in. wide as it moves at the relatively low speed of only 15 in. per sec. Instead of a single stationary recording head, the head assembly of the Ampex machine consists of four recording heads that are mounted on a rotating drum; this drum revolves at high speed across the width of the tape. During recording or reproduction (both of which processes are performed by the rotating head assembly) one or another head is in contact with the surface of the tape. At the instant when one head is leaving one tape edge, another head is engaging the other tape edge; both heads are physically in contact with the tape at this instant, during which the recording or reproducing function is in process of being electronically switched from one head to another. The peripheral speed of the rotating head assembly is 2000 in. per sec. Although the system of recording is longitudinal, the magnetic tracks are recorded transversely (across the tape) at approximately right angles to the direction of tape travel. The sound that accompanies the television signals is recorded by a conventional head along one edge of the wide tape. Along the other edge are recorded tape-speed-control signals. During reproduction these signals cause each section of tape to pass the reproduce head at the speed identical to that at which the same section of tape passed the record head during recording. The 2-in.-wide tape, which must remain perfectly smooth while it is in contact with the rapidly rotating (14,000 revolutions per minute) head, is held by suction against a concave shoe during the time it is in the vicinity of the rotating head structure. As the drum revolves, each reproducing head contacts the proper information track with a minimum of hunting and does not vacillate for any appreciable length of time (in millionths of a second) between two tracks of recorded information.

The first projected use of these new developments is that of magnetically recording, instead of filming, television programs for delayed transmission. The present methods of photographing and reproducing television programs provide, at best, less than the normal quality of picture that identifies the live program. Methods of motion-picture production possibly may change radically with the adoption of the video tape recorder. By use of television cameras and recorders costs can be cut considerably. Two or more scenes can be mixed electronically during recording, thus eliminating time-consuming and costly photographic processing. Scenes can be reviewed immediately after recording is finished, complete with sound, which has been magnetically recorded on the same tape. Cutting is simplified, since picture and sound are automatically synchronized during recording; neither leads the other. To edit both picture and sound one need only cut across the tape at approximately a 90-degree angle.

There is no doubt that the perfected videotape recorder will be found to have many extremely valuable applications in industry and research in addition to its present uses in television and film production. Already, military uses alone cover a wide field. Whether videotape will take the place of the present high-quality films in motion-picture theaters remains to be seen. However, it is possible that tomorrow's home audience will be able not only to record television programs from television receivers but also will be able to rent or buy videotapes for reproduction (through videotape recorders) on the television screen.

14

Information Recording

In the term "information recording" we include a multitude of applications and techniques, ranging from those involved in the use of a simple magnetic recorder for dictation to those in complicated computers.

DICTATING MACHINES

Any wire or tape recorder makes a fairly efficient dictating machine *for dictation only*. But the ordinary magnetic recorder, no matter how faithful its reproduction, does not offer the facilities for transcribing that the typist requires if she is to work quickly and efficiently. As one designer of dictating machines remarked, "A dictating machine is valuable only if it can be operated by the typist with a minimum of physical effort and mental strain."

Some of the advantages claimed by the makers of magnetic dictating machines over other types are these:

1. Since errors can be corrected in dictation by backspacing and recording again, the typist does not have to "listen ahead" for errors but can go right ahead and type.
2. The clarity of the recording minimizes typists' listening strain and fatigue and reduces the possibility of misunderstood words.

THE DICTOREL

A comparatively new departure in magnetic dictating machines is the "Dictorel" (Fig. 14-1). This machine, which records on magnetically coated sheets of paper or plastic clipped in place around a revolving drum, is the first example of the kind of dictating machine that will probably find universal acceptance in the future. It comes closest, perhaps, to filling all the requirements of the ideal dictating machine.

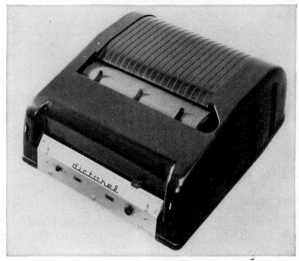

By the courtesy of Ateliers de Constructions Électriques de Charleroi, sole creators and manufacturers

Fig. 14-1. The Dictorel, a unique dictating machine.

The recorded sheets may be re-used for thousands of recordings. They may be filed or they may be mailed like ordinary letters. The reverse side is generally used for a signature or any reference in handwriting. Filing is done in special folders that can hold a very large number of copies. The recorded sheet, when folded at a distance approximately two-thirds down its length, can also be kept in a standard file.

It is advisable to avoid placing "dictograms" together with their magnetic surfaces in direct contact, as slight printing might result; they may be placed back against front without harm. The sheets may be mailed in any envelope in which the dictogram can be held in two or three folds parallel to its smaller dimension. Folds parallel with its long dimension should be avoided.

The Dictorel is manufactured by the Ateliers de Constructions Électriques of Charleroi, Belgium. Figure 14-2 shows another type

Courtesy of the Peirce Dictation Systems

Fig. 14-2. On this machine, dictation is recorded magnetically on an endless belt, or limp sleeve.

of magnetic recording machine, made in the United States, that is used for dictation.

TELEPHONE APPLICATIONS

DICTATION

Magnetic dictating machines of all types provide facilities for recording single or multiple conversations or dictation via the telephone. A businessman away from his office may call up, have the telephone induction-coil pickup placed under or near the telephone base, and proceed to dictate to the machine. The operation of this telephone pickup coil is based on the induction produced by the telephone transformer in the field where the pickup is placed. The strength of the currents picked up depends not only on the distance between the two coils but particularly on their mutual orientation. It is necessary to determine the best position for obtaining the maximum transfer of energy. This may be done by experimenting with any given telephone to find the position of the pickup coil which gives the best results.

CONFERENCE RECORDING

Recording a conference over telephones located in different cities usually requires that the conferee at the telephone where the conference is being recorded keep his voice slightly lower than the voices of other conferees. The machine's recording volume control should be turned up high enough to assure sufficient amplification of distant voices coming over the line for recording them clearly. Such amplification will cause the local conferee's voice to distort on the recording unless he keeps it fairly low in volume.

RECORDING OF ORDERS

Businesses having offices in many cities that conduct considerable business by long-distance telephone can effect savings by recording complete conversations at both ends of the line. Orders may be read rapidly and later typed, eliminating any need for repetition unless required by purchaser or seller. One businessman of the writer's acquaintance records his own telephone conversations in which he orders materials for delivery. The typed order, confirming the telephoned order, is sent by mail after it has been transcribed from the recording machine. The writer has been assured by this businessman that this method saves him the cost of his recorder every month by reduction of telephone expense.

STOCK-TAKING

There are many other ways in which use of a magnetic recorder in business offices and establishments saves time and money. Taking stock by using a microphone and a recorder saves many hours of tedious work and probably a considerable sum of money.

IN BUSINESS SYSTEMS

The next logical step in the use of magnetic recording in business is its employment as an erasable memory. The kind of work this magnetic memory performs depends entirely upon the application to which it is put in the system of which it is a part. In general, all businesses need information about the goods or services available at any particular time. This job can be done through the use of any medium that can communicate ideas—by means of words written or spoken, by pictures, or even by the senses of touch and smell. Up to this time written information has been the accepted medium. Businesses employ filing systems, card-index systems, and stock-inventory systems of many kinds and in many combinations. Magnetic recording can become a time-and-labor-saving part of such systems, especially where the time it takes to find, correct, and file written information, ready for use, is too long compared to the length of time in which the information itself changes. Thus, a business whose salesmen do not know at any given time exactly what they have available for sale will not realize its sales potential. Any procedure that will shorten the time lag in making information available to all concerned will be a boon to businessmen and many others.

INTELEX SYSTEM

A memory system, employing magnetic drum recorders as memory units, is exemplified by the Intelex Automatic Reservations System, developed by the International Standard Trading Corporation, an associate of the International Telephone and Telegraph Corporation.

Installation of the Intelex Automatic Reservations System in the Pennsylvania Railroad's gigantic terminal in New York City has resulted in making information regarding train space available in a matter of seconds instead of minutes. This speed-up in obtaining accurate information is a boon to the railroads and may very well become extremely useful to insurance companies, mail-order houses, and other businesses dealing in large and rapidly changing quantities of commodities.

The Intelex System uses magnetic recorders to provide information automatically. In railroad ticket-selling, the status of available space is recorded, by an operator, on Brush magnetic drum recorders, built to International Standard Trading Corporation's design specifications under contract. When the ticket-seller gets a request, he merely dials, on a special telephone set, the destination, date, and space desired. Then he (and the traveler, if desired) can hear, played back from the drum recorder, information on all space available on all trains for that destination on that date and also in some instances on alternative dates. The system enables the ticket-seller to dial only four digits to secure the desired information. The inquiry-sets on a ticket-seller's counter and on a telephone reservation clerk's desk are connected through a special automatic switchboard to the magnetic recorders (Fig. 14-3). The system is designed so that any number of inquiry-sets can be connected to enable the hearing of the same recording, or different recordings, simultaneously.

The very essence of this system of recording available space is that a ticket-seller, instead of listening to an attendant's voice over a telephone while he searches through train-space diagrams, now listens to a recording of exactly the same information that has been prepared in advance of his inquiry. He now selects the record he wants automatically, without disturbing the attendant. The latter now has only one job to do, that is, to enter in the car-space diagrams the reservations that have been made.

Automatic Space Control. The second main Intelex feature is Automatic Space Control. The ticket-seller, having determined from the recorded availability record the space that will be suitable for the customer and having pushed appropriate buttons on a newly developed device, a "key box," before him during his conversation with the passenger, has only to press a "send" button. This automatically assigns a serial number that, among other things, identifies

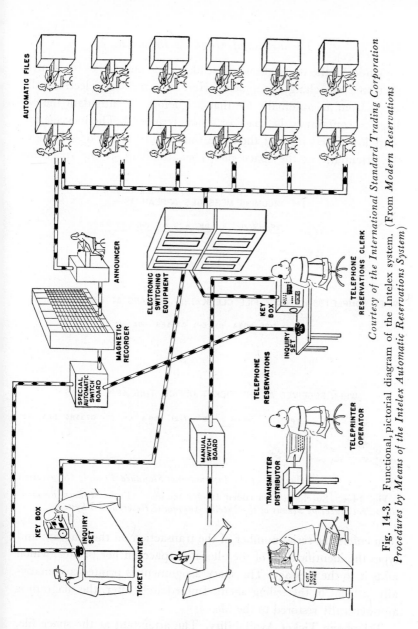

Fig. 14-3. Functional, pictorial diagram of the Intelex system. (From *Modern Reservations Procedures by Means of the Intelex Automatic Reservations System*)

Courtesy of the International Standard Trading Corporation

AUTOMATIC FILES

ANNOUNCER

ELECTRONIC SWITCHING EQUIPMENT

MAGNETIC RECORDER

SPECIAL AUTOMATIC SWITCH BOARD

KEY BOX

TELEPHONE RESERVATIONS CLERK

INQUIRY SET

MANUAL SWITCH BOARD

TELEPHONE RESERVATIONS

KEY BOX

INQUIRY SET

TICKET COUNTER

TRANSMITTER DISTRIBUTOR

TELEPRINTER OPERATOR

CITY TICKET OFFICE

the sender of the transaction and sends a code message to the central electronic switching equipment. Here the message electronically selects from an automatic file that lies before the attendant the car diagram containing the space or spaces requested. The message appears in printed form at the same time before the ticket-seller and the attendant at the space file. The attendant at the space file

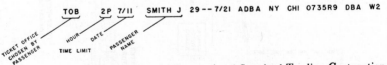

AS PRINTED IN FRONT OF SPACE FILE CLERK
THE INCOMING MESSAGES APPEAR AS:—

29 -- 7/21   A   DB   A   NY   CHI   0735R9

TRAIN NO. / DEPARTURE DATE / NO. OF UNITS OF SPACE / TYPE OF SPACE / MAKE DOWN / BOARDING PT. / DESTINATION / SERIAL NO.

WHEN COMPLETED BY SPACE FILE CLERK THIS APPEARS AT THE KEYBOX AS:—

29 -- 7/21   ADBA   NY   CHI   0735R9   DBA   W2

SPACE ASSIGNED / CAR NO.

WHEN RECEIVED AT THE TICKET OFFICE THIS APPEARS AS:—

TOB   2P 7/11   SMITH J   29 -- 7/21   ADBA   NY   CHI   0735R9   DBA   W2

TICKET OFFICE CHOSEN BY PASSENGER / TIME LIMIT / HOUR / DATE / PASSENGER NAME

Courtesy of the International Standard Trading Corporation

Fig. 14-4. Specimen of a coded Intelex message. (From *Modern Reservations Procedures by Means of the Intelex Automatic Reservations System*)

then enters the serial number of the transaction on the diagram and types the identification of the allocated space on her printer, which adds it to the message. The space assignment is printed automatically in front of the selling agent. Immediately after, the diagram is automatically restored to the file.

Telephone Ticket Availability. The attendant at the space file, who handles the entries on the diagrams, no longer answers public requests for reservations over the telephone. The telephoned requests are received by a reservation clerk who carries out the operations that have been described for the ticket-seller behind the counter. However, in the case of a reservation requested over the telephone, the telephone reservation clerk asks the customer his name and where he will pick up his ticket. The telephone reservation clerk, having received the space assignment from the attendant, adds to this information the data regarding the customer's name, the place where the ticket will be picked up, the time until which it will be held, and so forth. This information is then sent by printer to the sales office designated by the customer. At that point the message is put in an alphabetical file for ready reference when the customer arrives, or, if desired, the ticket can be prepared in anticipation of the customer's visit. This last, in brief, is the Telephone Ticket Availability feature of Intelex. A specimen coded message is shown in Fig. 14-4.

SOUND RECORDING FOR ANALYSIS

The technique of recording sound for analytical purposes is considerably different from that of recording for amusement purposes or even for ordinary musical instruction. When we record music we try to obtain sound that will be enjoyable to listen to when it is reproduced. If there is an apparent fault in the auditorium or studio where the musicians are playing, we may try to improve the sound before we record it, that is, improve it by the judicious use of reverberation and accentuation—in other words, by distorting the original sound to conform to our own judgment of what it *should* sound like. When we record sound for information, however, we *must* record the sound so that, when reproduced, it will sound *exactly* the same as the original, since otherwise the purpose of the recording would be nullified.

You may now ask, Why record sound for this purpose at all? Why not observe it directly? The reasons for recording sounds are: (1) to permit a number of people to listen to characteristic sounds at the same time and to form opinions as to their meaning, since it may not be convenient for all of them to make direct observations; (2) to permit comparison between two or more sounds recorded at different times and under different conditions; (3) to permit the keeping of audible progress records.

Sound information recording is valuable, then, only if the recording is faithful to the original sound. Also, as in any other kind of professional recording, the conditions under which recording and

Courtesy of the Minnesota Mining & Manufacturing Company

Fig. 14-5. Noise levels of experimental mufflers are determined by means of tape recorders at the Donaldson Company in St. Paul, Minnesota. The microphone at left allows an observer to record his comments on the same tape on which, at right, the muffler noise is being recorded.

reproduction are carried on must accord with strict standards. Apparatus used must be maintained in perfect condition at all times and should be tested for accuracy before and after use. No unknown variables are permissible, such as variation in the frequency of the ac supply or in the flutter of the recording-machine drive. If conditions are such that a variable quantity cannot be eliminated, it should be measured and noted on the record taken of conditions under which the test recording was made, also by voice recording on the reel of tape or wire containing the information recording, and again on the label affixed to the reel. (See Fig. 14-5.)

Precautions taken to reproduce conditions of recording while reproducing the record should include the recording of a calibrating tone, which, when played back at the same level, will ensure that the reproduced sound will be played back at the correct level of intensity. It is preferable to listen to noise recordings by means of headphones, since acoustic differences (for example, for sound projected from loudspeakers) would probably lead to incorrect evaluation. The phone diaphragms should be separated from the ear by small rubber cushions that perform two jobs: They exclude extraneous sounds and provide an additional small cavity that assists in giving accurate reproduction. (A 6-cubic-centimeter cavity is preferred by some.)

BINAURAL RECORDING FOR ANALYSIS

Methods of information recording for sound analysis should be based on all the precepts laid down for high-fidelity recording, including those ensuring that the sound will be reproduced exactly as it occurred. But now we are confronted by a contradiction that makes all our precautions seem useless. The observer listening to a sound *directly* hears with two ears, but the ordinary recording system is monaural. No matter how careful we are in recording and in reproduction, the monaural system is not capable of transmitting complete and precise information. Monaural recording in enclosed spaces produces frequency discrimination that is much more pronounced than that resulting from binaural recording. Monaural recording reproduced can convey to our hearing very little more than the character of the sound, its intensity, and its loudness. There are, of course, other informative effects—the frequency distortion effects caused by the proximity of the sound to the microphone or its distance from the microphone and those introduced by reverberation or its absence—but single-ear recording, or broadcasting for that matter, imparts very little sense of the direction from which the sound is traveling. This sense of direction is a needed part of the information recorded in many kinds of sound analysis.

Auditory Perspective. Auditory perspective—the ability to locate or "place" a sound in space—is a hearing ability compounded of several physical, neural, and mental abilities. Some of these abilities come under the heading of behavior and are modified by previous hearing experience and subsequent interpretation. We need not discuss them here since they vary considerably and are subjective in nature; also, space is lacking for a complete exposition. But, basically, we possess the ability to hear sounds in correct perspective, with certain exceptions. We can *place* sounds because we hear by means of two ears which conduct sounds—in the form of neural impulses—by two separate channels to the "diagnostic" center in the brain. Sound reaching our ears from a source to the right, for example, will give us the sense of coming from that direction mainly because the sound heard by the right-facing ear (assuming that hearing is normal) will be slightly louder than the sound from the same source heard by the left-facing ear. This effect may vary considerably with frequency; sound curls around the head at low frequencies (under 800 cy per sec, it is said) with little loss of intensity, and therefore very little directional effect may be noticed when the sound is one of low frequency. However, this intensity-directional effect increases with any increase in the frequency of the sound. As the wave length of sound becomes shorter with increase in frequency, the size of the head becomes more and more of a barrier; consequently, the ear facing the sound source will receive increasingly more as frequencies rise than the ear facing in the other direction.

However, offsetting our poor sense of direction in response to sound at low frequencies, due to the diffraction effect explained above, human hearing is more sensitive to phase differences of low-frequency sound than to phase differences of high-frequency sound. Thus the ear facing the oncoming low-frequency sound hears it a very short time before the other ear does. Although it has been repeatedly expounded that we have little phase discrimination in our hearing systems, apparently we have enough to aid us in deciding from which direction a low-frequency sound is coming. It is apparent that, by means of intensity and phase-discrimination and -differentiation, modified by other factors that depend upon the constitution of the sound and the listener's physical and mental idiosyncrasies, we are able naturally to sense direction.

In order, then, to "retain" in a magnetic recording all our natural abilities to discriminate in hearing, we must record and reproduce the sound as closely as possible to the way we naturally hear it—binaural recording on two tracks is indicated. The two microphones used in recording should possess pickup patterns resembling those of the human ear (good dynamic microphones are preferred) and should be set up in the same position on a dummy head as are the two ears on a human. For truly binaural recording the dummy head should possess the same acoustical properties as a human head does. The space between the two microphones is normally 7 or 8 in. Each microphone feeds its own pre-amplifier and recording amplifier and has its individual track on a dual-track tape or film. The tracks should be separated far enough, or the heads should be sufficiently shielded from each other magnetically, to prevent crosstalk between the two tracks. (See description of Westrex heads in the preceding chapter.) Before recording is begun, an accurate check should be made to ensure that operating conditions are exactly the same for each channel; true binaural recording cannot otherwise take place. Sound reproduced from the two tracks should travel through precisely similar channels, from the reproduce heads all the way to tested headphones.

Magnecord, Incorporated (Chicago, Illinois) was the first to produce a commercial binaural recorder, which (with similar tape recorders) has proved of inestimable value in industrial noise and sound analyses.

DATA RECORDING

Since magnetic recording is basically an electrical process, any information channeled to a magnetic recorder for preservation or for direct observation on reproduction must be in electrical form.

We cannot, without a complicated system, expect a magnetic recorder to read an ordinary mercury-column thermometer. However, if we fix things so that the mercury influences an electrical transducer, we can record variations in temperature as proportionate variations in electricity. The first step in data recording is to find a sensing device (sensory element) that will produce an electrical voltage (or cause changes to occur in an electrical voltage) as a result of the device's responses to changes in the condition being sensed. Such a sensory element responds to pressure, temperature, flow, strain, and/or other physical phenomena and converts its responses to the phenomenon being measured into electrical voltages that can be recorded magnetically.

DIRECT DATA-RECORDING

In order to record any information accurately, we need to know the time during which the event occurred. Thus any data-recording system should have at least two tracks on the tape, one track containing the magnetically recorded equivalent of the voltage representing a physical quantity, the other track having an accurate representation of time. Actually, modern data-recording systems provide for the recording of from 7 to 50 tracks (Fig. 14-6) simultaneously, separate tracks containing information about temperature, acceleration, strain, shock, pressure, humidity, air speed, velocity, displacement, vibration, frequency, time, and so on. The tape used may be up to 5 or 6 in. wide.

We have seen, in the chapter on the theory of magnetic recording, that sound is recorded on the tape by means of amplitude modulation, if you will permit a slight inaccuracy in terminology. Amplitude modulation is ordinarily not used in recording data on tape because of the present limitations of magnetic tape. These limitations are due, fundamentally, to a tendency of the iron-oxide coating on tape to be somewhat uneven and to clump in spots. Although these inconsistencies in tape coating are too minute and of too short duration at normal tape speeds to be noticeable to the ear, they can be the cause of inaccuracies in data recording. Thus, where the "clump" occurs, the signal level recorded may be half again as great as desired, whereas if we record a signal at a point from which coating is missing, the level, when amplitude recording is used, may be almost nil. Phase shift may also occasion errors in recording data accurately. For these reasons, magnetic data recording is usually performed by means of frequency-modulated carriers

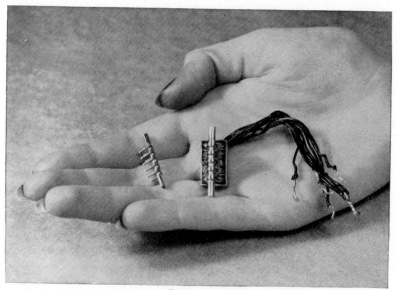

Courtesy of the Stancil-Hoffman Corporation

Fig. 14-6. Multi-channel head assembly.

that are modulated by the voltage outputs of various sensory elements.

A simple direct-recording data system may consist of the following elements:

1. Sensory elements
2. A multitrack tape recorder
3. Frequency-modulated oscillator
4. Frequency-modulation converters
5. A reading system

Such a system operates in this way: The sensing elements on becoming activated create voltages that frequency-modulate oscillators whose output is recorded on the tape on separate, respective tracks. At the same time a reference oscillator records a constant frequency on another track. On playback, this action is reversed, and the original voltages recorded are demodulated and either operate direct-writing oscillographic recorders or may be viewed on an oscilloscope. The reference signal, which has been modulated during recording by any irregularities, now acts as a control so that the final outcome accurately represents the original physical quantities. A system like this may be used to record shocks, motions, or vibrations occurring once a second or even less frequently and phenomena occurring up to several thousand times per second. Connected by wiring, the system may be made small enough to be used inside an automobile or an airplane.

FM-FM TELEMETERING

When conditions are such that they preclude the employment of a directly wired system for data recording, such as that above, we must make use of radio transmission. For instance, we may want to find out what happens to various parts of an automobile as it is tumbled down a hillside. We could put all the necessary equipment, including the recorder, inside the automobile and proceed with the test. After the wreck had come to rest, we could scramble down the hill, recover what equipment was not smashed, patch together the broken tape, if necessary, and play it back to get the needed data. Or, placing in the automobile only the sensory elements and a small radio transmitter, we could record the data at a distance by means of a receiver and tape recorder. The telemetering method is now preferred wherever it can be used, since it possesses several advantages. Small mobile recorders, since they operate from batteries or nonconstant sources of electricity, are by no means as free from drive instability as recorders operated from ac lines. Another factor in favor of telemetering information is that of economy: The equipment needed to transmit information to a stationary recorder is not anywhere near as costly in the long run as that needed to record data inside a moving vehicle that may—with the equipment—be irretrievably smashed during a test.

FM-FM telemetering is a system of recording information that can be used in all kinds of mobile testing and by persons conducting tests at a distance from the sensory elements, as would be the case in tests of explosives. The sensory elements pick up their information and translate it into electrical impulses. Each of these impulses, or electrical voltages, frequency-modulates a different part of a radio-frequency carrier wave, or what is called a "subcarrier." Thus, a change "observed" and responded to by the sensory element causes a proportional change in the frequency of its associated sub-carrier. Subsequently mixed together, all these sub-carriers form a composite wave that frequency-modulates a radio-frequency carrier which is transmitted. At the receiving point this frequency-modulated radio-frequency wave is demodulated and recorded as composite information, which is not yet "readable." On playback, the composite signal is separated into its original frequency-modulated sub-carriers by means of band-pass filters. Each filtered channel is then fed into a limiter and FM discriminator, a procedure that leaves intact the original information derived from the particular sensory element that measured it in the first place. This information may then be read on direct-reading instruments, transferred to recording paper, or viewed on an oscilloscope. Or, if desired, the particular band-passed tracks that are wanted for further study may be re-recorded on other machines. Later, they may be played back as continuous loops for constant observation or comparison with other loops of tape.

Flutter Problems. In the conventional tape recorder for recording sound, flutter and wow are kept down and cannot be noticed even in piano music unless they amount to a considerable percentage. With FM recording, random flutter (introduced by drive aberrations) cannot be tolerated to any appreciable extent because it causes errors in interpretation of instrument readings. Actually, frequency modulation is a controlled, *precision* "fluttering" of a radio wave, the number of flutterings per second constituting

the frequency of the wave. If during the recording and reproducing of this wave, flutter is also contributed by the drive
mechanism of the recorder, the machine flutter will cause error in
interpretation. If a sensory element produced a constant voltage, we
should see, in the final graph, a straight line. If flutter is introduced
by the machine drive, the line on the graph will have little "excursions," up and down, their values depending upon the amount of
flutter in the drive. Another factor that necessitates very low flutter
in data recording is this: The frequency-modulated sub-carriers that
are affected frequency-wise by the intelligence conveyors (that is,
the sensory elements or instruments) must be comparatively narrow
in bandwidth if all are to be accommodated in a radio-frequency
carrier link. These sub-carriers are deviated (or frequency-
modulated) only by ±7.5 per cent of their center frequency. This
imposes the requirement upon the recording system that its inconsistencies must total only a small percentage of this ±7.5-per cent
frequency deviation if the system is to be at all useful. In other
words, if we were dealing with a system of ±50.0-per cent deviation, the recorder could be of the normal kind, and very little trouble
would ensue. But with only ±7.5-per cent deviation from center
frequency, the total flutter of a data-recording machine must be
very low, since a greater percentage of flutter would obscure or cause
misinterpretation of the observation "sensed."

Therefore, in order to obtain accuracy in measurement of one per
cent or better, it was found necessary to do one of two things: either
to make an almost perfect mechanical drive or to use some kind of
feedback compensation. The Ampex Model 302 used electronic
compensation, of a type developed by the Raymond Rosen Company of Philadelphia. It works as follows: An unmodulated, frequency-stabilized subcarrier wave is recorded simultaneously with
the composite-information-subcarrier waves. During playback the
subcarrier wave that is frequency-stabilized is separated from the
other subcarrier waves by the usual means (band-pass filter, limiter,
and discriminator) and is then fed back *in opposite phase* and at
almost equal magnitude across the outputs of each separate information channel. By this means flutter components, or quotients, of the

various channels are canceled, in effect, and the desired accuracy of reading in the final measurement is obtained. (The foregoing is a typical example of feedback control.) Still another Ampex recorder, Model 500, utilizes a drive that reduces flutter to a point where, for many purposes, electronic compensation is not needed.

AC Supply Problem. Like sound recording, data recording is subject to momentary or prolonged variations in speed due to changes in the supply current. It can readily be appreciated that a recording made at one speed and played back at another speed, unless the speed ratios are accurately known and are constant, would be useless for measuring data. Therefore some method of achieving independence from power line changes is desirable. Such methods, as previously indicated in this volume, are predicated upon the use of a tuning fork or oscillator-controlled power pack for operating the capstan motor. Several of these packs have been designed and manufactured. One of them (the Ampex Model 375 amplifier) contains a tuning fork that produces a 60-cy-per-sec frequency, stable to within five parts in a million per degree centigrade. This tuning-fork amplifier's output is 60 watts of power, more than ample to drive the capstan motor at a constant speed.

Problem of Tape Stretch. The stretching of tape that was recorded under adverse conditions poses another problem in this kind of recording. (See Chapter 3 on recording media.) It is important either to avoid dimensional changes altogether or to provide some means for nullifying their effects in the crucial period between recording and reproduction. The latter type of means has been provided by several manufacturers. The Ampex Speed Lock System has achieved correction of error due to tape changes in dimension to within 1/1000 sec throughout 2400 ft of tape. Other recorders have achieved comparable results by the use of similar methods.

The Ampex Automatic Speed Control System operates in this manner: The tuning fork contained in the unit that furnishes ac power for driving the capstan motor also records a 60-cy-per-sec signal (reference frequency) on the tape. This same 60-cy signal is then mixed in a modulation unit with the incoming signal, and the total output is recorded on the tape. In reproduction, a "Differential Playback Unit" compares the reference 60-cycle frequency reproduced from the tape with the output of the tuning-fork oscillator; this Unit then generates the current necessary to correct the speed of the capstan drive so that the frequencies keep in perfect step with each other. The Differential Unit contains two synchronous motors, one controlled directly by the tuned-fork oscillator's output and the other controlled by the oscillator's output as reproduced from the tape. One motor is mounted in a fixed position, with only the rotor itself movable; the other is free to rotate. Therefore, if the two frequencies are not identical, one motor varies with respect to the other, thereby varying a potentiometer that controls the frequency of a variable-frequency oscillator. This oscillator in turn feeds the power amplifier that drives the playback motor. Thus, if the reproduced frequency does not match the standard frequency, the variable oscillator changes its frequency sufficiently to correct the speed of the capstan motor. (See Chapter 13 on motion-picture and television techniques.)

Tape Vibration. It seems that in tape recording we solve one problem only to be plagued by another. In the continuing development of tape we went from solid steel to coated paper, to homogeneous plastic tape, to coated plastic tape. After it was observed that coated tape vibrated excessively, all such tape was treated with a wax lubricant. This expedient reduced tape chatter considerably, so much so that at normal tape speeds no serious effects due to any vibrations that remain can be aurally noticed. But in data recording of the FM-FM variety, tape chatter can cause serious error. The only alleviative is use of a device which will not permit extensive excursions of the tape while it is in a vibrating state. The motion-picture industry was forced to adopt this expedient a long time ago, and it seems that it is now being applied to tape recording. The Rangertone drive and other drives built and contemplated embrace this idea of a heavily damped tape section in the head area. The Ampex Model 500 has solved the problem of chatter by employing a drive in which air suction is used to hold the tape tight to the capstan in intimate and unvarying contact with the heads.

It is claimed that the use of this device and associated equipment has resulted in tape flutter from all sources being reduced sufficiently to make feedback controls unnecessary in any effort to achieve an accuracy in final data of less than 0.7 per cent (using the normal ±7.5 per cent deviation in FM transmission).

USES OF RECORDED DATA

The information collected by means of data recording and telemetering may be stored in any one of a number of ways. It may be kept on the tape on which it was originally recorded, in the form of a number of information tracks. One or more information tracks may be re-recorded to other tapes for closer study. The information may be photographed, by means of a movie camera and a cathode-ray tube face (oscilloscope), and stored in the form of film strip for motion pictures. Or the multiple information tracks may be converted to inked graphs on paper, each graph related to the others by some common time scale.

There are two other ways in which information can be more or less directly used. In one technique each information track is used directly to govern the actions of the mechanism that produced it in the first place. In the other the mass of collected information is reduced, in translatable terms, to a formula or a short description describing the behavior of the mechanism that created each of the respective information tracks. In the first of these two techniques we have what is now termed "automatic control," in the second, computer systems.

AUTOMATIC CONTROL

"Automatic control" is a new way to describe what has long been known by other names—or by no name at all in those cases where it is taken for granted, as in the human body. The temperature-regulating system of the normal person is an intricate example of automatic control. The beating of our hearts is automatically controlled. We would not be able to walk if it were not for the automatic functioning of our balancing system, automatically controlled in part through the agency of the fluid in the balance canals in our ears. In each of the cases mentioned, the whole system functions as a tightly controlled unit; one cause creates one effect —this effect in turn becomes a causative factor in creating another effect; the whole chain of cause and effect is automatically controlled, and the end result is the result desired. Commonly encountered forms of automatic control outside the body are: the weather vane, which is kept heading into the wind, the speed-regulating ball governor, the thermostatic heat regulator in the home, the voltage-regulator systems used in electronics and industry, and, from our experience, some of the synchronous-drive systems used in tape recording. In a truly automatic control system any error in the result is fed back to the original source in such proportion that the error is eliminated or rather, almost eliminated.

The part that magnetic recording plays in automatic control is thus indicated: Information about the behavior of a machine in actual operation can be compared with theoretical information regarding the ideal behavior of the same machine or with information about its previous performances. Any difference between the two tracks of information may be fed back and used to control the actions of the machine; it can thus be made to conform to the ideal or desired norm. In order to do this work, the magnetic tracks should, ideally, contain no error of their own, and they must be convertible to a force that can actually effect regulation. We have just seen how magnetic tracks can be corrected for phase differences (Raymond Rosen System) and speed (The Ampex Synchro-Lock and Fairchild Pic-Sync Systems and others). Let us assume that we wish to control, by means of magnetic recording, a machine drilling holes in a steel plate. The resistance of the steel plate to the drill would depend upon a number of factors, all predictable: the increasing depth of the drill in the metal, the sharpness of the drill, its cutting shape, its temperature, lubrication, and so forth. The information needed to produce perfect holes, identically made and placed, in identical steel in the least possible time could be recorded on a number of information tracks on tape, each information track based on ideal or actually proved conditions of temperature of steel plate and drill, lubrication, speed, et cetera. The actual conditions obtaining during each drilling operation could then be compared instantly with the recorded ideal conditions, and corrective signals could be sent back, by means of amplifiers, motors, relays, and other actuators, which would cause the actual conditions to be made to conform to the ideal, or proved, conditions.

A machine called a "record-playback control" has been built for the above purpose by the General Electric Company's Specialty Control Department. A multiple-channel tape recorder is employed as a magnetic memory for the machine on which it is installed. In operation, a skilled machinist sets the machine to perform a series of operations that will produce the first piece of work. These motions are translated into electric signals by means of selsyns (self-synchronous motors), and these signals are recorded on magnetic tape. When the tape is played back through the machine, it automatically duplicates the machine's original motions and produces a part identical to that made while operations were recorded as electric impulses. Repeat orders can be produced economically— merely as a result of taking the specified tape recording from a file and inserting it in the machine. Studies are now being conducted into the possibility of using an electronic computer to convert numerical data into electric signals that would then be recorded on the tape. This would eliminate the first manual machining operation. Magnetic recording is expected to play an important part in automatic industrial control systems of the near future.

MAGNETIC RECORDING IN COMPUTERS

In order to understand how magnetic recording is employed in computers we must necessarily learn something about the functions and operations of computers. Possibly the very first thing to learn about computers as a whole are their limitations. A computer does not take the place of a brain. A computer, regardless of its intricacy or cost and despite the seemingly unlimited kinds of mathematical or computational functions it may fulfill, is still only an aid to the human brain. A computer has no imagination, no instinct. It does, however, have a memory that can be more useful than our own; it is not as subject to fatigue; it can be made to operate millions of times faster than man can with simple mechanical aids, and in other ways it is superior to the human computational system. A computer can even be made to exert something akin to human judgment in the comparison of values, but as yet it does not "think."

There are at present two basic types of computers, the analog and the digital computer. The analog computer solves problems in which physical quantities are represented by analogous quantities. The digital computer works with numbers, adds and subtracts them, fundamentally. The analog machine has been compared to a slide rule, the engineer's "slip-stick," which *measures* quantities; the digital machine is comparable to the abacus, which *counts* units— arbitrary numbers. Information may be processed directly by either type of computer, provided that the information is in a form that the computer can digest.

A digital computer, since it operates with numbers fundamentally, requires some finite time in which to compute and give an answer. Although the time it takes to do this is not long now, and with improved techniques is becoming shorter all the time, the digital machine does not take the place of the analog machine for instant-to-instant precise answers about information continuously being received.

It is possible to make a hybrid computer, one with the digital input and mechanism and the analog output, and vice versa, in order to provide facilities for handling specific problems. Our interests here, however, lie in the field of magnetic recording, which is employed mainly in conjunction with digital computers. This type of computer generally consists of four main sections: an input-output unit, a memory unit, a control unit, and an arithmetic unit. The input-output unit is the link between the machine and its human operators. By means of this unit (which in most cases is di-

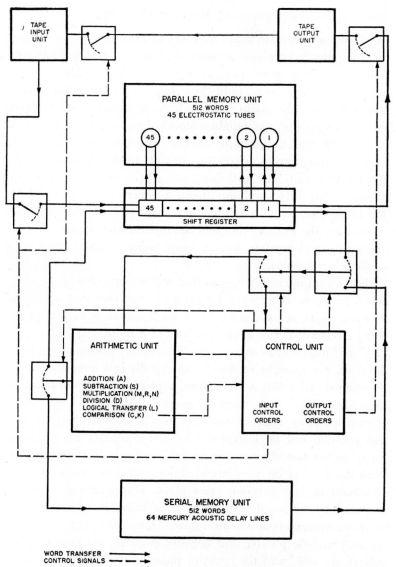

WORD TRANSFER ──────▶
CONTROL SIGNALS ── ── ── ▶

Courtesy of the U.S. National Bureau of Standards

Fig. 14-7. Over-all block diagram of the SEAC—the National Bureau of Standards Eastern Automatic Computer (digital computer). After the computer is supplied with coded instructions and numerical data, the control unit automatically directs the computer's operation. The diagram shows the various sequences of operations possible. The successive steps in a sequence are controlled by means of switches; switching time is about one microsecond.

327

vided into two separate units) numbers and instructions are fed into the computer proper and answers are fed out. The memory unit "stores" numbers, instructions as to what to do with the numbers, and also partial answers, until these items are needed. The control unit selects all the paths along which information must travel, searches its memory for numbers stored there, sends those selected to the arithemtic unit, returns answers to the memory, and finally directs the memory to deliver the answers to the operator via the input-output unit. The arithmetic unit carries out the actual computations that the control unit directs it to perform (see Fig. 14-7). The sections of digital computers in which magnetic recording may be used are the memory unit and the input-output units. (In some machines supplementary storage units, using magnetic tape as a medium, are employed.)

Digital computers, for reasons that will become obvious as we go along, make use of a special language of their own that consists of only two digits, one and zero. These digits can easily be interpreted by an electronic device as the presence of a pulse or its absence, as "yes" or "no," and as one or zero. This binary system of numbers, therefore, can easily be recorded magnetically in a number of ways. By using dc recording without bias, a positive pulse will make an identifiable "pip" on a magnetic surface that has previously been magnetized in the negative direction. The lack of any "pip" of positive polarity will be interpreted by the computer as indicating "zero" in the case of a number, or "no" in the instruction category. With this kind of dc recording no ac erasing is necessary, since dc saturation in one direction takes place. Direct-current recording may also be employed with previous ac erase, in which case the magnetic medium is in a neutral state. Thus, subsequent dc recording may include positive and negative polarity, the positive pulse indicating "one" and the negative pulse indicating "zero," or alternatively, "yes" and "no." These pulses are ordinarily accentuated or "spiked" before they are recorded (pre-shaped) in order to prevent the possibility of error that could occur in interpretation (by the machine) if there were slight flaws or "holes" in the magnetic medium.

MAGNETIC MEMORIES

The memory, or storage medium, of the digital computers employing magnetic recording usually takes the form of a drum. This drum, varying in size as the needs of use indicate, is made of a nonmagnetic metal and is either plated or coated with a magnetizable medium. The drum made by Remington Rand (Engineering Research Associates, a division of Sperry Rand Corporation) is coated with iron oxide, which is protected and held in place by sprayed-on lacquer (Fig. 14-8). Drums made by other companies are ordinarily of the plated variety. Plating is, in some cases, performed by the dc–ac method, the metallic molecules deposited being kept as small in size and as uniform as possible by means of their constant agitation by a supersonic component in the plating current.

Binary numbers, recorded around the surface of the memory drum, are readily available for reading (playback) when needed. If the computer is to operate rapidly, these numbers—or rather, the desired series of numbers represented by pulses recorded on any track of the many tracks on a typical drum—must, of course, be available in the least possible time. This requirement, basic in computer design, necessitates either very high drum speed or a multiplicity of magnetic heads. Most computer designs make some compromise between these two requirements, but even so, typical drum speeds may range upward from 1600 in. per sec. We have seen previously that ring heads, which are used in computer work, ordinarily have to be made of rather soft iron. Heads of this type, in contact with the oxide-coated or plated surface of a drum revolving at such high speeds, would themselves rapidly wear out and, in addition, would wear and abrade the drum surface. Problems resulting from such contact have been avoided, and one of the following arrangements is employed: (1) noncontact heads, with very sharply spiked pulses; (2) heads whose cores are made of magnetic ceramic, which is very hard and is capable of very good magnetic response at the high frequencies used in computer recording on drums; and (3) the ERA systems of recording called the "Boundary-Displacement Method," designed for use in analog computers.

ERA Boundary-Displacement Method. Recalling ordinary amplitude recording for a moment, we notice two or three failings inherent in it; although these may not cause any noticeable difficulty in sound recording, they can cause error and therefore failure in

Courtesy of Sperry Rand Corporation

Fig. 14-8. The magnetic drum and head assembly developed by Engineering Research Associates, now a division of Sperry Rand Corporation.

the primary function of amplitude recording in a computing system. Ordinary amplitude recording requires that contact between the head gap and the medium be unvarying; it is extremely difficult, if not impossible, to maintain unvarying contact between a rapidly whirling drum and a magnetic head, discounting the problems of wear and static charges. Even with the use of noncontact heads of normal design, if the distance between the drum surface and the head varies even slightly, there will be a noticeable difference in the level of the signal recorded or reproduced. In addition, slight imperfections in the drum surface, whether the drum is plated or coated, may cause enough difference in signal amplitude for the machine to interpret a noise "pip" as an information pulse; such imperfections could also result in failure of the machine to "recognize" a pulse recorded on an imperfect spot on the drum surface. (It is possible for a magnetic coating to acquire "holes" during manufacture because of dust particles in the oxide pigment.) Difficulties and failures due to any or all of the foregoing causes are in great part avoided in the Boundary-Displacement Method of recording. This method, characterized by a high degree of amplitude linearity, has no dependence upon the magnetization curve of the medium and does not require for optimum performance the critical adjustments found in conventional intensity recording systems.

The Boundary-Displacement Method attacks the problem of intensity nonlinearity by producing a record in such form that a continuous range of magnetization is not involved. A strip of tape recorded by this technique is effectively left in only one state—the relatively unvarying state of residual magnetic saturation.

With intensity recording, the *intensity* of magnetization increases or decreases along the length of the tape as the recording signal rises and falls in amplitude. With Boundary-Displacement recording, a small region of transition, which separates areas of *oppositely polarized* saturation, is displaced transversely from the center line of the tape by an amount proportional to the instantaneous signal intensity.

In playback, the Boundary-Displacement recording is reproduced by a conventional type of pickup head whose gap spans the entire range of displacement of the boundary. The net flux in the pickup head is proportional to the difference between the areas of the positive and negative saturation scanned by the gap, and hence to the amount of displacement of the region of transition, or "boundary" from the center line.

Unwanted modulation of the signal during recording, either by minute surface irregularities in the recording medium or by variations in spacing between the recording-head gap and the medium, is largely avoided by the Boundary-Displacement Method.

The oscillograms shown in Fig. 14-9 present a comparison of a Boundary-Displacement magnetic-drum recording and a dc bias

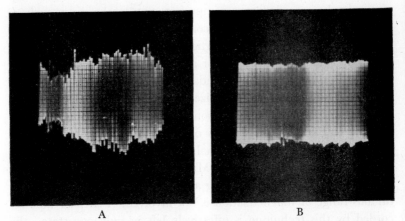

A   B

Courtesy of Sperry Rand Corporation

Fig. 14-9. Oscillograms of: A, dc bias recording and B, Boundary-Displacement recording. (The Boundary-Displacement System was developed by Engineering Research Associates, now a division of Sperry Rand.)

recording on the same drum. The drum, the medium, the frequency of the recording signal, and the pickup head are identical in both cases. The drum used for this comparison was deliberately constructed to provide an over-all eccentricity of 0.002 in. and also a series of relatively short-period surface irregularities. Oscillogram A shows the dc bias recording; oscillogram B shows, for the Boundary-Displacement recording, the marked reduction in modulation effects.

An interesting side light on the Boundary-Displacement Method is its adaptability to the production of visible records of recorded signals. Tapes recorded by this method, like tape recorded by any other magnetic method, may be "developed" by immersing them in a suspension of carbonyl-iron powder in alcohol or light oil. But on boundary-displacement recorded tape the carbonyl-iron particles give a far better indication of the recording. They adhere to the boundary region of the tape, giving a clear-cut visible indication.

The Boundary-Displacement Method makes use of dc bias recording, which restricts the signal-to-noise ratio to approximately —40 db. Capable of recording frequencies from 1 cy per sec to over 100,000 cy per sec, this method has been applied to the recording of sound and of data with excellent results.

AUXILIARY MAGNETIC MEMORY

Regardless of the type, an electronic digital computer has a limited storage capacity in its internal high-speed memory, in which partial solutions are stored until needed later in the course of the solution of a problem. In order to retain information for later use in solving many types of problems, provision is made for the machine to store information in an external memory; information is transmitted from the computer for storage and fed back into it later during the solution procedure for which it is needed. The speed with which this can be accomplished is a very important factor in the over-all operating speed.

A computer-controlled external auxiliary "memory," using magnetic tape as the recording medium, has been developed by James L. Pike of the Computer Laboratory of the U.S. National Bureau of Standards. The units in this external memory combine high-speed starting, stopping, and reversing with notable mechanical simplicity. They are used in conjunction with SEAC, the Eastern Automatic Computer of the National Bureau of Standards, which was built in 1950.

When teletype tape was used with SEAC for auxiliary storage as a temporary expedient, reading the information onto and from the tape often took more than 95 per cent of the problem-solution time. These new units represent the most promising method thus

*Courtesy of the U.S. National Bureau
of Standards*

Fig. 14-10. The complete auxiliary magnetic-tape memory unit, designed for SEAC, is shown at left; an enlargement of the right-most panel is pictured at right.

The tape rests lightly on the two large rollers on either side of the middle panel on the complete unit. Between these rollers are the magnetic heads for recording, playback, and erasing. The two rollers are driven continuously but in opposite directions. A corresponding jam roller (visible at right in enlargement) engages the tape against the large roller when a solenoid is energized, and the tape is consequently quickly started to move in the desired direction. The tape then falls in loose folds into a narrow glass tank, formed by spacing two glass plates just a little farther apart than the width of the tape. Electrostatic charges are eliminated from the tape by a strip of polonium (white bar at bottom in enlargement).

far offered in reducing problem-solution time. Computer-controlled auxiliary memory systems using magnetic pulses have been employed successfully in computers other than SEAC, but most of these systems have required complex and expensive mechanisms to start, stop, and reverse the magnetic tape with the necessary speed. This NBS* magnetic tape memory has the considerable advantage

* National Bureau of Standards.

of combining speed, simplicity, and economy, an advantage resulting from the successful elimination of reels and servomechanisms. Only two small masses need to be accelerated in starting the tape, a small jam roller and the tape hanging in a tank (Fig. 14-10). The magnetic tape, when at rest, rests lightly on two smooth-surfaced rollers that rotate continuously, the first in a direction opposite to that of the other. Between these two rollers the tape passes past magnetic recording, play, and erase heads. When either of two control solenoids is energized, a low-inertia rubber-covered roller presses the tape against one of the smooth rollers. The pressure quickly starts the tape moving in the desired direction. Tape inertia is kept low by letting each end fall in loose folds into a tank. Each tank consists of two plates of glass which are a little farther apart than the width of the tape. Although the tanks are large enough to hold several thousand feet of tape, 1200 ft is ample for most problems. Enclosed on all edges, the tanks have slots in the top through which the tape enters and leaves. Because the tanks are just wide enough to clear the tape, the loose folds in which the tape falls have no tendency to turn over or become tangled.

Tape Tank Problems. Several problems were encountered in developing the tape memory mechanism. For one thing, as the tape passes through the drive mechanism, it tends to acquire an electrostatic charge, which can become quite troublesome at intermediate high speeds and cause the tape to cling to the walls of the tank as soon as it leaves the drive mechanism. If the electrostatic charge is strong enough, the tape may continue to stick at the top of the tank until it backs up into the mechanism and is damaged by a sharp fold. The present solution, satisfactory at speeds up to 8 ft per sec, is to ionize the air where the tape leaves the drive unit, using strips of alpha-emitting polonium. Another possible answer to the problem, although somewhat inconvenient, would be to control the humidity within the tanks. The ideal solution would probably be to make the base material of the tape sufficiently conductive to prevent a static charge from collecting. Experiments indicate that base materials having a resistance of not more than a few megohms per unit square should be satisfactory.

Erasure Problems. A second limitation on the operating speed of the tape in a tape memory unit was imposed by the need to erase information from the tape. The necessary erase frequency increases as tape speed increases. A tape speed of 16 ft per sec, for example, requires an erase frequency of several hundred kilocycles per second. Because of hysteresis losses, ordinary magnetic heads cannot operate at such high frequencies. Fortunately, heads with powdered-iron magnetic circuits have solved this problem. Also, dc erasure can be advantageously used.

Tape-Coating Flaws. A major problem in using magnetic tape in computer work is the presence of flaws in the tape coating. Commercially available tape, although constantly increasing in quality, has many small imperfections in the magnetic-oxide coating, which are quite undetectable in ordinary audio work. In the recording of computer pulses, however, the loss of magnetic signals over a very small area in the tape may mean the loss of one or more digits of information. And in computer work the loss of a single digit—which may occupy less than 2/100 in. on the tape—cannot be tolerated. Some specially treated and selected tapes now available are nearly free from flaws, and improved manufacturing techniques may soon eliminate such difficulties.

LANGUAGE TRANSLATION BY MEANS OF COMPUTERS

Mathematics is a universal language, but ordinary languages are not universal in their communicative power. However, through the joint efforts of Georgetown University's Institute of Languages and Linguistics and the International Business Machines Corporation, sentences in one language have been translated into another by use of computer techniques. Leon Dostert, of Georgetown University, predicted at the New York headquarters of International Business Machines, where he performed the first "electronic translation" in January, 1954, that "five, perhaps three years hence, interlingual *meaning* conversion by electronic process in important functional areas of several languages may well be an accomplished fact."

Dostert assumes that electronic translation will begin with separate dictionaries for each technical area and that as experience with use of the dictionaries grows, enough will be learned to permit accurate translation of our common everyday language, in which are such illogical and unpredictable words as "charleyhorse."

Electronic Language Signs. What the electronic translators have actually done is to create an entirely new electronic language. They have taken normal—as contrasted with "charleyhorse"—words and attached to them "tags" or "signs" that give each word a precision it does not usually possess. These signs actually denote rules of grammar and meaning. And although only six rules were used in one demonstration, the six were enough to cover all the words in all the sentences the IBM 701 Computer was asked to translate. (These six rules apply only to selected words in Russian and English.)

The digital computer could translate only because these rule-tags were associated with normal words. It cannot think independently. It could only perform in obedience to detailed instructions prepared by the Georgetown linguists who could not give the "brain" dependable instructions until they themselves had worked out foolproof means of telling in advance how to translate a word that had more than one meaning.

The particular six rule-tags were chosen because they have a broader effect on language translation than do any other rules studied by the Georgetown linguists. These six basic rules govern transposition of words when that is required in order to make sense, choice of meanings if a word has more than one interpretation, omission of words that are not required for a correct translation, and insertion of words required to complete the meaning or thought.

The mechanics involved in the operation of one rule, which governs transposition of words when such inversion is required in order to make sense, follows.

We begin with the Russian *gyeneral mayor*. These two words must be reversed to arrive at the proper translation in English: *major general*.

The switch is assured in advance by attaching rule-sign 21 to the

Russian *gyeneral* in the bilingual glossary that is stored in the machine and by attaching rule-sign 110 to the Russian *mayor*.

The stored instructions, along with the glossary, say, "Whenever you read a rule-sign 110 in the glossary, go back and look for a rule-sign 21. If you find a 21, print the two words that follow it in reverse order." So the instant the "brain" is given *gyeneral mayor* to translate, it automatically acts accordingly—all in the twinkling of an eye.

After the six rules were formulated as the foundation of electronic translation, the linguists tested the rules on themselves. They wrote out sentences in Russian. Then they wrote out instructions for placing in the Russian-English glossary the rule-signs that would lead to the proper English translation. After that, they gave the Russian sentences and the instructions to government officials and others in Washington who know nothing about the Russian language or electronic "brains." The officials followed the instructions and came up with the right translations.

The first step in preparing IBM's computer to repeat this human performance of a mechanical task was to write electronically, in plus and minus charges on a magnetic-drum surface, 250 Russian words and their equivalents in English. Wherever a Russian word had more than one meaning, each meaning was given a rule-sign. This set of electronic words (rule-signs) then constituted the dictionary to which the "brain" could refer.

The second step was to store the detailed instructions—exactly like those the people in Washington had followed, except that these were written in electrical charges on the faces of cathode-ray tubes in the IBM 701 Computer's electrostatic memory. All that remained to be done was to give the computer the Russian words to translate. The "brain" responded at the rate of one full sentence every 6 or 7 sec.

This experimental demonstration can be rated only as a scientific sample. Nevertheless, the success of the project contains enormous implications for both linguistics and electronics. Students of language are now for the first time justified in undertaking serious study of language from a mechanical point of view.

From the viewpoint of the electronic "brain," language translation also has tremendous significance. Through the electronic "brain" it has been learned that the formulation of logic required to convert word meanings properly by electronics, even in a small segment of two languages, necessitates two and one-half times as many instructions to the computer as are required to simulate the flight of a guided missile!

15

Magnetic Recording in the Medical Field

Part I

RECORDING OF HEART SOUNDS

As this is being written, more and more members of the medical profession are turning to magnetic recording for use in teaching, diagnosis, and treatment. The magnetic recording method provides the medical practitioner and researcher with an exact recording of sound, something that was never before cheaply or easily available to him. Disk recording of heart sounds, for instance, required the presence of competent technicians; they can be dispensed with ordinarily in magnetic recording, since the physician or his assistant may operate the recorder during examination of a patient. To date, magnetic recording in the medical field has been most widely used in the recording of heart sounds and in teaching diagnostic methods in cardiology. It has also been used, but less widely, for listening to abdominal cavity and chest sounds, in the teaching of psychiatry, and the treatment of psychiatric patients. It is probably not too much to expect that magnetic recording will become a valued tool in all branches of medicine in the near future.

MICROPHONES AND AMPLIFIERS

The kind of microphone to use in recording heart sounds posed a problem that was solved by two different organizations in about the same way. Heart sounds are created by the various pumping actions within the heart. Frequencies as low as 30 cy per sec and as high as 10,000 cy per sec must be recorded faithfully if diagnosis is to be as exact as possible. Although it must be tightly coupled to the patient's chest wall, the microphone must not pick up noises generated by the friction of the microphone against the skin.

The Gallant Engineering Company of Washington, D.C., which developed the system now in use at the Georgetown Medical College and at Gallinger Hospital, Washington, D.C. for the recording of heart sounds, at first utilized a microphone that was made like a stethoscope, a captured column of air being used to transmit the sounds. Later, after considerable experimentation, a diaphragm type of microphone was employed; this proved to give more faithful recordings.

Dr. George David Geckeler, a pioneer in the recording of heart sounds and head of the Cardiology Department at Hahnemann Hospital in Philadelphia, Pennsylvania, developed a practical way of reducing pickup by the microphone of frictional skin noises. (He also standardized a diaphragm microphone, employing a Western Electric 618-A dynamic microphone.) In an attempt to reduce skin noise, Dr. Geckeler cemented a ring of surgical rubber tubing, 3/8 in. in diameter, around the edge of the front face of the microphone. For best results (that is, minimum frictional noise pickup), the rubber tubing had to be well aged, not new or too resilient. When properly used this rubber-fronted microphone will give the closest and tightest possible coupling to the chest wall, at the same time eliminating the "squealing" noises caused by new rubber. Dr. Geckeler found that by this method of coupling he achieved the closest approach to "stethoscope sound." (See Fig. 15-1.)

As noted previously, almost the whole audible spectrum is useful in recording of heart sounds, the sounds most useful for diagnostic purposes generally being those between 30 and 2000 cy per sec.

However, it is best to record the full frequency range and, in reproducing the recording, to narrow the range by filtering, if necessary, in order to make wanted frequencies more prominent.

Pre-amplifiers giving a total amplification of 90 db are used during recording. The need for this high order of amplification makes it necessary to avoid all extraneous noise that can possibly be avoided

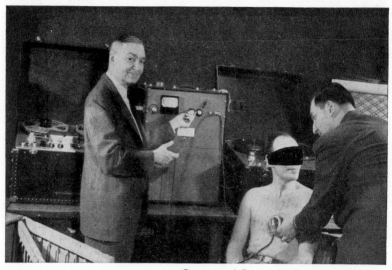

Courtesy of George D. Geckeler, M.D., and
Daniel Mason, M.D.

Fig. 15-1. Dr. George D. Geckeler adjusts the recorder, an Ampex 300, while an assistant, Dr. Daniel Mason, holds the microphone to the patient's chest.

while recording is in process and to keep the entire recording apparatus well shielded from electrically created noise and interference.

Recorders employed in medical recording, especially in the case of heart sounds, should be as free from speed variation and flutter as possible, since either would tend to make difficult the exact evaluation of the sound recorded. Professional grades of machines, like those primarily designed for radio broadcast and sound recording work, are completely suitable to medical use.

RECORDING PROCEDURES

At Gallinger Hospital, the cardiology staff utilizes what is called the "Multiple Screening" method. Recordings, each lasting two or three minutes, are made of the heart sounds of every patient who appears for treatment at the Outpatient Clinic, regardless of the nature of his illness. It is realized, of course, that this brief "screening" does not afford sufficient data on which to base a diagnosis of the heart's condition, but in this way any outstanding heart abnormality can thus be immediately noted. One advantage is that the tape recordings are available for later study and comparison, if and when needed, even though they are not needed when recorded. The tape recording is kept on file as part of the patient's clinical record.

Dr. Geckeler has kept at Hahnemann Hospital, since 1950, similar taped records of patients' heart sounds recorded periodically and has also inaugurated a system for filing heart sounds, classified according to the patient's name, age, and other pertinent facts, on endless loops of tape. These loops, about 3 ft in circumference, are used both as data against which to check during treatment of the respective patients and in teaching the diagnosis of heart trouble (Fig. 15-2). In the latter use, a loop is placed on the reproducing machine and played repeatedly. Students may listen on headphones to heart sounds, simulating those they would hear via stethoscopes, until they become familiar with the characteristic sounds of a particular heart complaint. By listening to different tapes, students of cardiology are helped to learn how to recognize rapidly the respective sound patterns of the different kinds of cardiac trouble.

The following description of the Geckeler method is quoted from a brochure entitled *The Teaching of Auscultation by Means of Endless Loop Tape Recording,** by George D. Geckeler, M.D., William Likoff, M.D., and Daniel Mason, M.D.

The original reel-to-reel tape recordings of normal and abnormal heart sounds, murmurs and arrhythmics are made in the conventional

* Report of a project supported, in part, by a cardiovascular training grant from the National Heart Institute, U.S. Public Health Service.

manner. From these, continuous loops are constructed by splicing the ends of a selected segment of tape containing several cardiac cycles. Where the heart rhythm is regular, this continuous loop is an accurate reproduction of what is recorded from the precordium over a long period of time.

For the uninitiated, a rapid heart rate often makes difficult the demonstration of a particular auscultatory finding and for this reason

Courtesy of George D. Geckeler, M.D.

Fig. 15-2. Heart sounds are recorded on endless loops of tape. The playback of such tape serves as an aid in teaching certain features in the diagnosis of heart trouble.

for student teaching it is an advantage to be able to reproduce murmurs at greatly reduced rates. Through phonocardiographic study it has been possible to determine the time which elapses between (1) the first and second sounds and (2) the second and next first sounds with the heart beating at different rates. The recording tape runs at a speed of 15 inches per second. With these two factors known, it is then possible to determine what length of blank tape must be spliced between the first and second, and the second and next first heart sounds in order to reduce the cardiac rate of any recording.

The student often finds it difficult to differentiate murmurs from heart sounds or to understand the relation of the two. The same method of splicing blank tape between murmurs and heart sounds permits these auscultatory features to be heard disassociated.

It has been noticed at the Hahnemann Hospital that students utilizing this method of study are able to advance much more rapidly than did those who used the old method. Sounds can be learned more easily and in less time by means of recordings than by examination of patients individually. Students are enabled to hear repeatedly sounds symptomatic of troubles that occur rarely and that might not be otherwise available to them for study.

Present and prospective recordists of heart and other sounds that are of significance in diagnosis and treatment may lighten their labors and produce more accurate and meaningful sound records by use of the revolving magnetic head, described in the following chapter. By means of this head the playing time of a recorded sound can be varied even though the original sound frequencies are simultaneously preserved. This ingenious device allows us to slow sound down—even to a point where the individual components of a complex sound may be accurately studied. To ensure optimum quality of sound the reverse re-recording technique previously described (pages 212–214) should be used wherever possible in order to minimize distortion, which is most destructive to the clarity of reproduction.

Part II

USES OF MAGNETIC RECORDING IN PSYCHIATRIC TREATMENT AND TEACHING

By Dr. José Comas, University of Buenos Aires
(Institute of Psychiatry of the Faculty of Medicine)

Diagnosis of mental and emotional disturbances is based particularly upon reactions of the patient—upon both his spontaneous behavior and his reactions, verbal and other, evoked by the doctor. Special attention is given, not only to the content of the patient's talk but also to his manner of speaking, vocabulary used, modulation of his voice, and other behavior. We are here principally interested in all facets of his speech behavior, however. For these reasons it proves very helpful for the teaching staff to have available specimen recordings of patients' spoken reactions that are suitable for lectures and practical demonstrations. Recordings are particularly helpful because (unfortunately or fortunately, depending upon the viewpoint) it is not possible to have whenever "needed" a supply of patients in significant stages of pathological processes and in such frames of mind as to be disposed to self-expression to an extent that may benefit students without causing loss of too much time. Besides, the patient very often, justifiably, puts up a stubborn resistance in the presence of a large audience and keeps persistent silence, refusing to show again the symptoms noticed by the attending doctor during previous private conversations.

All these circumstances make it necessary to have a stock of recordings typical of different illnesses available at all times—in the form of magnetic tape, disk records, or sound pictures—as an alternative, or sometimes as a complementary, tool to the clinical presentation of patients.

The best single illustrative medium, of course, would be sound pictures, since these allow students not only to hear the patient but also to note his general behavior, way of dressing, gestures, facial expressions, and bodily movements, so important in certain cases and especially in those where the central nervous system is involved. This is a valuable but expensive procedure, since only part of any film taken can be used, the remainder representing sheer waste. To this may be added the inconvenience of having to work in a brightly illuminated studio, with a camera generally in sight of the patient, which circumstances deprive the film of the spontaneity—perhaps even of characteristic reactions* that are so highly important—on the patient's part. Moreover, the projection of film requires a darkened projection room and also a projectionist or other person trained in handling the equipment, two essentials not al-

---

* Use of items (such as bright lights and cameras) that cause the patient to behave atypically will yield pictures of little or no value for study.

ways available at the time of lectures. For these reasons, talking pictures are ordinarily employed for (1) diseases where overt manifestations are of primary importance and (2) the purpose of illustrating various techniques of examination and treatment, such pictures of the *modus operandi* enabling the students to observe procedures in detail.

Recording on disks presents inconveniences similar to those of recording on film. Much material is wasted before one is able to record something significant; very often, perversely enough, the patient begins to say something of importance just when the disk's last groove is being cut. Apart from this, proper operation of disk-recording equipment requires highly trained personnel.

Recording on magnetic tape has produced far better results than on disks, since tape is free from the inconveniences mentioned above and presents the following advantages.

Tape makes necessary fewer interruptions for loading and preparing cutting machines. Recording usually continues for a period of from 30 to 60 minutes, making it possible to record on one tape reel all that the patient and physician say to each other during one treatment session. (See Figs. 15-3 and 15-4.) Afterwards the tape can be edited, and selected material, generally limited to only a few minutes' playing duration, filed, the remainder of the tape being erased and re-used. Because there is no waste of materials, as in film or disk recording, magnetic tape recording is very economical. Finally, since the recording process is very easy to learn, specially trained personnel are not needed.

For practical use, the more interesting parts of the selected material are re-recorded on disks, mainly because disk playback machines and phonographs are available to students who can themselves play these records at will. The tape originals are kept on file.

Magnetic tape recording has another important use in psychiatry —for patients under therapy that includes so-called "poly-shock" treatment. This treatment, which commonly yields good results in some cases of mental illness, consists of the administration at brief intervals of a series of electric shocks, perhaps three or four times daily. The purpose is to produce a confused state of mind in the

Fig. 15-3. A table ready for use during an interview with a patient. The microphone is installed beneath the screened aperture in the table top. Passing through the wall into the next room, the microphone cable connects to the magnetic tape recorder, also ready for use.

Courtesy of José Comas, M.D.

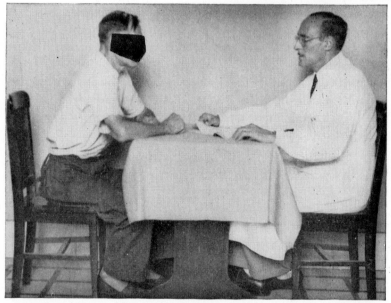

Courtesy of José Comas, M.D., and Mario Sbarbi, M.D.

Fig. 15-4. A patient, seated at the table shown in Fig. 15-3., is unaware that his conversation with Dr. Mario Sbarbi is being recorded.

patient. After shock treatment he is subjected to continuous and repeated psychotherapeutic procedures in the form of talks by the attending physician; these are aimed at the introduction of new ideas into his mind. Reproduction of post-shock discussions by means of magnetic tape has proved an important adjunct to therapy. The recordings of the parts of the talks that are adapted to the requirements of therapy are played many times a day to the patient by a nurse in his room. As his condition and needs change, the parts of his post-shock discussions that are played back to him vary accordingly.

A talk recorded by the physician in charge on magnetic tape that was played back repeatedly to a patient during the first days of treatment succeeding poly-shock therapy will serve as a sample of the use of recordings in this phase of psychiatric treatment.

Mr. N. N., your physician, Dr. Sbarbi, is talking to you by means of this record. We are at the beginning of the year, and you have undergone a treatment aiming at your recovery from a derangement of your nervous system. At present your recollections are not very definite, and there are many things you are not able to remember. Your ability of concentrating your thoughts is impaired, for the time being. You should not worry about this because this is a consequence of the treatment applied in your case, and this is its regular effect. You are going to recover your memory and your abilities, day by day, and in a short time your recovery will be complete.

Over a year ago, the disturbance of your nervous centers set in gradually. This brought about difficulties in your mental work and some strange sensations. At another opportunity we will talk the matter over and add more details.

Now you are on the way to regain your health, and the attending doctors are satisfied with your progress since your reactions are becoming quite normal.

In addition, recordings permit the study and treatment of speech disorders, which are frequently associated with certain types of mental illness. A record of each patient's progress in speech correction is kept on tape. Sometimes a patient becomes discouraged and has the feeling of not improving rapidly enough; he can then be encouraged and convinced of his progress by listening to specimens of his own speech recorded during successive stages of treatment. In addition, exercises consisting of specially chosen sounds, words, and phrases are prepared for imitation and practice by the patient as a means toward his recovery. A file of a great variety of well-classified recordings of speech anomalies is kept at hand. These are most useful for the illustration of lectures and for practical demonstrations.

Magnetic tape recording has proved to be an easy, practical, and inexpensive aid in teaching wherever the study of sound is of primary importance. In the teaching of psychiatric treatment methods, recordings are not a substitute for the direct presentation of patients, but they are an extremely useful supplement, allowing the student to hear a great variety of verbal and other symptoms which are audible. In some cases recordings prove to be more useful than observation of patients, since recordings make it possible, within the course of a few minutes, to illustrate the changes produced over a long period of time during the development of the pathological process or by the patient's response to therapeutic measures. Thus it is possible for an instructor to present the audible reactions of a great number of patients in a short time. He can easily illustrate even minor similarities and differences—in the same patient and also those between different patients. Magnetic recordings can illustrate the instructor's explanations and make them clear and vivid to a class.

16

Magnetic Recording in Education

Magnetic recording in education is used in many applications, from classroom use in the primary grades through graduate research in phonetics. In all these applications it has proved itself an extremely adaptable tool.

Teaching by means of recorded sound is a method as old as the phonograph itself. In the United States the U.S. Office of Education has operated for many years a transcription exchange that makes disk-recorded material available to teachers all over the country. However, as users have found out, transcriptions retain their high quality only for a limited number of playings, after which time they are no longer usable in class work. Additional factors accounting for the limited use of transcriptions in teaching are the storage difficulties and high cost of shipment, which make the regular use of transcriptions costly.

One of the first experiments in the use of tape for teaching was that undertaken in 1949 by the Department of Education of the State of Minnesota. The Department decided to use magnetic tape for distribution of teaching materials and, according to its report,* considered it "to be ideal for the following reasons:"

* A two-year report (mimeographed), *Tapes for Teaching,* on the Minnesota Experimental Tape Recording Project, prepared by the Department of Education of the State of Minnesota, Code XXXIV–B–37, and issued in July, 1951.

351

1. *The original investment in a tape master is comparatively low.* While the original price exceeds that of a high quality disc, it may be played over thousands of times without quality deterioration, making the per-use cost negligible in comparison.

2. *Tape duplicates can be erased and re-duplicated.* The major cost of securing the necessary tape for a state-wide service could be widely distributed and met by local schools with a small investment in tape. This eliminated the heavy investment by a state agency in sufficient tape to be circulated and returned to a central depository.

3. *The cost to the schools would be nominal.* With duplication provided without charge as a state service the cost aside from the original investment in a recorder and tape would be postage.

4. *The master tapes could be put into further use once the original program had served its usefulness and was scheduled for withdrawal.* This provided an additional though a relatively unimportant economy.

5. *The technical aspects of tape duplication were considered to be simple* when compared to the process necessary in making a master recording and subsequent pressings.

Many other educational institutions have come to the same conclusions reached by the Minnesota Department and are now utilizing tape recording extensively.

SOURCES OF EDUCATIONAL MATERIAL

Material may be obtained from many different sources—radio broadcasts, film sound tracks, transcriptions, and recordings made in class. Copies of lectures originating anywhere in the world may be obtained from agencies, such as Sound Seminars in Cincinnati, Ohio. Dr. George W. Kisker, head of Sound Seminars, has already contracted with several hundred authorities in various branches of the arts, sciences, and humanities to record their lectures, which are now used in more than 50 colleges and universities in the United States and abroad. Cornell University, the Minnesota Department of Education, the U.S. Office of Education, the Lowell Institute in

Boston, and the National Association of Educational Broadcasters are but a representative few of the many agencies, public and private, that are recording, broadcasting from, and cataloguing libraries of, educational tapes. In addition, copies of radio broadcasts that may be of value in education are often made available by commercial radio stations and networks.

In the New York City school system, tape recording has been used for several years. The Board of Education's radio station, WNYE, broadcasts a variety of programs designed to fill the needs of classes in the public schools. These are often recorded on tape, by teachers or others, and utilized at more opportune times. The broadcasts by WNYE cover a wide range of subjects, varying in content and treatment according to the students or classes expected to use them. Recordings are also made of broadcasts of historic events, speeches, plays, debates, and any other material that may be used as it is or after being edited for use in the classroom. Many classes record their own activities—acting of plays, reading of poems, singing, speech correction, and many others.

Tape makes it possible for much valuable work to be done easily, for instance, the recording of folk songs, regional forms, and relics of ancient dialects, in this way preserving them for future study. The United States Library of Congress has for many years sponsored the recording of American folk music sung and played by "mountain ballad-singers, Negro prisoners, Mexican vaqueros, New England farm wives," as Archibald MacLeish, the then Librarian of Congress, wrote in 1940. Writing in that year* about the creation of the Library's Recording Laboratory, he said, "it will be possible for a student in Washington to study the fiddle tunes of the Carolina mountains, for a poet in Florida to hear the ballads of the Evangeline country of Louisiana, for a musician in California to hear the songs of the pioneer Forty-Niners."

Besides making it possible to record original material that would otherwise not be preserved, magnetic recording plays its part in the process of re-recording material from other forms of recording. From

* In Press Release No. 778, issued by the Library of Congress in 1940.

magnetic tape it is possible to edit out defects in the original recordings and to rearrange the originals in forms that will serve definite purposes. Such a project, performed in the Library of Congress' Recording Laboratory under the supervision of George Steele, chief engineer, is typical of work of this kind. It consists of re-recording from wax cylinders, made in the early 1900's, to magnetic tape, which, after being edited, is recorded to phonograph records by the Library, which subsequently distributes them. The music of one album, consisting of 30 different songs of the Chippewa tribe of Indians, was originally recorded by Dr. Frances E. Densmore of Red Wing, Minnesota, for the Smithsonian Institution in Washington, D.C. Many of the songs are accompanied by the traditional drums, rattles, and other musical instruments of the Indians. Dr. Densmore, in *Papago Music,* Bulletin 90 of the Bureau of American Ethnology of the Smithsonian Institution, preserved for posterity the "songs of dreams, dances and games, songs of the warpath and camp, love songs and the songs used in the treatment of the sick, as well as songs of the Midewiwin (Grand Medicine Society), the great religious organization of the Chippewa."

THE TAPES FOR TEACHING PROJECT

The following examples of the mechanics of duplication and distribution are taken from *Tapes for Teaching.**

The Catalog:

In order to make ordering simple and to prevent confusion of titles, it was decided to list the available materials by code number for ordering purposes. The following codes were used:

(A) art	(E) English	(SC) science
(DT) drivers training	(G) guidance	(CD) child development
(FLL) Latin	and	(FLG) foreign language
(HE) home economics	occupations	(H) health
(MU) music	(HS) history	(MA) mathematics

* *Op. Cit.*

(SS) social studies	(P) professional	(AG) agriculture
(HR) human relations	(teachers	(CL) commercial law
(C) conservation	education)	

In the catalogue the code numbers will run from 1 to infinity in sequence as material is added. It is planned to abandon a number completely as a tape is taken from the library, thus eliminating any possible confusion of orders as time goes on and as revisions of the catalogue are made.

After each code number the material is listed with a title tending to be descriptive, and in some cases a short descriptive paragraph.

HE45 How to Use White Sales
HE46 How to Buy Towels
HE47 How to Buy Frozen Fruits and Vegetables
HE48 Evaluating New Textile Finishes

. . .

E140 INTRODUCTION TO SHAKESPEARE. Introduces the material which is to follow in the remaining programs by pointing up some of Shakespeare's outstanding contributions to literature.

E141 THE SHAKESPEARIAN PLOT. Discusses the three parts of a play—the beginning, the middle and the end and illustrates these parts from *Romeo and Juliet*.

The following page from the catalogue lists the information on ordering.

HOW TO ORDER MATERIALS

1. Mail your magnetic tape to us, postpaid, in standard 400′ fiber film mailing cases.
2. Enclose a list of the code numbers of the programs desired and the make of the recorder you will use. Place this information on a separate card (preferably 3″ × 5″) inside the shipping container. *Include machine speed.*
3. Fill out a card, cut to fit the holder on your shipping case, or a gummed label with your name and address. Attach to this the

stamps necessary for *return postage*. Enclose in the case or put it on the back of a card containing our mailing address as below.

4. Mail to: Minnesota Department of Education
                 Experimental Recording Project
                 TNM Room 21
                 University of Minnesota
                 Minneapolis 14, Minnesota

Your only expense will be the cost of postage *both* ways. This will be about 15 cents maximum for each 15 minute program and may be reduced to 2 or 3 cents per program when larger fiber mailing cases, holding up to a dozen rolls of tape, are secured. These cases may be obtained through any school supply or audio-visual dealer.

Courtesy of the Minnesota Mining & Manufacturing Company
Fig. 16-1. In this room, used by the Tapes for Teaching Recording Project of the Minnesota State Department of Education, orders for tape reels are processed and filled.

We duplicate one way (single track) only, at 7 1/2" or 3 3/4" speed. This enables you to edit the tape as you choose without spoiling a program that might be on a dual track. In this way, anything you might want can be added to the tape or eliminated.

Be sure to enclose your *return address and return postage*.

Figure 16-1 shows reels of sound tape, usually sent in one or two at a time by the schools. Note the open file of master tapes in the background. So much in demand was the Minnesota tape library that the master file grew very quickly, necessitating additional wooden filing shelves. One advantage of tapes is that they can be conveniently and compactly stored. Open filing shelves are now preferred.

DUPLICATING (RE-RECORDING) EQUIPMENT

While tapes are recording automatically, they are logged on a daily report sheet, as shown in Fig. 16-2. All the tape duplicating

Fig. 16-2. Tapes are recorded on the equipment shown. A log is kept for each tape reel.

Courtesy of the Minnesota Mining & Manufacturing Company

equipment can be seen in the background. The top two tape units on the right rack are for master tapes; the bottom unit on the right and the tape unit on the left are for the duplicates. Thus two tapes can be recorded simultaneously from two separate masters. Or if the top right tape unit is used as the master, a duplicate can be made simultaneously on each of the three other units. Master tapes, too, are made on the equipment, since the laboratory has three direct lines to the University of Minnesota radio station, KUGM. That station, turn, has direct lines to local and network radio stations in the Twin Cities. Thus network radio programs can be recorded for distribution to schools.

The following more detailed description of the equipment and its use is taken from *Tapes for Teaching*.*

The following equipment was used. Two complete magnetic recording units Magnecord Model PT6-R and Model TT6-J2 are in operation. These are professional type, high quality recorders that meet the specifications for broadcast standards. This equipment is considered to be minimum. . . .

As the acoustics of the average classroom are poor, and low priced recorders are none too good, the best recording possible should be made available to the teacher. . . .

Every effort has been made to maintain highest standards of quality. The amount of equipment needed will depend upon the volume at which a recording project operates. An average of six 15-minute copies or three 30-minute copies can be made on each duplicating unit (two recorders) per hour. One engineer can conveniently operate two duplicating units and take care of the associated clerical work. If clerical help is available, it is considered probable that an engineer could efficiently operate three duplicating units.

From these figures the amount of equipment and personnel needed to attain any given volume of duplicating can readily be determined. The auxiliary equipment needed will depend upon the nature of the installation. If some of the program material is to be transferred from disc to tape, it will be necessary to have available a good transcription turntable and pickup. . . .

In duplicating all duplicators are run at double speed so it is impractical to make a continuous auditory check on recording quality. Therefore it is necessary to have available recorders operating at both 3 3/4" and 7 1/2" speeds so that checks for quality may be made. This direct check supplements the continuous checking of equipment and head alignment necessary to insure proper recording of broadcast standard materials. For checking, the following equipment was used.

* *Op. cit.*

1–Signal generator – Hewlett – Packard, Model 200 CR –
> To put single frequency audio tone signals on tape for frequency checks

1–Distortion Meter – General Radio – Model 1932A –
> To check the audio distortion in all equipment

1–Vacuum tube voltmeter – for general service

1–1 Mil. Wavelength Azimuth Head Alignment Tape–L. S. Toogood Recording Company, Chicago
> For weekly aligning of recording and play-back heads

1–Special recorded 1000 cps Wow-Free Tape –
> For auditory check of wow and flutter

Also desirable:

1–Oscilloscope – Dumont Model 208 –
> For checking bias and erase wave forms and general distortion tests

1–Wow Meter – Furst Electronics Co. – Chicago Model 115R
> For precise checking wow and flutter contents of tape

It was early in the project determined to make single track duplicates only. In order that duplicates give the best efficiency in dual track machines, a full width recording head was used. This single track recording enables teachers to easily and conveniently edit the tape to suit their particular classroom needs. It also prevents confusion in locating recorded materials on the tape. There is at present no intention of doing dual track recording because of the many serious handicaps that would be involved in such duplication. It may be found desirable to record dual track at some later date, but there is no present advantage for the cost of tape involved is a negligible factor.

In recording and re-recording on the many types and makes of tape received it was determined that each tape should be completely erased before being placed upon the recorders for further duplicating. For this purpose a Goodell Magnetic Noise Eraser is used. With such a unit a reel of recording tape can be erased in a matter of seconds. While this should not be necessary with a good recorder, some of the tapes received have been over-recorded and so are difficult to erase under normal conditions on a recorder. Complete erasure also eliminates the possibility of old program material being left on the tape at the beginning and end of new materials. . . .

Double Speed Recording:

In order that copies can be made at double speed and still maintain a frequency response from 100 cps to 7,500 cps $\pm$ 3 db duplicating equipment must be capable of a flat response to 15,000 cps at 15 inch speed. Double speed recorders capable of both 7 1/2 inch and 15 inch per second are necessary for making 3 3/4 inch speed copies from the 7 1/2 inch masters. In this operation a master plays at 15 inches per second, while the copy is running at 7 1/2 inches per second. This maintains the necessary 2 to 1 ratio between 7 1/2″ and 3 3/4″. To do this without deterioration of quality it is necessary to properly equalize the circuits for duplicating at each speed. In the Magnecorder equipment used, the 7 1/2 inch equalizer is used for 3 3/4 inch duplicating and the 15 inch equalizer used [for] 7 1/2 inch duplicating.

Master Tapes:

All program masters are recorded on lubricated plastic base tape with red oxide coating. The 15-minute programs are stored on 600′ reels and 30-minute programs on 1200′ reels. The few programs longer than 30 minutes are split into two or more parts, no part being longer than 30 minutes. In cases where there is more than one part to a complete program, the material is given a single code number and each part is given a letter as:

SS232 – Madam Pandit Nehru – 2 hours parts a b c & d.

The desirable length for a program, if it can be arranged, is 14 and 28 minutes. This allows a margin of safety in duplications on tapes that have become shorter through splicing and editing. . . .

All masters should be equipped with leaders long enough to take the whipping action resulting from fast re-winding that could damage the actual recorded portion. Special leader tape is also commercially available.

As each master tape is recorded, it is marked as being a master and is given a code number and title. This information is placed on special marking tapes developed for this purpose and now commercially available. The tape storage carton is suitably marked on both back and edge.*

* From *Tapes for Teaching.*

CLASSROOM USE OF TAPE

Edward G. Bernard and Clifford Ettinger suggest* that it is advisable for teachers to take the following steps before they use recorders with their classes:

1. Select the recording specifically to contribute to what the class is currently learning.
2. Avoid choosing an excessive amount for any one class period . . . .
3. Listen to the recordings in advance of the class. Prepare your comments and follow-up activity.
4. Plan for any necessary related aids, such as maps, readings, pictures, or other materials.
5. If several short excerpts are to be used, check your place finders. Splice in leader and timing tape to help find your place . . . .
6. In the class situation prepare the group for listening. Pupils should understand why the recording is to be used and what they are particularly expected to listen for. A few key questions may be placed on the blackboard.

Tape recording has many and varied uses in class and group activities (see Figs. 16-3 through 16-12); it is also an ideal instrument for helping handicapped children. For the pupil required to stay at home because of illness, a tape recorder can be the means of bringing him verbatim reports of class activities, subject matter, assignments for study, and practice exercises. By this means, also, most of the study material for the blind can be prepared. The tape recorder may be expected to provide ever-increasing extra help to slow learners. Pupils, irrespective of their mental and physical abilities, can listen to languages, music, and sounds of any kind that may contribute to their total understanding. Shorthand students find in dictated material on tape an excellent help for extra practice. Used as administrative or instructional aids, tape recordings may be piped to classrooms by means of a central address system (Fig. 16-13).

* Edward G. Bernard and Clifford Ettinger, *Using the Tape Recorder*, copyright 1953, and published, by The Board of Education of the City of New York.

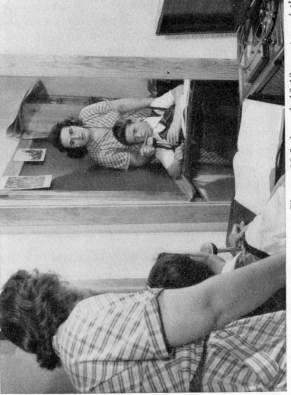

Fig. 16-3. Tape recorders and mirrors when used in conjunction can aid teachers in all grades to help students correct their speech defects.

Figures 16-3 through 16-13 *courtesy of the Minnesota Mining & Manufacturing Company*

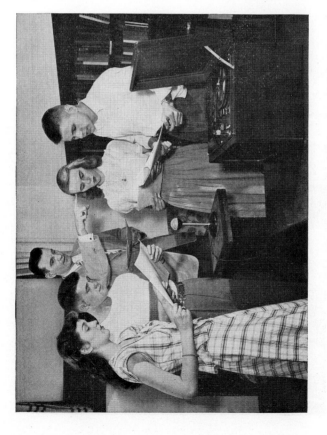

Fig. 16-4. Students in a "radio shop" class at Duluth (Minnesota) Central High School. Interest in speech improvement is heightened by use of a tape recorder, which enables students to discover their speech errors and to improve their diction.

Fig. 16-5. Sales training in a vocational high school in Minnesota gains in effectiveness when the student records and later plays back his conversations with "customers." By this means he is able to analyze and criticize his sales techniques. Similar self-criticism has been found by many teachers to be the most effective method of improving students' sales and speaking techniques.

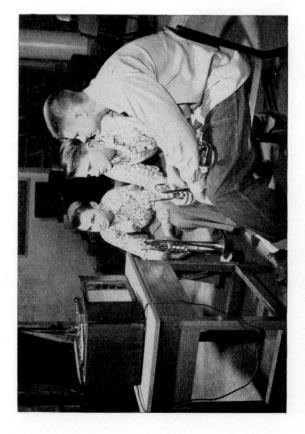

Fig. 16-6. A trumpet trio in a Minnesota high school "takes five" and listens to a tape recording they have just completed. Teachers have noted marked improvement among students of various subjects (music is high on the list) after tape recorders became available to the students.

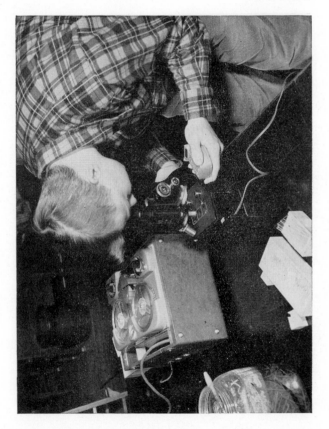

Fig. 16-7. Tape recording of laboratory data and of observations has been found to shorten considerably both the time required initially for some types of experiments and the time for their repetition.

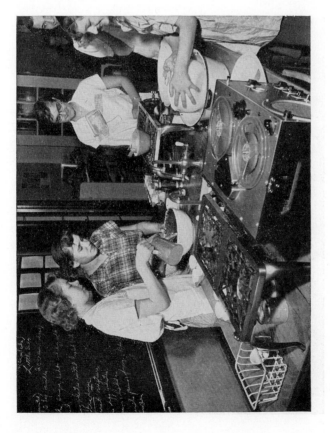

Fig. 16-8. A tape-recorded report of steps taken by members of a high-school home economics class in following a cake recipe serves as a play-by-play description of the entire process, from mixing to eating.

Fig. 16-9. After recording the speeches of their puppets on tape, students are then free to concentrate on the manipulation of the puppets. The tape is used both for rehearsals and for performances. Students have found that a puppet seems to come to life when he acquires a voice.

Fig. 16-10. No need for the band to be present when the drum majorettes want to practice. Tape recordings the band made earlier serve rehearsal needs.

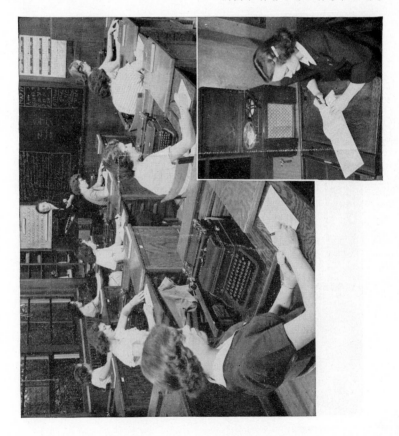

Fig. 16-11. Tape recordings in shorthand and typing classes lighten teachers' loads and provide students with dictation under controlled conditions. Materials at the different speeds—though the same speed is maintained throughout each dictated test, or practice—required as the student progresses are easily dictated to tape. The same dictation test may be used repeatedly—for the same or different groups, as well as for individuals who missed the test or who must take it again. The teacher can put to good use the free time such recorded dictated materials provide her.

Fig. 16-12. Even very young children gain confidence from the use of recording equipment. These first graders will hear their songs played back after they have finished taking turns singing with piano accompaniment. Wherever recording and playback serve as educational aids they add a new element of interest to that particular phase of school work.

Fig. 16-13. At Cleveland Junior High School in St. Paul, Minnesota a public-address system is here fed from a tape recorder. By this means, recorded radio programs and educational recordings can be piped as they are needed to any classroom or group of classrooms.

ELECTRONIC LANGUAGE LABORATORY

An example of the methods that can be used in adapting magnetic tape recording to the teaching of languages is found in The Institute of Language and Linguistics at Georgetown University in Washington, D.C. Established as the result of the efforts of Leon Dostert, Institute Director, the laboratory was designed to take full advantage of the possibilities of magnetic recording for group instruction.

Inaugurated in November, 1950, the Electronic Language Laboratory's employment of the use of recording in teaching languages was based on the following reasoning:

Language is the natural medium for meaningful human expression. The spoken form is the primary means of human communication. The program of instruction aims at giving the student an active command of language as a whole, and not merely of some one aspect such as "reading knowledge" or "auditory recognition." Spoken language being the primary form of language use, the program of instruction strives to achieve a rational balance between theory and explanation on the one hand, and audition and imitation on the other. The method is also based on the recognition that the acquisition of skill in the use of foreign languages is largely a matter of intensive repetition and practice, and that "language learning is over-learning."*

OPERATION

Truly a custom-engineered laboratory for languages, the Georgetown installation was engineered by Educational Laboratories, Inc. of Washington, D.C. Its operation is described as follows:

The Language Laboratory is intended to serve a total of approximately 1200 students of foreign languages enrolled in the College of Arts and Sciences and the School of Foreign Service. Language courses in both schools are conducted on a basis of three periods a week of class instruction supplemented by three laboratory periods, thus giving the student six "language contact" periods weekly. The use of recorded language repetition drills, especially prepared by the

* From 1950–1951 catalogue of The Institute of Languages and Linguistics, Georgetown University School of Foreign Service.

faculty to synchronize with the work done in the classroom, affords to the student the opportunity for intensive repetitive drills not possible in the classroom. In broad terms, the "speaking" possibility offered by laboratory drills represents a total of some 50 hours, during the school year, of speech drill in the laboratory, as contrasted to less than five hours per school year in the classroom. In other words, the student is able to speak the foreign language in the laboratory for from 14 to 20 minutes during each period, whereas he can speak for only one minute during a given class instruction period.

One account of the Language Lab offers the following information:

The tapes are so prepared as to give the student the opportunity to repeat the words and sentences recorded and to formulate replies to questions based on the recorded text.

The laboratory is equipped with a public address system of five loud speakers. A lecture can be recorded at the time it is delivered and thus remain available for future use.*

Installation. The following description of equipment in the Language Laboratory is from the same *Audio Record* article.*

1. There are 120 individual, semi-soundproof booths, with collapsible fronts to permit the use of visual aids (pictures, film strips, and moving-picture films).

2. Each booth is provided with a language-selector switch with six possible positions, which enables a student in any booth to select any one of six language tapes that are being played at any given time. Each booth is also equipped with a pair of headphones (it has been found that listening through headphones permits more complete and spontaneous concentration as well as more accurate reception).

3. A total of 12 magnetic tape machines are installed in the console. Six of these are reserved for the use of language students of the School of Foreign Service and six for the use of those in the College of Arts and Sciences. Each of the machines may play a different language

---

* From "Electronic Language Lab Opens at Georgetown University," *Audio Record,* published by Audio Devices, Inc., vol. 7, no. 1, Jan. 1951.

at the same time, or more than one may play the same language at different levels of instruction.

4. The 120 booths are divided into three sections of 40 booths each, and a switch makes it possible to achieve considerable flexibility in transmitting language drills to the various sections. For example, elementary French may be played on Channel 1 in Section 1 (the first 40 booths), and intermediate French can be played on the same Channel 1 in Sections 2 (the next 40 booths) and 3 (the remaining 40 booths). Laboratory drills are scheduled at regular hours for the various language classes and are conducted on a group basis, each group having a block of seats assigned to it for three given periods per week.

We quote further from the *Audio Record*.*

The whole concept of laboratory drill work in language study is based on the fact that magnetic tape recording permits the reproduction and dissemination of the *spoken* form of language, just as the printing press [is] . . . the means for dissemination of the *written* form of language . . . .

The facilities of this laboratory will permit approximately 3600 student contact hours per week, or a total of 108,000 student contact hours during the academic year of 30 weeks. To make possible the same amount of language contact drill through individual instructors would require the addition of 15 members to the present language faculty.

The laboratory located in Room B is the audio-visual and recording laboratory. It is equipped for the diversified use of visual-auditory teaching methods, and pictorial material used in teaching languages can be projected on the screen. Sixteen individual soundproof booths are provided for the students to make their recordings, and in each booth is installed a tape recorder, which may also be used for auditory drills.

In the student listening laboratory (Room C) thirty tape recorders have been installed, for auditory drills only. The teaching material is recorded by the professors on a master tape, from which the required copies are prepared for the individual use of the students. For example, a recorded lesson of a half hour's duration in the Swedish

* *Op. cit.*

language can be heard several times over by the student in the auditory laboratory, until he has thoroughly mastered it. When he feels that he has attained reasonable proficiency with that particular material, he then makes a recording of a summary of such a lesson, using the recording equipment in Room B.

The program of the Institute calls for the oral use, exclusively, of the foreign language during the first three months of instruction. This means that no written text is introduced during this introductory period, and the student assimilates the language only by means of sounds, visual material, and demonstration. The written form of the language is introduced to teach the student to read and write and to develop his vocabulary, after the basic elements of the language have been assimilated through this strictly oral method.

TAPE USES IN TEACHER TRAINING

The tape recording of class activities may be used in teacher training to demonstrate proper and improper teaching methods. The recording of the actual events may be edited and a commentary inserted for pin-pointing the techniques used. By means of this training method, trainees may the sooner be exposed, at second hand it is true, to various kinds of actual situations they probably will soon be facing. Also, by means of recording, teachers may "visit" each other's classes and supervisors "observe" teachers and students without disrupting of class activities.

As Bernard and Ettinger* report further:

Demonstrations of effective procedures with children may be prepared . . . for use with pupil teachers or teachers in service.

Conferences which yield valuable insights are often recorded and pertinent excerpts are circulated [via tape rerecording] to inform teachers and supervisors unable to attend.

Lectures and reports recorded on tape are often valuable to committees at work on school problems. Talks by visiting consultants are recorded for reference use; sounds and situations resulting from experimental procedures in classrooms, gym, lunchroom or elsewhere in school, may be studied and evaluated.

* *Op. cit.*

"SLOWING DOWN" SOUND FOR TEACHING

Before we leave the subject of the classroom we might consider one more phase of the use of sound in teaching; this—the "slowing down" of sound so that the component parts may more easily be analyzed—has already been touched upon. In studying phonetics it is sometimes of value to hear the component parts of a compound sound in slow motion, as it were. Obtaining such slow motion is not too difficult. The instructor need only play a tape in which a sound or word, pronounced normally, is "stretched," that is, played back two, ten, or more times more slowly than it was pronounced while it was being recorded. In order to keep the sound understandable, it must be stretched or "slowed down" without the frequencies of the individual component sounds being changed. As we have pointed out before, sound can be stretched by the editing together of similar sounds or by use of the German "Tonschreiber" revolving reproducing head. "Stretched sound" may be produced by the following process: A compound sound is recorded many times (or, preferably, recorded once, this original sound being re-recorded several times to get copies of the same sound), and each compound sound is cut apart—into its separate constituents. All similar components are spliced together, and then the compound sound is reconstituted by the splicing together of these "stretched" sections in the correct order. Of course, this technique requires fine editing and takes considerable time. After enough examples have been thus stretched and copied, however, they may be used numberless times in teaching.

THE FAIRBANKS–EVERITT–JAEGER METHOD

The method just described—extending or expanding sounds for study purposes—is of necessity a tedious, time-consuming job. Several experimenters have tried to expand sound in other ways, but no satisfactory method was found until Grant Fairbanks, W. L. Everitt, and R. P. Jaeger, at the University of Illinois, hit upon the idea of employing multiple, rotating magnetic heads for this purpose. By use of their method it is possible to expand or contract sounds and to reproduce them at the original sound frequencies. Their method was described in a report, "Method for Time or Frequency Compression-Expansion of Speech," presented at the National Convention of the Institute of Radio Engineers on March 26, 1953 (published in the 1953 *Convention Record of the IRE, Part VIII*). Although the title mentions "compression-expansion of speech," the method will work with any sound.

The first known use of the principle of the rotating magnetic head was on a tape machine, one of the Tonschreiber recorder models developed by technicians of the German Army during World War II. In looking for a way of transmitting messages secretly, they built a machine in which the velocity of the tape and the speed of rotation of a revolving four-section playback head could be adjusted independently. This feature of independent adjustment of the two speeds made it possible to transmit messages at various speeds of one or the other component from one Tonschreiber to another on which the coded message could be reproduced in its original form only after these two variable speeds of the "decoding" Tonschreiber had been set to correspond exactly with the two respective variable speeds of the Tonschreiber on which the message had been "coded." If tape speeds *or* rotating speeds of the playback heads of the two machines vary, the coded message cannot be properly decoded.

The Tonschreiber rotating head has not been used to any great extent since World War II, although it is employed by some German film studios in editing tape and film. The ease afforded by a revolving head in editing magnetic tape or film is obvious: The track may be moved slowly past a revolving head that is rotating at the speed necessary for correct reproduction until the sound at which one wishes to cut the track is heard; at this point the exact spot may easily be marked for cutting. The CBS Edispot, developed by Richard S. O'Brien, employed this same principle (see Chapter 12 on radio broadcasting practice).

Although an intrinsic component of the Fairbanks-Everitt-Jaeger machine is also a four-part rotating head, their method, according to Professor Fairbanks, was developed without any knowledge of the Tonschreiber head. The purpose of the machine developed at the University of Illinois is to facilitate the study of speech sounds; the stretching or compressing of sounds is very helpful in such study. Explanation of the method used, as given at the 1953 National Convention of the Institute of Radio Engineers,* is as follows:

Theory of Time Compression and Expansion by Sampling

For purposes of explanation assume two different phonemes, A and B, which are of equal duration and joined without interruption as shown (Fig. 16-14). Assume that A' and B' are valid samples of A and B, and that each is of adequate duration for perception. Assume that samples A' and B' are extracted from A and B and abutted in time as shown without discontinuity, and that $A — A'$ and $B — B'$ are discarded. If, now, A', B' is reproduced, the time will be shorter than the original A, B, but the phonemes should be perceptible.

When this proposition was advanced several years ago it was validated for connected speech by cutting and splicing magnetic tape at arbitrary points, without regard to the phonemes. It was discovered that substantially more than 50% of the total time of connected speech could be discarded by this means without destroying intelligibility. That is, $A — A'$ could exceed A'.

In the case of expansion, assume that phonemes A and B are caused to be repeated, as in the middle portion. If A, A, B, B are reproduced, the time will be longer and the auditory effect, given the above assumptions, should be that of prolongation of A and of B.

Finally, assume that A and B are first compressed to A' and B', and then expanded to A', A' and B', B' as shown at the bottom. Here the original time for A and B has been restored. A and B have been reconstructed from A' and B'.

Apparatus

Figure [16-15] shows a photograph of the essential part of an experimental model of a device for compression or expansion along the lines of such a theory. Basically, the device is a continuous loop magnetic tape recorder, mounted at the bottom of the rack containing

* G. Fairbanks, W. L. Everitt, and R. Jaeger, "Method for Time or Frequency Compression-Expansion of Speech," published in the *1953 Convention Record of the IRE, Part VIII.*

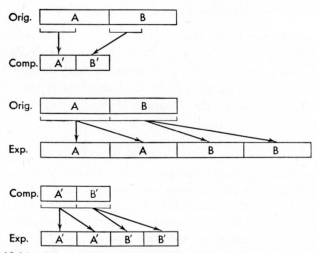

Fig. 16-14. Diagram illustrating the theory of time compression and expansion by sampling.

Fig. 16-15. A portion of the experimental model of a machine that compresses and expands sound.

(The two illustrations above are taken from G. Fairbanks, W. L. Everitt, and R. Jaeger, "Method for Time or Frequency Compression-Expansion of Speech," *1953 Convention Record of the IRE, Part VIII—Information Theory*, pages 120–124. Illustrations above *courtesy of the authors and of the Institute of Radio Engineers*) the other components. The tape loop, approximately 12 feet long, rises along the right edge of the rack to a pulley under slight spring tension at the top. Its pathway is shown by arrows. Entering the device, the tape is directed by means of rollers over a Magnecord erase head, and then over a fixed Magnecord record head where the input is temporarily recorded. Passing over another roller, the tape then descends to a revolving playback head assembly enclosed in a mu-metal box, where signal recorded on the loop is scanned. Next the tape passes to the drive capstan, around a roller, and, finally, over a Brush permanent magnet erase head.

The revolving head assembly consists of a brass drum with four Brush playback heads equally spaced around its periphery. The output of the heads is taken off by means of a slipring-brush unit. The circumferences of both drum and capstan are 7.64 inches. Drum and capstan are mounted on shafts supported in sleeve bearings at the back of the panel. Massive flywheels are also mounted on the shafts. The two units are driven by twin 1/15 hp DC Bodine motors with independent speed controls by means of GR Variacs. Speeds are measured with a GR Strobotac.

The remaining components are conventional. An independent Magnecorder PT6-A is used for storage and playback. This has been modified for continuously variable speed reduction and furnishes about a 15 to 1 range of tape velocities.

Compression Process

Operation of the revolving head assembly is shown at the left of Fig. [16-16]. The four playback heads are identified by letters. The tape passes over the drum and is in contact with 1/4 of its circumference, or a distance equal to the peripheral distance between any two adjacent playback heads. The tape is retained by flanges around the drum periphery. Tape direction is constantly counterclockwise. In the compression application the direction of drum rotation is also counterclockwise. Under load the top tape velocity is approximately 190 inches per second. The top peripheral drum velocity is about 225 inches per second.

For purposes of explanation the tape is divided into hypothetical numbered segments, each equal to the distance between heads. The relative positions of tape and heads are shown at representative times. The diagram shows 50% time compression as an example.

COMPRESSION PROCESS

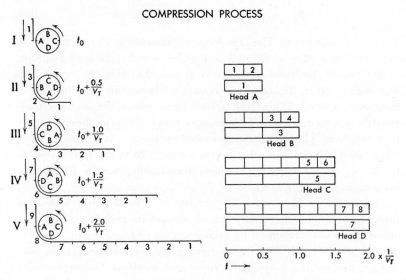

Fig. 16-16. Functional diagram of the compression process.

EXPANSION PROCESS

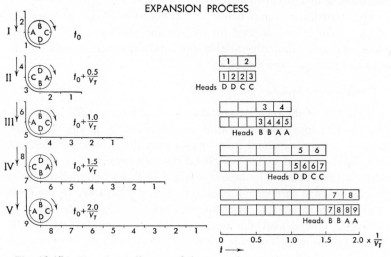

Fig. 16-17. Functional diagram of the expansion process.

(Illustrations above from G. Fairbanks *et al., op. cit., courtesy of the authors and of the Institute of Radio Engineers*)

In Part I segment 1 is shown at t_0 when it first comes into contact with the drum. At this time it is intercepted by head A, which is moving in the same direction. If the drum were stationary, reproduction would be one-for-one. If its velocity were equal to the tape, no signal would be reproduced. Between times I and II, however, head A moves through 1/4 of a revolution. During the same interval tape segments 1 and 2 pass the 9 o'clock point where head A was at t_0. As a result, head A reproduces segment 1 during that interval. The *effective* tape velocity is $V_T - V_H$. In the example diagrammed V_H equals $V_T/2$ which equals the effective velocity. Therefore, the frequencies of segment 1 as reproduced by head A are divided by 2.

. . . time II head A is at 6 o'clock . . . B is at 9 o'clock, while segment 2 lies between them in contact with the drum. Head A is about to leave the drum, while head B is about to begin reproducing segment 3. Accordingly, although there is no discontinuity, segment 2 is not reproduced by any head. The remaining diagrams show how the process continues, the odd-numbered segments being discarded. It is evident that various durations of either reproduced or discarded segments can be realized by varying the absolute and relative velocities of tape and head, and that a range of sampling frequencies and compression ratios can thus be produced.

The output of the device with respect to time is diagrammed in Fig. 16-16. Between times I and II, for example, segment 1 is reproduced by head A in the time necessary for both segments 1 and 2 to pass a point. Head B then reproduces segment 3, etc. The final yield is segments 1, 3, 5, 7. When these segments are stored at a given speed and then reproduced at an appropriately higher speed, their original frequencies are restored and the elapsed time is shortened.

With respect to duration the odd-numbered segments are termed *sampling intervals;* the even-numbered segments *discard intervals*. The reciprocal of their summed durations is the *sampling frequency*. The discard interval divided by the sum of the two intervals will be termed the *compression percentage*. Since sampling is periodic the ratio applies also to the total message time, and describes the percentage by which that total time has been reduced.

Assuming that the process results in intelligible speech, it becomes evident that the processed message may be transmitted over a system with smaller bandwidth than originally necessary. The capacity of a

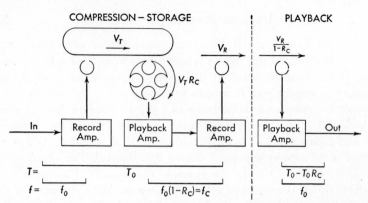

Fig. 16-18. Diagram illustrating the method used for time compression.

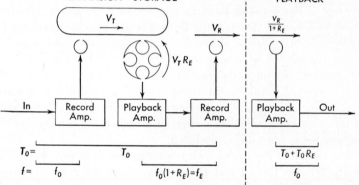

Fig. 16-19. Diagram illustrating the method used for time expansion.

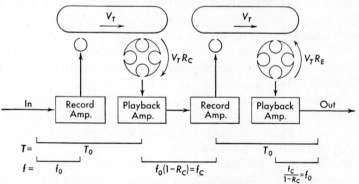

Fig. 16-20. Diagram illustrating the method used for frequency compression-transmission-expansion.

(Illustrations above from G. Fairbanks *et al., op. cit., courtesy of the authors and of the Institute of Radio Engineers*)

384

conventional transmission link for handling simultaneous messages will be a function of the amount of compression, or frequency division.

Expansion Process

Figure [16-17] is a similar diagram for expansion. Here the drum bearing the playback heads revolves in a direction opposite to that of the tape. The illustrative example shows the condition when these velocities are equal. The effective velocity is equal to their sum.

At t_0, shown at I, segment 1 is in contact with the drum between heads A and D. During the next interval head D, as it moves from 6 o'clock to 9 o'clock, will reproduce both segments 1 and 2 and then leave the tape. At that time it will be replaced by head C, which has moved to the 6 o'clock position to intercept the tape at the beginning of segment 2, and which will reproduce segments 2 and 3 during its sweep. The result, shown at the right, is that between time I and II, while segments 1 and 2 are passing the 6 o'clock point, segments 1, 2, 2, 3 are reproduced. The rest of the figure shows how this process continues.

Since the effective tape velocity has been increased by the opposite movement of head and tape, frequency multiplication has been incurred. The original frequencies are restored by reproducing the processed message in an appropriately longer time. The amount of time thus added divided by the original time is the *expansion percentage*. In the diagram this equals 100%.

Method of Time Compression

Figure [16-18] summarizes the various stages in compression. The comparative times and frequencies are indicated at the bottom. In an original time T_0 and with original frequencies f_0, the input is recorded on the loop at the velocity V_T and scanned by the revolving head unit moving in a positive direction at $V_T R_C$. This yields the compressed frequency f_C shown at the bottom. Simultaneously the compressed signal is stored at a recording tape velocity which will be taken as V_R. This recording is reproduced at a later time at the higher tape velocity shown, in the relative time indicated, and with f_0 restored.

The smaller values of compression affect intelligibility and perceived speed of talking very little. Although both factors are perceptibly affected as compression is increased, intelligibility persists with surprisingly large compression percentages.

Method of Time Expansion

Figure [16-19] is a similar diagram for speech expansion. Head movement is negative with respect to the tape, and equals $V_T R_E$. In the original time the original frequencies are multiplied by 1 plus R_E, yielding f_E as stored. The message is then reproduced at the lower velocity shown, f_0 being restored with the time expansion.

Small percentages do not affect the perceived speed of talking very much; the details of speech become more readily heard as expansion increases. An echo-like sound occurs when the interval repeated exceeds the duration of one phoneme. This is a size limitation in the experimental model and not a limitation of the method.

Method of Frequency Compression-Transmission-Expansion

Figure [16-20] shows a system which involves the following: (1) compression, (2) transmission of the compressed message, (3) expansion of the compressed message. The steps are carried on simultaneously with two units. A transmission link, undiagrammed, is inserted between the two at the arrow. Velocities, times and frequencies are labeled.

Conclusion

Apart from its theoretical interest, the method appears to have several practical applications. For one thing, the smaller compression and expansion ratios should be useful in the programming of re-broadcast speeches in radio, since they furnish "tailor-made" time without the audience's knowledge. A saving of 10 minutes per hour is completely realistic. Conversely, and we advance this suggestion with diffidence, thinking of commercials, more intelligence can be communicated to an audience in a given amount of time.

Straightforward compression by larger amounts should be useful wherever high-speed communication is crucial, as in certain military situations. Expansion should facilitate branches of study such as experimental phonetics and linguistics where auditory analysis is important.

Finally, of course, the method gives promise as an approach to the long-standing problem of bandwidth reduction.

THE SPEECH SYNTHESIZER

A different kind of magnetic recording machine that uses a rotating head was built by Professor Cyril M. Harris, director of the Acoustic Laboratory of Columbia University in New York City, and formerly with Bell Laboratories. Professor Harris' study in-

Courtesy of the Bell Telephone Laboratories

Fig. 16-21. The Speech Synthesizer, developed to create speech artificially. (From Cyril M. Harris, "A Speech Synthesizer," *J. Acoust. Soc. Am.,* vol. 25, no. 5, Sept. 1953, pages 970–975)

volved not the contraction or expansion of speech sounds (phonemes) but the creation of artificial connected speech from recorded individual speech sounds. He found that individual speech sounds, although fundamentally the same, varied considerably in what he called "the influence factor." As is apparent to any careful listener, vowel and consonant sounds are influenced by the manner in which the sounds preceding and succeeding the vowel or consonant are voiced. Accordingly, to synthesize speech, many forms of each speech sound must be recorded and made available for use in building connected, intelligible speech. The "Speech Synthesizer," according to a paper by Dr. Harris in the September 1953

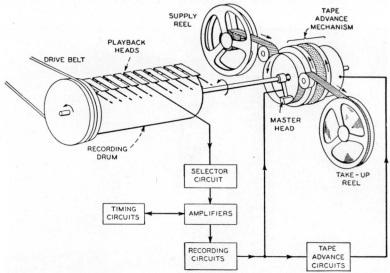

Courtesy of the Bell Telephone Laboratories

Fig. 16-22. Diagram showing the method of operation of the Speech Synthesizer. (From Cyril M. Harris, *op. cit.*)

issue of the *Journal of the Accoustical Society of America,* works as follows:

When buttons on a keyboard are pressed, a sequence of corresponding speech modules are automatically recorded on tape exactly in tandem. The modules are selected from a group stored on a rotating magnetic drum. The pressing of a button causes an electrical signal corresponding to a module to be reproduced—the electrical switching so arranged that only one complete module is reproduced for a single button pressing. This electrical signal is amplified, biased, and then fed into a constantly rotating recording head which makes contact with stationary magnetic tape and records the signal on it. A 10 kilocycle signal superposed on each stored speech module controls an electromagnetic clutch which (a) measures the length of the recording accurately, and (b) advances the tape at the completion of the recording by the correct amount so that the next recording forms a connected sequence with it. The same module may be used any number of times and in combination with different stored modules, thereby introducing wide experimental control in standardized speech studies. The principle of this type of device could be applied to other classes of problems involving communication of information, as the conversion into speech of typing or of electronically read printed matter. [See photograph and drawing, Figs. 16-21 and 16-22.]

17

Home Uses and Telephone Recording

The great majority of magnetic recorders in use today is the "home" type of machine. They are employed in three general ways —for entertainment, for education, and for home-conducted business and hobbies. Another kind of machine, the telephone message recorder, although generally used in the home, may be installed anywhere that a telephone connection is available.

HOME ENTERTAINMENT

RECORDING RADIO OR TELEVISION SOUND

Many home recordists assemble libraries of taped music either by purchasing commercially recorded tapes or more usually by recording from their radio receivers the compositions that they want to preserve. This procedure may not be restricted to music but may include dramatic programs, plays, and lectures. When recording the sound output of a radio or television receiver one must not forget that the quality of the recording cannot be appreciably better than the quality of the receiver employed. For this reason, it is better to record from a frequency-modulated receiver than from an amplitude-modulated receiver, especially in localities where a great deal of electrical noise is received along with the amplitude-modulated radio signal.

Since most magnetic recorders designed for home use have what is called "high-impedance inputs," they can be connected to almost any output circuit of the normal receiver with fair results. The hookup that is the least trouble to make is shown in Fig. 17-1.

This type of hookup simultaneously reduces the level to the loudspeaker for monitoring and provides a properly terminated output

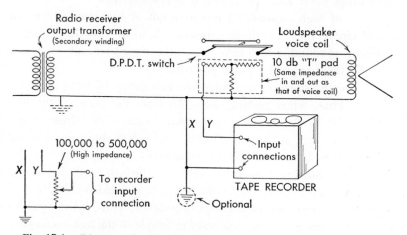

Fig. 17-1. Diagram of a simple method of connecting a recorder to the output of an ac-operated radio receiver. The lower left-hand portion represents the insertion of a level control, or potentiometer.

for the recorder input to bridge. Distortion that might otherwise be introduced by the changing impedance of the loudspeaker at different frequencies is thus avoided. This type of circuit will give excellent results with any of the high-impedance input recorders. The loss of audio voltage incidental to the use of this method makes it unlikely that the first audio stage of the recorder will be overloaded in normal use. However, if you find that this hookup consistently gives distorted recordings, insert a potentiometer with a resistance from 100,000 to 500,000 ohms, as shown in Fig. 17-1.

When the recorder input circuit contains a 500- or 600-ohm input, the same method may be used; only the size of the potentiometer need be changed. If better quality is desired, the audio signals may be picked up from the output of the first audio stage in the receiver and fed to the recorder at high impedance. If the recorder is at some distance from the receiver, a high-impedance circuit cannot be used without using a shielded cable of very low capacity. (Incidentally, shielded wire, with the shield grounded, must be used for any connections to the input circuit of the recorder.) If the receiver's output contains good high-frequency response but the recordings made from it do not, it is possible that the connecting cable is of high capacity. The end result of high capacity in an input circuit that is of high impedance is to by-pass the high frequencies of sound, which never reach the recorder at all. In a case like this there are two possible procedures:

1. Use transformers to couple the two pieces of equipment together. Thus, when picking audio up from the plate of the first audio tube of the receiver, use a plate-to-line (500 ohms or so) transformer and, at the recorder end, use a 500-ohm-to-grid transformer, if the input is of high impedance. Of course, if the recorder has a 500-ohm input, as some have, you do not need the second transformer. It is best to have the connecting shielded cable in that part of the circuit with the lowest impedance. Thus, if the recorder has a 500-ohm input and you want to couple to the first audio tube of the receiver, hook up the transformer near, or in, the receiver, so that the connecting cable will be carrying the lower impedance current from the 500-ohm side of the transformer. The lower the nominal impedance, the closer to ground potential is the circuit, and the less chance there is of picking up hums and noises from surrounding lamp cords and other ac wiring.

2. The problem may also be solved by means of cathode followers. The cathode follower is an amplifier using a tube circuit that is hooked up in such a way as to give a high-impedance input and a low-impedance output. The cathode-follower tube may be fed with audio voltage from any appropriate point, and its output may be connected either to a high- or low-impedance circuit without pickup of noise and hum or appreciable loss of high frequencies. (These amplifiers are commercially obtainable.) It is advisable, when using

an ac–dc receiver as the program source for recording, to isolate the recorder from the receiver in all cases by hooking them up through a transformer. In this case the recorder should be grounded independently, and no attempt should be made to ground the recorder "ground" to the ac–dc receiver at any point. Those recordists who do not have enough knowledge of basic electronics to perform these operations would be well advised to get a qualified technician to make their connections for them.

Repetition of advice about impedance matching is in order at this point. In connecting two pieces of apparatus, we may either "match" them or "bridge" the output of the one (feeding) with the input of the piece of equipment it is feeding. For instance, if we have a transformer with an impedance of 500 ohms that constitutes the output of a radio receiver, we may connect it to a 500-ohm input on a recorder and get good response with little loss of voltage. If we connect this 500-ohm line to a high-impedance input, for example, 500,000 ohms, we are actually "bridging" the 500-ohm line. The quality will be good, but there will be a loss of voltage, which in most cases is desirable, since we will not then overload the first tube in the recorder amplifier and cause it to distort. Never, however, feed a high-impedance source to a low-impedance input. Such a procedure produces serious frequency discrimination, and recordings made from such a hookup will be of poor quality, no matter how fine the recorder may be.

In connecting pieces of equipment, all ac polarities should be the same. The practical way to achieve this is to connect the equipment and make a test recording with the radio receiver detuned and the volume control turned down. If the amount of hum recorded is negligible, everything is fine. If the hum is excessive, reverse the recorder ac plug in the ac outlet, and try recording again under the same conditions as before. There should be less hum with the plug inserted one way than the other. When you have ascertained the best way, mark the plugs so that thereafter you will always insert them in the same position.

Radio receiver-recorder combinations may be connected to a time clock that will switch them on in time to record a program when no one is home to do it manually. Time-clock and relay combinations, together with a motor-tuned receiver or a number of separate, tuned receivers, may be connected so that recordings may be made of selected programs for a period of twenty-four hours.

RECORDING FROM RECORD-PLAYERS

A record-player or phonograph equipped with a piezoelectric crystal pickup requires no other apparatus to copy a phonograph record on a magnetic recorder. The crystal output is normally high enough in voltage and impedance for it to be connected directly to the high-impedance input of the usual home recorder. Connect a low-capacity shielded cable—the "high" side to the output of the equalization circuit following the pickup and the "low" side to the ground. If the output of the crystal is too low after the equalizer for effective recording (in other words, if you record more hum than sound), you may take your choice of connecting the recorder input to the output of the following audio stage or to the output transformer, in the manner previously described.

Magnetic phonograph pickups of all types generally do not provide enough power, after their response has been equalized, to record properly on the average recorder. Most of them are followed in the circuit by a pre-amplifier whose output is of high impedance. The pre-amplifier may be coupled to the recorder input through a capacitor or by means of a cathode follower or transformer. Of course, one must pick a method for hooking up the recorder that is in keeping with the design of the pre-amplifier and the recorder, ensuring that no loss of fidelity takes place.

LIVE SOUND RECORDING

The rules regarding the use of microphones in recording have been adequately laid down in preceding chapters and in the literature. There is not much to add here except this: Do not try to avoid recording all the sounds that in the aggregate mean "home." It is well to avoid outside noises that are not characteristic of the situation you are recording, but one should not try for "studio" quality in home recording. It is the atmosphere of home and homely sounds, as background for the voice or music, that will make the home recording more and more valuable to you as time goes on. If, however, you want to record your daughter's or your sister's piano playing, or other instrumental music, observe some of the rules in Chapter 6, and your efforts should produce good results.

Do not record the sounds coming from your loudspeaker as a quick and easy way to avoid making a proper hookup. The loudspeaker is the part of any sound-reproducing system that contributes most to distorting sound. There is no good reason for adding this distortion to your magnetic recording.

Most home machines are equipped to work best with crystal microphones, although any kind of high-impedance microphone will produce good results. The kinds of microphone from which you may choose can be ascertained after you find out the input impedance and the amplification available in the recording amplifier. For most home uses there is nothing wrong with a well-made crystal microphone, of which there are many on the market. If you want to use a dynamic microphone, however, whose nominal impedance is 50 ohms, and if your recorder input is of high impedance, of the order of 500,000 ohms, you may find that not enough recording voltage will be generated through the amplifier to permit a good recording to be made, even with the volume (or "gain") control turned on all the way. In a case like this there are two things you may do: (1) Use a transformer to match the 50-ohm microphone to the 500,000-ohm grid, thereby obtaining enough voltage from the combination to record properly (miniature transformers of this type are available) or (2) use a pre-amplifier with a 50-ohm input, a volume control, and an output that matches the input of the recorder. Of course, you may also use a high-impedance dynamic microphone.

There is one prime disadvantage connected with the use of high-impedance microphones, whether the actuating mechanism is a crystal or is magnetic: They are prone to pick up hum and noise and can be properly used only a short distance from the recorder amplifier. A crystal microphone is normally provided with a cable not more than 25 ft long, since the use of longer lengths would cause voltage-loss and would pick up hum. Any high-impedance device actually extends the grid of the first amplifier tube to the device itself and is thus sensitive to any hum pickup, as anyone who has ever touched the grid of the first tube in a high-gain amplifier knows. Low-impedance devices, however, lose very little in voltage and fidelity even through long, high-capacity cables. They are easier to work with for this reason. Besides, magnetically operated microphones are not damaged by dampness or reasonable heat, whereas some kinds of crystal microphones can be made inoperative by temperatures over 125° F or by absorption of moisture.

There is little necessity, in ordinary home recording, for the use of more than one microphone. If, however, more than one is needed, it is possible to hook two up *in parallel* without too much loss. It is much better to use a "mixer" if more than one microphone is used. The "mixer" is an assembly of controls so arranged that each microphone is matched into its correct impedance and the mixer, as a unit, is matched properly to its load (or bridged by its load). Microphones may be purchased to match almost any impedance. If the loss in gain through the mixer makes recording at the proper level difficult, a mixer-amplifier should be purchased; by this device each microphone output is amplified, then "gained," and finally permitted to go through the rest of the mixer to the recorder input. The type of mixer you need for any particular microphone and recorder can be determined from the specifications of both pieces of equipment.

HINTS FOR BUYING RECORDERS

Directions for cleaning and maintaining recorders will be found in the chapter on "Maintenance." Do not forget that although magnetic recording permits you to forget the practical hazards of disk recording, you will get good results only by being careful to use your microphone, recorder, and controls correctly. The choice of a recording machine is one that should be made carefully. It is good business sense to buy on performance only. The points to look for are: (1) a quiet "erase" system—test the recorder by erasing a recording of "tone" or a whistle at a little more than full level. The tape should be completely erased. A good system will reproduce erased tape as a steady "s-s-s-sh," without irregular bursts of noise. (2) If you can afford it, buy a machine with a meter level-indicator, which is much more accurate than the usual neon tube or "magic-eye." (3) There is a trend toward the use of half-track reproducing heads on full-track machines. A full-track head gives better reproduction and less noise, normally, but is more difficult to align and keep in service. For highest quality, use full-track-head machines. (4) Machines that operate with minimum "flutter" and "wow" are preferable to machines with poor drives that claim to record sound up to 20,000 cy per sec. The lack of high-frequency response is not a deterrent to good reproduction of sound, but flutter and wow are. Test the machine you intend to buy by recording piano tones with it. If they sound like piano tones on being played back, the machine is good; if not, the machine's flutter is too high. (5) Components of a good tape recorder will not overheat in normal temperatures. Check this condition, especially as the motors and magnetic heads are affected. The motors are in good order if you can keep your hand on them after they have been operating continuously for four or five hours. If the erase head, which warms up more than the recording head, heats too much, it may cause sticky and erratic tape motion, as mentioned earlier. If the record or reproduce head (sometimes the same head) gets too hot, it will not record or reproduce with top fidelity.

Remember, a magnetic recorder is a mechanical *and* an electronic apparatus. *Both* systems must be in good operating condition, or the recording will suffer. In most instances the manufacturer who makes a good mechanical unit also makes a good electronic unit.

SLEEP-LEARNING

There is no need here to tell you, in detail, the many ways in which you can use your home recorder. We have taken up the subject of learning a language in detail in Chapter 16 on educational uses. Languages may be learned at home in the same way.

But another method of committing material to memory usually can be applied only at home. This is the method of memorization called "sleep-learning." The principle guiding the "learning" action is that the memory can be more easily imposed upon when one is asleep than when awake—therefore memorization occurs much more quickly and lasts longer in the "new" memory section of your brain. In order to use this method with tape one requires certain items. (1) A single headphone or tiny loudspeaker that can be placed under the pillow, or in it, without causing discomfort, is essential. (It is possible to purchase a "pillow-speaker.") Those who do not use pillows may install a small loudspeaker within the mattress, near the head position. (2) A machine so arranged that it can be turned on and caused to operate automatically by a relay controlled by a time clock is also needed. The positions needed are: turn on recorder, start reproducing, stop (on the contacting metal, or metallic-painted, strip at the end of the tape section you want to memorize), reverse to beginning of tape section (upon contacting another metallic switch-contact), and, finally, reproduce again. This cycle can be performed more easily by any ordinary automatic phonograph, but, unfortunately, the material one wishes to commit to memory is rarely recorded on a disk, unless it is a language lesson. The sleep-learning method requires that one set the time clock in such a way that the machine will begin to play back, at low volume, after you are asleep.

OVERCOMING SPEECH DEFECTS—VOICE AND MUSIC PRACTICE

Recorders may be advantageously used in the home either to supplement or to supplant supervised speech training in schools established for the purpose. Almost everyone is deceived as to the sound of his own voice; it is only by listening to a high-quality recording that we can really hear ourselves as others hear us. We are then, and only then, conscious of defects in our speech, whatever they may be; this is the first step toward overcoming them. (See Chapter 16 on educational methods.) Note, incidentally, that for high-quality voice reproduction you must record properly. Do not over-load the microphone or the recorder. Try to establish a normal pro-cedure; then stick to it.

Musicians and vocalists make use of magnetic recorders for a rea-son similar to the one noted above: Only by listening while not playing or singing can the performer become his own critic and analyze defects in his playing or vocalization. Especially is this true of players of wind instruments whose aural passages cannot func-tion properly while the performer is playing.

VOICE "LETTERS"

A popular use of magnetic recording is found in recording and mailing tape, or paper magnetic disks, to friends and relatives. Peo-ple who would otherwise never, or only infrequently, hear the voice of the recordist are able to do so by this means. Both correspondents must, of course, have access to the same type of recorder.

THE IPSOPHONE TELEPHONE RECORDER

The "Ipsophone," manufactured at present in Switzerland, is one of the most ingenious machines ever devised to record and answer telephone calls automatically. In order to discharge its various func-tions, it makes use of a multiple-spool wire recorder, 71 telephone relays of various kinds, amplifiers, timing cams, gears, and manual switching circuits. The Ipsophone has been in use for several years in Europe, largely taking the place of the "personal telephone-an-swering service" used in the United States. In addition to record-ing incoming calls, this machine may be used to record dictation and telephone conversations; by means of a secretly coded, voice-impulse-operated relay system, it will play back to its owner, when he calls it from any telephone set in the world, all the messages that have been recorded since his last call. The owner may then, either from any remote point or from his home or office, cause these messages to be completely erased and the Ipsophone to be made ready for any new messages. It has provisions for recording or transmitting messages over either of two independent telephone

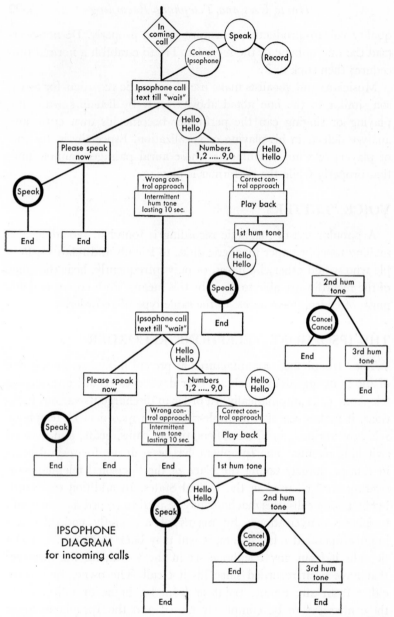

Courtesy of Ipsophone Exploitation, Ltd.

Fig. 17-2. Block diagram of alternative sequences of operations an Ipsophone can perform when an incoming call is received. (From *Technical Description 729 E,* published by Ipsophone Exploitation, Ltd., Zurich, Switzerland)

400

Courtesy of Ipsophone Exploitation, Ltd.

Fig. 17-3A. The inside of an Ipsophone. The six wire spools are seen from this view.

Fig. 17-3B. Another view of the inside of an Ipsophone; from this view the belt drive can be seen.

(From *Technical Description 729 E*, published by Ipsophone Exploitation, Ltd., Zurich, Switzerland)

A

B

lines. Figures 17-2, 17-3A and B illustrate the operation of the Ipsophone and its mechanism.

Suppose that you were to call Mr. Smith, whose telephone line is connected to an Ipsophone. If your call is not answered within 13 sec, the automatic answer of the Ipsophone (previously recorded on one of the reels of wire), after 20 sec at most, will be, "This is Mr. James A. Smith's Ipsophone. Your message will be automatically recorded—wait—please start speaking now."

After this invitation to you, the Ipsophone is switched over to recording (on the second pair of wire reels which have a capacity of 5 min), and your voice, whose sound intensity has been increased or decreased as needed, by an amplifier, is recorded on the wire. If you do not begin speaking within 12 sec after the invitation, "please start speaking now," the Ipsophone automatically disconnects from the line. It also automatically disconnects when you replace the receiver, no further acoustic impulses reaching it until the next call.

SECRET CODE ON THE IPSOPHONE

Ten push buttons on the Ipsophone control panel, numbered from 1 to 0 (0 succeeds 9), are the "secret code" buttons. Any desired combination of 2 or more numbers can be formed by means of these buttons, the ones selected to form the code being pressed down. Turning the key on the panel *sets* the code according to the buttons selected, let us say 3, 5, and 9, and pushes out any depressed buttons, which cannot be pressed down again until the 3, 5 and 9 are released. Only Mr. Smith, or someone in his confidence, knows this code.

PLAYBACK BY MEANS OF SECRET CODE

Your call to the Ipsophone has been recorded now, along with some others. Mr. Smith, whose phone and Ipsophone are in London, is in Paris on a business trip. He calls his phone from Paris for his recorded messages. The Ipsophone answers his call, since no one is there to forestall (by picking up the receiver) its going into action. About 15 sec later, the Ipsophone announces: "This is Mr. James

A. Smith's Ipsophone. Your message will be automatically recorded—wait—" The word "wait" informs Mr. Smith that he may cause the Ipsophone to play back by twice saying the word "Hello." The first "Hello" must be said immediately after he hears the word "wait," that is, within 3/4 sec. The two "Hellos" must be clearly separated from each other, since they actuate voice-impulse relays. The Ipsophone, after "hearing" these two "Hellos," instead of repeating "please start speaking now," calls out the numbers 1 to 9 and 0, leaving a two-sec interval of silence between each number and the next. Mr. Smith then enunciates the words "Hello—Hello" after each of the numbers that constitute his own secret code—that is, after each of the numbers 3, 5, and 9. If he follows procedure correctly, the Ipsophone will then begin playing back all the previously recorded messages just as soon as it finishes counting up to 0.

If Mr. Smith makes a mistake, by saying "Hello—Hello" after the wrong number or by saying "Hello" only once, the machine will not play back. Instead, after counting up to 0, it will send out a buzzing sound lasting 10 sec and repeat the previous routine, thus giving Mr. Smith another chance to get his messages played back to him. If Mr. Smith does not get his "Hellos" said after the correct code numbers this time, the Ipsophone switches off and disconnects the phone.

If Mr. Smith has followed procedure correctly, all the messages received since his last check with the Ipsophone will be played back. At the end of this reproduction period, which is indicated by the machine emitting a short buzzing signal, Mr. Smith may avail himself of one of three procedures:

1. *Recording after playback.* If, after playback of all the accumulated messages has been completed, Mr. Smith wants to transmit a message for recording by the Ipsophone, he calls "Hello" twice within 2 sec after hearing the first buzz following the completion of playback. The Ipsophone is then ready for recording. When recording is completed, Mr. Smith replaces the receiver, and the Ipsophone is automatically disconnected.

2. *Erasing recordings after playback.* If Mr. Smith, after having heard the messages, decides to erase them, he waits for the

second buzzing signal that is sent out by the Ipsophone about 2 sec after the first buzz, which indicated the end of playback. After this second buzz, he says: "Cancel—Cancel" into his telephone mouthpiece. Again, these two words must be spoken separately from each other and clearly. The message-recording reels of wire are then reeled back into starting position, undergoing erasure in the process.

3. *Repeating playback.* Should Mr. Smith decide, after hearing his messages, that he wants to listen to them again some time later, he need only put the receiver down immediately after hearing the first buzzing signal. In this case, any subsequent message will be recorded in correct order, and no erasure will take place.

AUTOMATIC DISCONNECT

If Mr. Smith, for some reason, does not put down his receiver after the first buzz and gives no orders (either "Hello—Hello" after the first buzz or "Cancel—Cancel" after the second buzz), a third buzzing sound of slightly longer duration than either of the other two will be emitted, indicating that the Ipsophone is being disconnected from the line.

RESULTS OF ERROR IN APPROACH

If Mr. Smith should have forgotten his code, should say only one "Hello," or make some other error in his attempt to get the Ipsophone to play back its messages, the machine, after counting up to "0," will give an intermittent buzz for 10 sec and then repeat its "call text." If Mr. Smith, or an interloper, should again not give the proper replies in the secretly coded order to the relays that are "waiting" for the correct voice impulses, the 10-sec buzz will repeat, and then the Ipsophone will be switched off and disconnected from the caller's telephone line.

THE TELE-MAGNET

The Tele-magnet (Fig. 17-4) is a telephone-answering machine, made in the United States, that uses wire in recording. When the phone rings, the receiver is lifted and a phonograph record, previously prepared, gives instructions to the caller in the owner's voice. Each incoming message is registered on a counter as it is recorded, thus enabling the owner upon his return to learn how many calls

Courtesy of the Mohawk Business Machines Corp.

Fig. 17-4. The Tele-magnet, a wire-recorder telephone-answering device.

were received by the machine during his absence. The recorder capacity is one hour of recording; it shuts off automatically between calls.

LEGAL ASPECTS OF TELEPHONE RECORDING IN THE UNITED STATES

In most European and other countries (except the United States) telephone recording is subject to a minimum of restrictions. In this country, however, the use of telephone-recording equipment is forbidden in connection with interstate and foreign calls unless the recording is made through equipment that transmits a periodic warning tone, thus indicating to the parties to the telephone conversation that their voices are being recorded. The legality of recording local or intrastate calls must be decided by the Public Service Commission or Bureau having jurisdiction over this matter in the particular state or region involved.

The warning tone, which must be transmitted approximately every 15 sec during any recording made of an interstate or foreign telephone conversation, should be 1400 cy per sec and of a strength equal to "the average telephone talking signal strength." American telephone companies will install and service a device that produces this tone during the recording of a telephone conversation. Telephone companies will also aid in equalizing incoming and outgoing signals over the telephone line, thus making it possible for recording to take place at a more or less even level. (Readers interested in this question should read Federal Communications Commission Public Notice 60591, issued March 28, 1951, and Public Notice 5569 and Docket No. 6787, adopted March 24, 1947.) Companies of the Bell System are now equipped to provide automatic telephone message-recording machines for subscribers. These machines record on a rubber belt impregnated with an iron-oxide mixture.

18

Public Entertainment, Advertising, and Warning Methods

Magnetic recording machines, in use for some time in the fields of public entertainment and advertising, have also served to give instructions and safety warnings automatically. The machines that do these jobs differ considerably in design, just as the functions that they perform are different: In other words, the machine fits the job.

ENTERTAINMENT MACHINES

For several reasons, magnetic recording is being used increasingly for entertaining the public. The most important reason is that magnetic reproduction can take place under conditions that make it impossible to play the ordinary phonograph record. Thus, aboard trains, planes, buses, and even some ships, where disk machines would fail unless they were designed and made to withstand the various kinds of shock encountered—a very expensive procedure, magnetic reproducers are able to produce high-quality entertainment. Another reason is absence of discernible wear; either wire or tape can be played many thousands of times before any loss of quality occurs. In addition, tape machines, running at low speed, may furnish hours of continuous music without any servicing becoming necessary. With modern, improved playback heads and tape, a playback machine running at 3 3/4 in. per sec furnishes good-quality sound, providing the drive is reasonably free from flutter. It is now possible to reproduce sound at this speed with comparatively good fidelity up to 7000 or 8000 cy per sec.

Recorders have been used with great success in the entertainment field. Installation of these machines in multiple units may provide for one unit, when it stops playing, automatically to trip a relay that starts the next unit; thus, one unit is going while the "played-out" tape or wire is being noiselessly rewound. If the medium should break accidentally, the same relay action stops the defective unit and starts the next one. Wire recorders of this type are being superseded by long-playing tape recorders, some of which can provide high-quality sound for eight hours from one 2400-ft reel of tape. The sound is pre-recorded on two tracks. After one track has played for four hours, the direction of the drive is reversed; then a different playback head is switched into operation or the same playback head is moved; either arrangement permits reproduction of the second track—for another four hours' time.

ADVERTISING MACHINES—ANNOUNCE MECHANISMS

An application in which magnetic recording excels is that of announcing mechanisms. The first such use occurred in Germany in 1920, when a telegraphone was adapted for use in a German railway.

Announce mechanisms now being manufactured are of two general types: one employing a continuous loop of tape (or a coated narrow cylinder), and the other a tape magazine (Fig. 18-1). The second type may be subdivided into two kinds: One makes use of an endless reel of tape enclosed in a magazine; the other uses an endless loop of considerable length, the loose tape dropping into a glass tank where it cannot tangle or get damaged.

Machines employing removable compact tape magazines are

most popular. In one kind of machine the tape may be erased and recorded again; in another no provision is made for recording new messages—the magazine must be removed and another magazine, which has been pre-recorded with the new sales talk or message, must be installed.

Courtesy of the Mohawk Business Machines Corp.

Fig. 18-1. The "Message Repeater," a tape recorder of the magazine-reel type.

Small enough to be hidden and connected to a public-address system, announce mechanisms may be used in numerous ways— their use being limited in scope only by the imagination of the user. Among present services performed are: description of an article of merchandise when a prospective buyer stops to look at it; announcement of train, bus, and plane arrivals and departures;

and giving directions to special sales areas in department stores. Indeed, these little machines may be put to a myriad of uses.

Announce mechanisms may be triggered in a number of ways. In a gasoline station, for instance, the announce mechanism may be started by a "hose activator." When an automobile wheel passes over a small-diameter flexible hose, a relay that turns on the machine is thrown. In those cases where actual contact devices, such as concealed switches under rubber mats or micro-switches that are activated by the opening or closing of a door, cannot be used for some reason, interruption of an "electric-eye" beam may be used to start the message machine. The method and means of starting the unit depend entirely upon the circumstances surrounding its use.

To stop the tape, a switching arrangement whose operation is very simple is generally provided. In the tape's path of travel there are two light, metal contacts that bear against the base side of the tape. Shorting of these contacts activates a relay that switches off the current to the drive motor. Metallic paint or foil, applied to the tape at the exact location where it is wished to stop the sound, shorts the contacts. Once stopped, the machine must be restarted by use of a switch, manual or automatic. By means of synchronous motors and different combinations of gear assemblies, automatic restarting devices can cause the machine to start and stop at predetermined and precise intervals. The availability of various methods and accessories permits a variety of choice; by use of different combinations one may cause a message to be played continuously, in rotation with others, or with time intervals between repetitions of the same message or varying messages.

WARNINGS AND SAFETY MESSAGES

Mechanisms identical to those discussed above may be used as warning devices on machines; for safety messages in factories, schools, and theaters; to issue directions in case of fire; to warn of road conditions; and to instruct tourists at points of interest. It is possible to construct warning devices to instruct drivers to slow down at dangerous spots on a road, during travel on parts under construction or obscured by fog, or because of other hazards. In addition, they may be used on trains to signal, in understandable language, the approach to a station. Or they may even be used to give instructions in several languages; for instance, one may be hooked up to a high-speed grinding wheel in a factory shop to warn the operator in Polish or Italian to put on his safety goggles. Another may be actuated by a smoke-detector to give directions for fire-drill or for escape from a fire-threatened building.

It is impossible to give in detail all ways in which these ingenious devices may be used. Suffice it to say that a machine may be automatically started by the very condition it is to warn about.

19

Legal Uses and Their Limitations

SURREPTITIOUS RECORDING

The author of this book has never made any recording without the knowledge and consent of the "recordee." He is, consequently, not qualified by personal *experience* to write authoritatively about the manner in which setups for surreptitious recordings are made. Since such setups can be concealed in little space, the unwary are apt not to detect them. Resulting recordings can be "doctored" in a way to damn an innocent person. Accordingly, some information, even though not "authoritative," may be in order.

This kind of recording may be accomplished in a number of ways. We know that telephone lines can be "tapped" and conversations on such lines recorded. An induction coil placed under or near a telephone instrument will pick up enough energy for a good recording to be made. Microphones may be concealed under a desk or a divan; in a cushion, light fixture, or lamp; behind a drape; inside a telephone set; and scores of other places. Tiny microphones, no larger than a dime, may be hidden almost anywhere. But for most recording, wires must be drawn from the microphone to the recorder, wherever that may be located; obviously, wires are difficult to hide, especially in modern offices. If an office is carpeted and access can be gained to the floor directly below it, the microphone wire can be pulled through a small hole drilled in the floor beneath

412

the carpet. If time permits, a microphone can be hidden and wire run through existing conduits for ac line, temperature controls, and the like, the wire being eventually fed into the recorder, which is in a "safe" location. Binaural (or dual-setup) systems, which allow the listener to "hear through" ordinary masking noises and to distinguish voices intelligibly, may be used if it is important to avoid masking effects.

Since the technique of the microphone "plant" is laborious and time-consuming, other methods of recording secretly have been devised. The latest of these makes use of a tiny ultra-high-frequency FM transmitter, which can operate automatically. The transmitter may be "planted," or it may be given to a "trusted" friend of the person whose conversation is to be surreptitiously recorded while the two are together. This transmitter is modulated by means of a tiny microphone and amplifier, both also hidden on the "friend." The whole apparatus, including a transmitting antenna hidden up the sleeve, need be no larger than the usual hearing-aid. The FM signal is received and recorded at the recording "station." At this writing there are several magnetic recording machines small enough to be hidden on the person; they permit recordings to be made without anyone other than the wearer becoming the wiser. The German "Miniphone," a battery-powered wire recorder, may be slung underneath a jacket, the sound being recorded via a tiny microphone which ostensibly is a good-looking wrist watch. A tape recorder, approximately 5 in. long, 2 in. deep, and 4 in. high, that will record efficiently for approximately 5 min, has been manufactured.

FALSIFIED RECORDING

Recordings are admissible in court as evidence *under certain circumstances*. In some courts their admission rests with the discretion of the court. There are many ways to trap the unwary, to record damning testimony and admissions that may afterwards be offered as evidence in court, and, if admitted, this evidence, "true" or falsified, may be used to convict the defendant, guilty or innocent though he may be. For, mark this well, there is no *sure* way to prevent recorded testimony from being slanted—tampered with—by editing and re-recording of the tape or wire in such a way that the "edited" testimony will favor one party in a trial at law.

It is sometimes (but not always) possible for an expert who is experienced in recognition of sound and in recording and editing methods to expose falsified recorded testimony. But it is indeed a horrid thought that men may be—perhaps have been already—convicted and sent to prison wholly or largely through the agency of tampered-with and altered recordings presented and accepted as legal evidence.

Two examples of falsified recording will be described here. Although the cases were actually tried in court, of necessity no names will be mentioned.

In the first case a man and his wife agreed to a legal separation, the man to retain custody of their only son for six months of the year and the wife to have custody for the remaining six months. The man, in hope both of obtaining his wife's self-made admission of her inadequacy as a wife and mother and of blackening her character, installed a wire recorder near his telephone to which he then had his recorder connected. Thereafter, he left instructions with his maid that the wire recorder was to be turned on whenever the wife called to speak to her son, who was permitted to talk with his mother over the telephone only when the father or maid was present. The boy, under the father's influence, rejected his mother's loving advances and, in doing so, used quite loathsome language for a child of his age. During his own telephone conversations with his wife, the man took every opportunity to goad her into some unguarded statement. The recorder was also turned on when the father was playing and talking with his son at home. Nine or ten hours of this kind of wire recording were made.

When the wife sued the husband, he presented his recordings as evidence and swore that they were bona fide recordings of her telephone conversations. This writer, called in as an expert witness, demonstrated falsification of the recordings. The wife, supposedly, swore viciously at her son over the telephone; the voice, however, was not that of the wife but of someone else. A voice had been disguised to simulate the wife's voice, but the voice frequencies of this recorded voice were considerably greater in range than could be passed by the husband's telephone line. Upon learning that he was on the point of being exposed as a perjurer, the man hurriedly capitulated, and the case was settled out of court—in favor of the wife.

If the trial of this case had continued, it would have been necessary in that particular court (according to attorneys) to present pictorial evidence of the fact that the voice alleged to be the wife's had been recorded directly, by means of a microphone and not from the telephone line in the defendant's (husband's) home.

Pictorial evidence of this nature, although difficult to obtain, can be procured. The first step is to isolate identical bits of sound from the taped voices of the persons concerned. These sounds are then re-recorded to tape, high fidelity equipment being used. Leader tape is inserted between the samples of sound. Next, the ends of the re-recorded tape are spliced together to form a continuous loop, which permits the sounds—in this case the telephone voice and the microphone voice—to be repeatedly reproduced in close succession. The next step is connection of the output of the tape machine to a cathode-ray oscilloscope, on which the sounds are reproduced in the form of tracings of light. These light traces may be photographed by any one of several slightly different methods. Direct comparison of the photographs of these sound patterns will make it obvious that they are not at all the same, and two facts can be demonstrated.

1. The voices are not identical phonetically.
2. The modes of transmission to the recorder input were not similar, and the voice current recorded from the microphone contains frequencies that could not be passed by the telephone line.

THE SOUND SPECTROGRAPH

A much better and faster method for making sound comparisons is that of the Sona-Graph. This machine, which is a sound spectrograph, is much used for rapid analysis and positive identification of sound; it was developed under Dr. Ralph K. Potter at Bell Laboratories and is manufactured by the Kay Electric Company in Pine Brook, New Jersey. By means of this apparatus any sound whose duration is no longer than 2.4 sec can be transformed into a shaded picture in about 5 min. The process is described below.

The sound to be transformed is first recorded on the magnetic surface of a drum. The recorded sound, whose fluctuations are converted into corresponding fluctuating high-frequency current, is reproduced in visual form upon a second drum. The drums, whose radii are the same, run in synchronism. With each revolution of the drums a successively higher band of sound frequencies (either a 45- or 300-cy-per-sec band) is passed through a filter and is converted into high-frequency current. The sound frequencies passed through the filter in any single revolution of the drums are transmitted in the form of current by means of a stylus to current-sensitive paper mounted on the second drum. The intensity of the sound controls the shading (from black to white) of the line registered by the stylus on the sensitive paper. Progressively higher frequencies are represented by the stylus' lines, ranging from 85 cy per sec, the lowest frequency that can ordinarily be registered by this means, to the normal top limit of the spectrograph's frequency range of 8,000 cy per sec. Thus, if the 45-cy filter is used, the first line drawn on the second drum's paper represents sound frequencies from 85 to 130 cy per sec, the second line frequencies approximately from 130 to 175 cy per sec, and similarly to the upper limit of the last frequency band that can be registered on the second drum.

The drums revolve at a speed which permits the stylus to make a complete shaded picture with a definition of 400 lines per in. within 5 min. Since the machine can be adapted to analyze waves ranging from subsonic through supersonic frequencies, it can be said to provide "fingerprinting" of sound. An equally detailed analysis would require hours of work if other methods were used.

The second case to illustrate falsification of recording is one in which a man was accused of perjury. A surreptitious recording was made in this man's office by a trusted "friend." The recording was purportedly made on a wire recorder, and the wire reel was deposited in court as evidence of perjury. Lawyers for the defendant, the supposed perjurer, engaged the writer as an expert witness. An exact copy, on magnetic tape, of the wire recording was obtained for examination. Except in certain portions that, by themselves, were damning to the man accused of perjury, the sound was obscured by the noise of hammering.

After thorough examination of the recording on tape, re-recordings through various kinds of filters were made in order to check several suspicions of the writer. Certain facts stood out like sore thumbs—the wire had been stopped twice and restarted twice, and there was evidence of editing at one point.

It was decided to play the recording in court before the jury. The recordist during cross-examination said that he did not know how many times the recorder had been stopped and started but emphatically affirmed that the wire had not been edited before it was deposited in court as evidence. The case was then adjourned until the next morning.

The writer advised the attorney for the defense that he (the writer) could positively prove that editing had occurred; either the wire reel presented in evidence had been edited, or it was actually a *copy* of an edited, intermediate re-recording of the wire on which the original recording had been made. In short, there had been an edit, and this fact could be proved.

The next morning the attorney for the plaintiff asked for permission to remove the wire recording from evidence on grounds that its lack of clarity would confuse the jury and that its sense, due to the confused jumble of sound, could not be grasped. Permission was granted. The case, shortly thereafter, was given to the jury, which voted to acquit the defendant.

Did knowledge of the fact that editing could have been proved persuade the plaintiff's attorney to eliminate the magnetic recording as evidence? There is no sure answer. The fact remains, however, that the case was won by the defendant—probably because the magnetic recording was withdrawn.

The sound that convinced the writer that an edit had been made, although crudely, was a sound that was *not natural*. It was *part* of the sound of a *reverberating hammer blow*. The actual sound does not have as abrupt an onset as did that on the recording. The recorded sound started in the middle, rather than at the beginning, of the operation of whose sound it was, presumably, a complete reproduction. The recorded sound could have been obtained only by *cutting out*, by editing, the first half of the natural sound of the hammer blow. Since the pitch of the beginning of the remaining sound agreed in pitch with the "middle" of recorded reverberating actual hammer blows, it could not be argued that recording had been started in the middle of a hammer blow; if such had been the case, there would have been a slight change of pitch as recording started—a recognizable beginning "wow."

SAFEGUARDS AGAINST FALSIFIED RECORDINGS

It is the belief of this writer that because of the ease with which complicated editing can be performed on tape, making possible perversion of a speaker's statements, sound recording should be outlawed as legal evidence.

It is possible to design recording machines that cause progressive time signals to be recorded on the tape at supersonic frequencies, a break in these indicating (in most cases) any editing of the original tape. Such machines could be placed under the immediate surveillance of the court itself; these "safeguards," however, do not *guarantee* that an original recording will not be altered.

RECORDED COURT RECORDS

Magnetic recorders have been used, although not yet widely, to record testimony, counsel's pleas, and similar material for use in court proceedings. Such recordings are later transcribed for the court records. This method of taking accurate "minutes" has some advantages over the usual method of two court stenographers or stenotypists taking verbatim notes. In the first place, the voice recordings may be played back in court, if necessary, and accents and emphasis may clarify an otherwise ambiguous statement read from stenographic notes. In the second place, with microphones placed in front of the judge, attorneys, and witnesses, recorded sounds *should* be clearer and more intelligible when reproduced than the voices originally heard in the usually large and sometimes noisy courtroom. One obvious difficulty in such use is that the person operating the recording machine for the court (court reporter, probably) would have to memorize the voices of the respective witnesses, lawyers, and others, if he is to be able to identify them later. This difficulty may be overcome by means of a dual-track recorder—an adaptation of a standard dual-track recorder or a dictating machine of the magnetic-cylinder type that is equipped for dual-track recording. On the second track of such a recorder the court clerk may record directions, names of witnesses, and any other needed memoranda. Such comments of the reporter could be a valuable aid to anyone trying to gain proper comprehension of the case. If this system were now in use, it is possible that it would be a great boon to judges, attorneys, and juries, not to mention plaintiffs and defendants.

Binaural recording, because of certain added features, would be of even greater value in this kind of court reporting. A person listening to binaural recording is able to locate the respective locations from which sounds come and can therefore hear them in their spatial relationships.

VOICE-RECORDED CONTRACTS AND AGREEMENTS

Magnetically recorded contracts and agreements have not yet, to the writer's knowedge, been accepted as valid instruments in any law court. That they may be so recognized in the future is doubtful, in view of the various things pointed out, here and elsewhere, including the ease of falsifying magetic recordings and the difficulty of ascertaining the existence of such falsification. The latter problem necessitates recourse to experts, who are few in number in this still relatively small field.

20

Some Techniques in Communication

When Valdemar Poulsen demonstrated his telegraphone at the Paris Exposition in 1900, telephone engineers were interested, as we have seen, in the possibility of using the telegraphone as a "message-repeater" to extend the range of the telephone. At the same time, telegraph engineers were shown how the transmission time of a tele-graphed message could be shortened and also how a message could be made more or less secret by means of the telegraphone. Poulsen demonstrated two ways of using the telegraphone for message transmission. By the first method, he recorded and transmitted the message at the telegraphone's normal speed; since the operator who transcribed the message could not copy the coded message as rapidly as he received it, it was necessary for him to slow down the playback to the speed at which he could transcribe the coded message accu-rately. Poulen's second method consisted of recording the message in code in the normal manner but transmitting it while the wire was rewinding, the effect being that the message was transmitted in reverse. The operator received a reversed message which he could copy only while playing it back in reverse, a procedure that, of course, gave him the original message.

The advantages gained by the second method were two: (1) A certain degree of secrecy was achieved, since a wire-tapper lacking a recorder would not easily be able to interpret the reversed code. (2) Some economy was possible in the use of a telegraph line, since one machine could continuously be transmitting previously recorded messages while on a second machine messages received over the same line were being recorded. However, the receiving station's operator, if he had only one machine, was forced to wait while it rewound before he could transcribe the next message; accordingly, this operation was not economical of time.

In connection with these early techniques of telephony, it is interesting to remember that it was while Carpenter and Carlson were working on a method to speed up code transmission by means of magnetic recording that they discovered ac bias.

SPEED OF CODE TRANSCRIPTION

Today, speed of direct transmission of coded messages—either Morse Telegraphic Code or International Code—is limited only by the speed with which messages can be transcribed. Codes are automatically transmitted and received at the rate of several hundred words a minute, the transcription speed limited merely by the maximum speed of the automatic receiving typewriter. This mechanical limit can be overcome in either of two ways. The first is that of recording the message on magnetic tape (or wire) and storing it until facilities for typing the message are available. The other is use of facsimile facilities, recorded or direct; this subject will be given attention later in this chapter.

TRANSMISSION FREQUENCIES

The frequency or tone of a recorded sound increases in the same ratio as the speed of motion of the medium on which it is recorded. Whether we transmit coded bursts of sound in dots and dashes, voice, or music, this rule does not change. For instance, if we record a 1000-cy tone at a tape speed of 7.5 in. per sec and transmit this tone at 30 in. per sec, the transmitted tone will be one of 4000 cy. Maximum speed at which a recording can be faithfully transmitted is governed by the upper limit of the transmission band of the wire line or radio-frequency link over which the signal will be sent. Pass bands of wire lines and radio bands vary in accordance with the respective uses for which they are designed and differ greatly in capacity. If the frequency of a transmission tone is to fall within a particular transmission band, it is essential that the frequency at which the tone is recorded and the speed at which the recorded tone is to be transmitted have a relationship that will limit the tone's transmission frequency to the frequency range available in the wire line or radio band over which transmission will be made. Obviously, when traffic does not warrant, it would be uneconomical to tie up a line that is capable of passing 10,000 cy with messages whose upper frequency does not exceed 3000 cy. If conditions do warrant, however, a wide-range circuit may be economically employed to carry messages recorded and transmitted at very high speeds and, therefore, at very high frequencies.

FACSIMILE SYSTEMS

By means of a modern facsimile system* (such as that of the Times Facsimile Corporation) a photograph, a drawing, or a page of print or writing may be transmitted over an ordinary telephone circuit and duplicated at the receiving point. Occasionally the need arises for retransmission of such a duplicate or facsimile. For instance, a photograph transmitted by facsimile from Albany to New York by wire may then be transmitted to Europe by radio. If, at the time transmission is to be made, the radio circuits to the destination in Europe are not available, or not usable because of adverse atmospheric conditions, the photograph would be "stored" in New York until conditions permitted satisfactory use of the circuits. Storage can take the form of a facsimile photograph or a recording of the facsimile impulses on a disk or magnetic tape. If the facsimile is a photograph, the usual procedure is to record it photographically and to retouch it before its next transmission. This is the method commonly used by a great many newspapers for reproduction of pictures. The original photograph is sent by facsimile to the main

---

* By facsimile, here, is meant the conversion of light to electrical impulses for transmission over telephone lines or by radio-frequency waves.

office of a news service; there it is copied, retouched, and then simultaneously relayed to possibly three or four hundred newspapers or periodicals. But should the matter that is "facsimiled" convey incorrect information if it were retouched and then relayed, photography by facsimile would not be used; instead the facsimile impulses would be recorded on disk or tape for retransmission.

PRINCIPAL NEEDS FOR FACSIMILE RECORDING

The principal need for magnetic tape recording of facsimile material arises in organizations, such as the armed forces, that transmit weather maps, graphs, and pictures throughout the world. In many cases it is necessary at various relay stations to retransmit the same map or picture many times. Sometimes, as mentioned above, there is considerable delay before atmospheric conditions permit satisfactory radio transmission of the facsimile.

HOW FACSIMILE SYSTEMS WORK

Optical (photographic) recording and retransmission of such data as weather maps would result in serious degeneration of the maps or pictures, since all types of recording paper limit to some degree contrast and range of photographic tone. (The Times Facsimile System normally permits a range of 18 shades between black and white.) An audio-level range of 15 db is required to print facsimile in full contrast—from black, through the 16 intermediate shades of gray, to white. In optical facsimile light and dark signals are transmitted as amplitude modulations of an 1800-cy-per-sec carrier wave. Normally, in a positive picture made at the receiving point, lack of modulation would result in a light or white spot and full modulation in a black spot; intensities of modulation between would yield corresponding shades of gray. Pictures up to 12×18.5 in. in size may be mounted (for transmitting) on a drum 12 in. long and 18.5 in. in circumference. The drum rotates at 60 revolutions per minute on a lead screw of 96-threads-per-inch pitch, while a narrow beam of light "scans" the picture, causing more or less intensity of modulation of the carrier wave, the degree depending upon the shade of the area being scanned at a given instant. At the receiving location a similar drum and apparatus reconvert the varying signals into varying intensities of light that produce corresponding areas of gray and black on photographic paper, which areas together reproduce the original material transmitted. Time needed to reproduce a picture by this system is a little less than 20 minutes.

Although the scanning method employed for optical facsimile is comparable to that used in television, there is one significant difference: Unlike television scanning, no synchronizing signals are transmitted at the start of each line to be scanned. As noted above, scanning, continuous, is at a pitch of 96 threads per inch. Synchronizing signals are transmitted only at the start of the transmission; they permit the receiving operator to "line up" or "frame" his picture. Synchronization of the lines throughout the picture is implicit in the system, resulting from the use of synchronous motors on transmitter and receiver drums which operate from two tuning-fork-controlled power supplies. These supplies maintain accurate enough frequency to keep the drums rotating at 60 rev per min (rpm) with variation no greater than one part in a million. Failure of either the transmitting or the receiving power supply to hold frequency within this accuracy will result in "skewing" or distortion of the picture. Similarly, variation in the drum's speed would produce fuzzy lines, and these would form a poor reproduction of the picture.

If transmitted facsimile impulses are recorded on a tape recorder and then reproduced on a facsimile machine, reconstituting the original material, any differences or irregularities in the reproduction that are contributed by the tape recorder will correspond to those caused by similar variations in the drum speed, itself. The effect of a steady error in speed may be easily computed from the characteristics of the facsimile machine. For example, suppose that there is a speed error in playback of one part in 200,000. During the transmission of one average-sized picture, which takes roughly 1150 sec (96 rev per in. times 12 in. at one rev per sec), the resulting time error is 1150 divided by 200,000, or 0.00576 sec.

Since the drum speed is one rev per sec or 18.5 in. per sec, this time error corresponding to 18.5 times 0.00576, or 0.106 in.—a skew of nearly 1/8 in. in the picture; this is the maximum distortion that can be tolerated in most reproductions.

Tape-Stretch Error. Most of the difficulty in the recording of facsimile signals on tape is due to the "stretchiness" of plastic-base (cellulose acetate) tape. (Plastic-base tape of this type stretches about 1 to 2 per cent, depending upon the humidity of its surroundings. Paper-base tape of the improved type stretches about one half as much.) Since a change in tape length has an effect similar to that caused by a variation in tape speed, it is obvious that good facsimile pictures cannot be recorded and reproduced unless the amount of tape-stretch is compensated.

The Fairchild Pic-Sync system (described in the chapter on motion pictures) has been found to correct for dimensional errors in tape sufficiently to produce a timing accuracy of better than 0.5 millisecond, which, as we have seen above, is more than adequate in facsimile recording. This system provides very low flutter content and minimum tape slippage at the capstan, both features contributing to excellence of facsimile results.

TRANSMISSION OF SECRET MESSAGES

Recording on a predetermined "secret" path on a magnetic medium, cylinder, or disk, is a simple way to send secret messages. In the Brush Electronics Company's "Mail-a-Voice," for example, a secret guide disk was placed over the magnetized paper disk during recording. The guide forced the recording head to travel along a complicated, secret path known only to the recordist and persons to whom he gave copies of the guide. Duplicates of such a "secret guide" may be kept by those "in the secret" and used to decode an otherwise unintelligible recording.

Another method for transmitting secret messages is the Tonschreiber method, discussed in Chapter 16. In addition, the interested reader will find described in the literature many electronic methods, commonly called voice or sound scrambling, for transmission of secret messages.

Glossary

attenuator – a potentiometer (see also gain control).

audio oscillator (**audio-frequency oscillator**) – an apparatus that produces power at audio frequencies.

balance to ground – this kind of circuit aids in reducing line noise and is a necessity in certain audio circuits where the two sides of a line must be made to balance each other in power.

beat oscillator (**sometimes called "beat frequency oscillator"** – a dual radio-frequency oscillator, whose frequencies mix with each other to produce an audible frequency. One of the radio-frequency oscillators can be varied, a variable tone resulting.

blend – to join two sequences in editing or recording so that the point where they join cannot be noticed.

break-away cue – the cue upon which a broadcasting station breaks away from a network program to make a local announcement.

bug – a trade term indicating generally a design error which can be found and eliminated only by practical tests.

bypassing – the process of providing a low-impedance path to ground for radio or audio signals not wanted.

calibrated oscilloscope – a cathode-ray oscilloscope with a scale imprinted on the tube face for the purpose of permitting visual measurement of voltages.

carrier wave – the unmodulated frequency band transmitted by a radio station.

cathode-ray tube – a kind of vacuum tube in which electrons are shot from a gun structure at one end and strike a fluorescent coating inside the tube face at the other end, causing the portion

427

of the coating struck to emit light. This electron beam can be bent by means of pairs of horizontal and vertical electrodes in the gun structure.

choke (**coil**) – an inductor designed to limit the flow of alternating current while permitting direct current to pass through it.

clapsticks – two sticks used to synchronize sound and action in motion-picture production. The collision of the sticks is photographed, along with the scene marker or slate, while the sound of the same act is being recorded. In editing and re-recording the picture and sound are thus synchronized by clapsticks.

clipped – refers to a wave from which the top and bottom extremities have been eliminated.

commutator ripple – the pulsations present in the output of an unfiltered or in an inadequately filtered direct-current generator.

compressor amplifier – an amplifier which compresses the volume range of a sound or signal.

condenser – apparatus, which stores electrical energy, consisting of two or more conducting plates, insulated from each other.

contact printing – the process of producing a photographic positive print by allowing light to pass through the negative film to the positive film while both films are held together positively.

crossfade – to manipulate gain controls in such a way that, as one constituent sound decreases, another increases; the total output of sound is thus kept constant.

crosstalk – leakage of sound (or light) from one channel or recorded track to another.

cue – a signal for switching or fading from one sequence or pickup to another, or for adding, or cutting away from, another source or signal.

dead – a trade term used in describing sound-absorptive properties of an enclosed space. Thus, one room may be "deader" than another, i.e., may absorb more sound than another.

decay – the dying out of a sound or other wave to an insignificant or predetermined lesser intensity.

diffraction – the bending of sound or other waves—around an obstacle or when passing extremely close to an object.

disperse – to distribute particles uniformly in a suspension, as in the manufacture of magnetic coatings.

dynamotor – a rotary converter, ordinarily used to convert a low ac voltage to a high dc voltage for use as a plate voltage supply.

dyne – unit of force in the centimeter-gram-second (cgs) system. It is that force which will give in one second an acceleration of one centimeter per second to a free mass of one gram.

electron motion – the motion, proportional to absolute temperature, of the electrons of which all matter is theoretically composed.

fidelity – the degree of faithfulness with which reproduced sound copies the original.

filtering (**of a power pack**) – the purifying of rectified ac current by means of combinations of capacity, inductance, and resistance, which results in the delivery of almost pure direct current for plate (and occasionally filament) current.

fluff – a trade term used to denote an error in an actor's delivery.

foot frame – the film frame which marks the beginning of a given foot of film.

Frahm frequency meter – the Frahm frequency meter contains a number of steel reeds, each having a different natural frequency. When the meter is connected to a source of alternating current, the reed closest in frequency to that of the current will vibrate.

frame – a single picture of a motion-picture film.

frequency meter – an instrument that measures the frequency of an alternating current (see Frahm frequency meter).

gain control – the potentiometer used in gaining.

gaining – a term used in the broadcasting, recording, and electronics industries. It refers to the manipulation of controls by an operator in order to maintain a relatively constant output level. Also called "gain-riding" or "riding-gain."

grease pencil – a very soft, china marking pencil used to mark disks, tape, and film for cueing or editing purposes.

grounding – the connecting, to a conductor buried in the earth, of any electrical apparatus. A large conducting mass may take the place of actual earth, e.g., the frame of an auto, the steel hull of a ship.

harmonic – a wave whose frequency is an integral multiple of the frequency of another wave which is called the fundamental, e.g., fundamental = 100 cy per sec, the second harmonic = 200 cy per sec, and the third = 300 cy per sec.

harmonic-distortion meter – an apparatus which measures the total amount of harmonics produced within an amplifier by a measured tone fed into the input.

hunt – the searching by a drive component for stability, or its mean speed.

impedance – the vector sum of all the resistances and reactances in a circuit or branch. The alternating current equivalent of resistance.

Kraft paper – a particular kind of strong paper.

lamination – the individual components, or layers, in a magnetic core, each made from a thin sheet of metal. Coil and transformer laminations are generally stamped out of silicon steel and are insulated from each other.

lapping (of head-core faces) – polishing by means of a gently acting abrasive.

leader tape – paper or plastic tape, uncoated, for providing leader for threading a tape in a machine. It is also used for visual cueing and for timing recorders.

line level – the power level or quantity of audio power transmitted over a line between studios or transmission points.

live – a. reverberant. b. actual performance as opposed to a recorded performance.

loading (as with resistance) – connecting a resistive or other impedance to the output of an amplifier in order to absorb all or part of its power output. This stabilizing factor acts to minimize variations in power or frequency.

log – an exact timed record of any operation or performance.

magic eye – an electron-ray tube containing a small fluorescent screen; the tube is used as a voltage indicator.

masking – occurs when the presence of one sound makes it more difficult to hear another sound also present.

mixing – a term used in the motion-picture and broadcast industries to denote the combining of the outputs of several program sources (microphones, reproducers) in order to produce the desired effect.

monitor – a. to listen to a radio program, or to listen and view a television program, critically. b. shorthand term for the monitor amplifier whose output operates the loudspeaker.

neon tube – a glass tube filled with neon gas under low pressure and containing two or more electrodes. The gas ionizes and glows pink or orange under the influence of electric current.

neutral condition (of coating) – completely demagnetized state of magnetic coating. (In this condition there is no preferred direction for recording.)

optical sound – sound recorded on photographic film by means of a sound-modulated light beam.

oscilloscope (cathode ray) – an apparatus which converts varying currents or voltages into visible traces. Can be used to measure voltages. The outmoded mirror oscilloscope performed the same function by means of a rapidly rotating mirror.

overtone – a harmonic frequency which a vibrating body can generate in addition to the lowest, or fundamental frequency, which it is capable of generating. The lowest possible frequency is the fundamental; the second harmonic is the first overtone; and so forth.

pad – a network made up of resistances used to couple two lines or impedances. Use of a pad minimizes the possibility of frequency distortion when two impedances are coupled.

pip – trade term meaning a pulse or a wave peak.

potentiometer – a variable resistor for measuring voltages.

pre-erased – magnetic medium which has been erased, by means of a bulk eraser, before a recording is made on it.

presence – the quality of sound which makes it seem actually in the foreground.

pressure-pad – a cushion, generally of felt, which presses the tape or other medium against the surface of the magnetic head.

production log – the sheet which contains accurate timings of parts of a program, notes regarding music, and so forth. Filled out by the production man or the assistant director.

protection copy – an original recording held in storage until after the production or program is completed. During broadcasting, the protection or safety copy is run off at the same time as the air copy but is switched to air only if the air copy fails.

random motion – haphazard motion, not governed by any fixed purpose or known physical law.

random noise – noise with energy components uniformly distributed throughout the frequency spectrum under consideration. Also called "white noise."

reflection – the directional change of a wave after it strikes any surface. The angle of reflection equals the angle of incidence to a plane surface or the angle of incidence to a tangent of a curved surface.

refraction – the change in direction of a wave which passes from one medium to another, due to differences in the transmission characteristics of the media.

relay – an electromagnetic switch in which the presence or absence of current-flow through the iron-cored armature coil causes contacts to close (make) or open (break) other current-carrying circuits.

Rochelle salt crystal – artificially grown crystal of sodium potassium tartrate having piezoelectric properties.

roll-off – the curve of attenuation versus frequency of a recording or reproducing device.

room-tone – a trade term used in describing the acoustic character of a room or studio.

rotary converter – a rotating device for converting alternating to direct current or vice versa.

running time – the actual time needed to play back a program.

safety copy – see protection copy.

safety film – photographic film made from cellulose acetate, which, compared to nitrocellulose film, is relatively safe and not inflammable.

scanning – the basis of the method by which scenes are viewed and reproduced in television. The scene is not "captured" as a whole but is scanned, line by line, by an electron beam that traverses the scene so rapidly that the action appears to be instantaneous.

sequence – a section of film or tape containing program material that is uninterrupted by breaks, titles, announcements, and similar material.

sine wave – a wave containing only one frequency.

sine-wave oscillator – an oscillator producing a pure, single frequency oscillation.

sound-head – a common term for optical-sound transducers.

spot news – news that is of immediate interest.

sprocketed film – film with (sprocket) holes punched in either or both edges. The film drive's sprocket teeth engage in these holes.

stage (of amplification) – the parts, including a vacuum tube or transistor, of any single, complete amplifying circuit.

standard tone – one of the tones adopted as standards for test purposes.

standing wave – a wave phenomenon produced by the addition and cancellation of alternate cycles of a direct wave and of a reflected wave. A stationary wave.

steady-state signal – a signal of constant amplitude.

stereophonic – the "perspective" effect produced by reproducing sound, by means of two or more completely separate sound channels, so that original spatial and directional relationships are simulated.

stroboscope – a device containing a source of light and also a means for causing this light to appear and to disappear at a rate controlled by the operator. The flickering light is beamed at a rotating part of a machine and its rate of flicker synchronized with the speed (or some multiple of the speed) of the machine part. When the rotating part appears to be stationary, under this illumination, its speed is the same as the rate of flickering of the stroboscope.

stroboscopic disk – a disk or card, especially marked with a series of lines, for determining the speed of rotating shafts or parts. The disk is attached to, or placed upon, the rotating part and viewed under the proper light. When a series of lines appear stationary, the speed of the rotating part is the same as the speed designated by that particular series of lines marked upon the stroboscopic disk. Used for adjusting the speed of phonograph turntables, capstans in tape recorders, and so forth.

sub-carrier – part of a carrier wave.

taxonomy – the classification of animals and plants according to their natural relationships.

tight drive – a film- or tape-drive system in which the medium is allowed the minimum of slack in any direction, is closely supported by guides, and is kept under constant tension.

tonal balance – musical balance between bass and treble.

tone – usually refers to a single frequency.

transducer – a device which converts energy from one form to another, e.g., microphone, loudspeaker, photoelectric cell, magnetic record, or reproduce head.

transients – short-term phenomena, electrical or audible, having no periodicity of recurrence.

tuning fork – an instrument shaped like a two-tined fork, which, when struck, vibrates at a fixed frequency and produces a pure, audible tone. Can be used as a frequency standard, or as a standard of musical pitch.

under – a trade term indicating that one or more sounds are partially submerged in the background of a dominant sound, e.g., "Hold the music under for twenty seconds." (Underneath is also used in this sense.)

wide-range sound – high-fidelity sound; sound which covers the audible spectrum.

wolf-tone – a resonant tone, generally produced by a singer, which is amplified out of proportion to its original intensity.

vibrator – an electromagnetically operated chopper which changes direct current into pulsating direct current (or simulated alternating current). The output of the vibrator can be magnified by means of a step-up transformer and then rectified to provide a source of high-voltage direct current.

viscosity – the property of a liquid, or of a solid, which permits it to flow more or less readily.

Abbreviations Used in Bibliography

Audio	*Audio*, formerly *Audio Engineering*
Bell Labs. Record	*Bell Laboratories Record*
B.I.O.S.	*British Intelligence Objectives Sub-committee*
Brit. J. Appl. Phys.	*British Journal of Applied Physics*
IRE Proc.	*Proceedings of the Institute of Radio Engineers*
J. Acoust. Soc. Am.	*Journal of the Acoustical Society of America*
J. Am. Inst. Elec. Engr.	*Journal of the American Institute of Electrical Engineers*
J. Aud. Engng. Soc.	*Journal of the Audio Engineering Society*
J. Brit. Inst. Radio Engrs.	*Journal of the British Institute of Radio Engineers*
J. Inst. Elec. Engrs. (London)	*Journal of the Institution of Electrical Engineers*
J. SMPE	*Journal of the Society of Motion Picture Engineers*
J. SMPTE	*Journal of the Society of Motion Picture and Television Engineers*
O.S.R.D.	*Office of Scientific Research and Development*
Proc. Inst. Elec. Engrs. (London)	*Proceedings of the Institution of Electrical Engineers*
P.B.	*Office of Publication Board*
Rev. Sci. Instr.	*Review of Scientific Instruments*

Selected Bibliography

References given below contain additional material on topics discussed in the text. No attempt has been made to make this an all-inclusive bibliography.

Aldous, D. W., "Duplicating Tape Recordings," *Wireless World* 42, 320 (August, **1952**).
———, "Magnetic Recording," *Electrician* 133, 138–140 (August 18, **1944**).
———, "The Textophone," *Wireless World* 44, 611–612 (June 29, **1939**).
Andrews, D. R., "A Solution to the Magnetic Tape Timing Problem," *Audio* 34, 49 (October, **1950**).
Anker-Rasmussen, Svend, "Magnetic Tape Used in Sound Letters," *Audio* 35, 42 (February, **1951**).
Apps, David C., "Use of Binaural Tape Recording in Automobile Noise Problems," *J. Acoust. Soc. of Am.* 24, no. 6, 660–662 (November, **1952**).
Ashman, G. L., "Magnetic Recording," *Wireless World* 50, 226–228 (August, **1944**).
Axon, P. E., "An Investigation into the Mechanism of Magnetic Tape Recording," *Proc. Inst. Elec. Engrs.* (London) 99, 109–126 (May, **1952**).
Barrett, A. E., and Tweed, C. J. F., "Some Aspects of Magnetic Recording and Its Application to Broadcasting," *J. Inst. Elec. Engrs.* (London) 82, 265–288 (March, **1938**).
Baruch, R., "High-Fidelity Tape Recording," *Communications* 28, 16–17, 32–33, 37 (November, **1948**).
Beachell, C. E. and Graham, G. G., "Dual-Purpose Optical Sound Prints," *J. SMPTE* 59, 1–10 (July, **1952**).
Begun, S. J., "Limitations of Sound Recording," *Communications* 29, 28–29, 33–34 (August, **1949**).
———, "Magnetic Field Distribution of Ring Recording Head," *Audio* 32, 11–13, 39 (December, **1948**).
———, *Magnetic Recording,* Murray Hill Books, New York, 242 pp. (**1949**).
———, "Magnetic Recording," *Scientific Monthly* 69, 192–197 (September, **1949**).
———, "Magnetic Recording-Reproducing Machine for Objective Speech Study," *J. SMPE* 29, 216–218 (August, **1937**).

———, "Magnetic Recording and Some of Its Applications in the Broadcast Field," *IRE Proc.* 29, 423–433 (August, **1941**).

———, "Recent Developments in the Field of Magnetic Recording," *J. SMPE* 48, 1–13 (January, **1947**).

———, "Recent Developments in Magnetic Sound Recording," *J. SMPE* 28, 464–472 (May, **1937**).

——— and Wolf, S. K., "On Synthetic Reverberation," *Communications* 18, 8–9 (August, **1938**).

Bernard, E. G., and Ettinger, C., "Using the Tape Recorder," *Board of Education of the City of New York* booklet (**1953**).

Bick, J. D., "Methods of Measuring Surface Induction of Magnetic Tape," *J. Aud. Engng. Soc.* 1, 4–9 (January, **1953**).

Bigwood, R. F., "Applications of Magnetic Recording in Network Broadcasting," *Audio* 32, 31–33, 38, 40 (July, **1948**).

Bishop, H., "Electromagnetic Sound Recording Machines," *Electrical Review* 97, 45–47 (July 10, **1925**).

Bixler, Otto C., "A Commercial Binaural Recorder," *J. SMPTE* 59, 109–117 (August, **1952**).

Blakesley, Jay, "Performance Plus Economy Tape Recorder," *Audio* 34, 20, 47, 48 (November, **1950**).

Booth, A. D., "Magnetic Digital Storage System," *Electronic Engineering* 21, 234–238 (July, **1949**).

———, "On Two Problems in Potential Theory and Their Applications to the Design of Magnetic Recording Heads for Digital Computers," *Brit. J. Appl. Phys.* 3, 307–308 (October, **1952**).

Boothe, Kenneth B., "Magnetic Tape Recording for Telemetry Analysis," Part I, *Tele-Tech* 11, 44–46, 116 (May, **1952**). Part II, *Tele-Tech* 11, 56–57, 90 (June, **1952**).

———, "Uses of Magnetic Tape Recording in Telemetering," *Instrument Society of America* Paper No. 50–9–2 (September, **1950**).

Boyers, J. S., "Factors Affecting Frequency Response and Distortion in Magnetic Recording," *Audio* 32, 18–19, 46–47 (May, **1948**).

Braunmühl, H. J. von, "Magnetic Sound Recording in Broadcasting Service," *Funktechnische Monatshefte* No. 12, 483–486 (in German) (December, **1934**).

———, "Sound Recording in Broadcasting," *Funktechnischer Vorwärts* 5, No. 4 (in German) (**1935**).

Brubaker, Paul M., "Multi-Channel Magnetic Recording," *Audio* 34, 49 (October, **1950**).

Camras, Marvin, "Magnetic Recording on Steel Wire," M.S. thesis, Illinois Institute of Technology (May, **1942**).

———, "Magnetic Records for Home Entertainment," *Proc. National*

Electronic Conference, Chicago, No. 4, **1948**; (*Ann. Telecommunication* 4, 25238 (August-September, **1948**). Also in *Proc.* Natl. Electronics Conference (Chicago) No. 4 (**1948**).

————, "Magnetic Sound for Motion Pictures," *J. SMPE* 48, 14–28 (January, **1947**).

————, "Magnetic Sound-on-Film," *Electrical Engineering* 67, 136–141 (February, **1948**).

————, "Magnetic Sound on 8 mm. Film," *Tele-Tech* 9, 25–27 (May, **1950**).

————, "New Magnetic Recording Head," *J. SMPTE* 58, 61–66 (January, **1952**).

————, "Stereophonic Magnetic Recorder," *IRE Proc.* 37, 442–447 (April, **1949**).

————, "Theoretical Response from Magnetic Wire Record," *IRE Proc.* 34, 597–602 (August, **1946**).

————, "Wire Recorder," *Radio News* (Radionics Section 1) 30, 3–5 (November, **1943**).

———— and Herr, Robert, "Duplicating Magnetic Tape by Contact Printing," *Electronics* 22, 78–83 (December, **1949**).

Carter, J. M., "Designing a Tape Recorder," Part 1, *Wireless World* 42, 108–110 (March, **1953**).

Chinn, H. A., "Magnetic Tape Recording in Broadcasting," *Audio* 31, 7–10 (May, **1947**).

————, "The Measurement of Audio Volume," *Audio* 34, 48 ff. (October, **1950**).

Clark, D. L., and Merrill, L. L., "Field Measurements on Magnetic Recording Heads," *IRE Proc.* 35, 1575 ff. (December, **1947**).

Cole, F. E., "Magnetic Tape Editor," *Bell Labs. Record* 30, 420–421 (November, **1952**).

Conner, Robert, "Magnetic Sound and Negative Picture," *TV Engineering* 3, 10–11 (April, **1952**).

Cookson, Frank, "Northwestern University Experiment," copyright by Frank Cookson, Brush Development Company pamphlet (**1949**).

Cooter, I. L., "Magnetic Fields Surrounding Recording Wires," *Electrical Engineering* 68, 433 (May, **1949**).

————, "Pulse Packing in Magnetic Recording Wire," Research Paper 2067, *Journal Research National Bureau of Standards* (Washington, D.C.) 44, 163–172 (February, **1950**).

Corddry, C., "Aerial Eavesdropper," *Flying* 35, 67 ff. (August, **1944**).

Costrell, Louis, "FM Data Reduction from Magnetic Tape Recordings," *Rev. Sci. Instr.* 24, 76–77 (January, **1953**).

Crane, G. R., Frayne, J. G., and Templin, E. W., "Supplementary Magnetic Facilities for Photographic Sound Systems," *J. SMPTE* 54, 315–327 (March, **1950**).

Crane, G. R., Frayne, J. G., and Templin, E. W., "A Professional Magnetic-Recording System for Use with 35–, 17 1/2– and 16–mm. Films," *J. SMPTE* 56, 295–309 (March, **1951**).

Crawford, J. M. C., et al., "Plastics in German Sound Recording Systems," *B.I.O.S.* Final Report 1379, Item 7, 22, *P.B.* L87901 121 pp. (April-May, **1946**).

Culver, C. A., *Musical Acoustics,* The Blakiston Company, 215 pp. (**1951**).

Curtis, Roger C., "Noise Test for Magnetic Recording Media," *Electronics* 20, No. 7, 216 (July, **1953**).

Daniels, H. L., "Boundary-Displacement Magnetic Recording," *Electronics* 25, No. 4, 116–120 (April, **1952**).

Darragh, J. B., "Planetest Magnograph," *Aero Digest* 37, 96 ff. (September, **1940**).

Davis, Arthur C., "Steps to Improve TV Audio," *Video Engineering,* (March, **1950**).

———, "Sprocket Hole Tape in Magnetic Recording," *Audio* 34, 50 (October, **1950**).

Davis, C. C., Frayne, J. G., and Templin, E. W., "Multichannel Magnetic Film Recording and Reproducing Unit," *J. SMPTE* 58, 105–118 (February, **1952**).

Dimmick, G. L., and Johnson, S. W., "Optimum High-Frequency Bias in Magnetic Recording," *J. SMPE* 51, 489–500 (November, **1948**).

Dolan, K. J., "Presetting a Tape for Broadcasting," *Electronics* 25, no. 4, 196–200 (April, **1952**).

Eidson, Herbert G., Jr., "Tricks in Tape Recording," *TV Engineering* 2, 14–16, 28–29 (March, **1951**).

Emigh, C. R., "Wire-Recorded Magnetic Pulse-Timing Circuit," *Rev. Sci. Instr.* 21, 142–144 (February, **1950**).

Endall, R., "Magnetic Tape Data-Recording Systems," *Radio-Television News* 47, 3–6, 30 (March, **1952**).

Fairbanks, G., Everitt, W. L., and Jaeger, R., "Method for Time or Frequency Compression-Expansion of Speech," *Convention Record of the I.R.E., Part VIII,* (**1953**).

Fairbanks, Grant, and Jaeger, Robert, "A Device for Continuously Variable Time Delay of Headset Monitoring during Magnetic Recording of Speech," *Journal of Speech Disorders* 16, 162–164 (June, **1951**).

Frayne, J. G., "Comparison of Recording Processes," *J. SMPTE* 59, 313–318 (May, **1952**).

———, "Magnetic Recording in Motion Picture Techniques," *J. SMPE* 53, 217–235 (September, **1949**).

—— and Livadary, J. P., "Dual Photomagnetic Intermediate Studio Recording," *J. SMPTE* 59, 388–397 (November, **1952**).

——, and Wolfe, Halley, *Elements of Sound Recording*, John Wiley and Sons, Inc., New York (chapter on Magnetic Recording) (**1949**).

Frederick, H. A., "Recording and Reproducing Sound," *Rev. Sci. Instr.* 5, 177–182 (May, **1934**).

Friend, Albert W., "Adjustments for Obtaining Maximum Performance in Magnetic Recording," *RCA Review* 11, 38–54 (March, **1950**).

Godfrey, J. W., and Amos, S. W., *Sound Recording and Reproduction*, Iliffe & Sons, Ltd., London (**1952**).

Gould, K. G. and Falkner, R. I. T., "The Application of Magnetic Recording to Sub-standard Film Projectors," *British Kinematographer* 16, 55 (February, **1950**).

Gratian, J. W., "Noise in Magnetic Recording Systems as Influenced by the Characteristics of Bias and Erase Signals," *J. Acoust. Soc. Am.* 21, 74–81 (March, **1949**).

Green, Paul E., Jr., "Magnetic Tape Recorder for Very-Low-Frequency Phenomena," *Rev. Sci. Instr.* 21, 893–895 (November, **1950**).

Gunby, O. B., "Portable Magnetic Recording System," *J. SMPE* 52, 613–618 (June, **1949**).

Hansell, C. W., et al., "Report on the Magnetophone," *P.B.* 1346, 13 p. (**1945**).

Hanson, R. O., "Bell Telephone Labs. HI-FI Tape Recorder," *Columbia University Division of War Research* Memo P37/R1320, *P.B.* L80603, 37 p. (January, **1945**).

Hare, D. G. C., and Fling, W. D., "Picture-Synchronous Magnetic Tape Recording," *J. SMPTE* 54, 554–566 (May, **1950**).

Harris, C. C., "Portable Magnetic Tape Broadcasting Recorder," *Communications* 29, 6–7 (December, **1949**).

Harris, Cyril M., "A Speech Synthesizer," *J. Acoust. Soc. Am.* 25, no. 5, 970–975 (September, **1953**).

Haynes, N. M., "Magnetic Tape and Head Alignment Nomenclature," *Audio* 33, 22–23 (June, **1949**).

Henslow, M., "Sound Recording for the Medical Profession," *Medical World* (London) 73, 549–551 (February 9, **1951**).

Herr, R., "Magnetic Tape Erasure by Permanent Magnets," *Audio* 33, 14–16, 29–30 (August, **1949**).

——, "Mixed Ferrites for Recording Heads," *Electronics* 24, no. 4, 124–125 (April, **1951**).

——, et al., "Some Distinctive Properties of Magnetic Recording Media," *J. SMPE* 52, 77–88 (January, **1949**).

———, and Von Behren, R., "Selective Erasure of Magnetic Tape," *Electronics* 25, 114–115 (August, 1952).

Hickman, C. N., "Delayed Speech," *Bell Labs. Record* 11, 308 (June, 1933).

———, "Magnetic Recording and Reproducing," *Bell Labs. Record* 16, 2–7 (September, 1937).

———, "Sound Recording on Magnetic Tape," *Bell Labs. Record* 16, 165–177 (April, 1937).

Hildebrand, T. A., "A Magnetic Tape Eraser," *TV Engineering* 1, 20 (June, 1950).

Hittle, Carl E., "Twin-Drum Film Drive Filter System for Magnetic Recorder-Reproducer," *J. SMPTE* 58, 323–328 (April, 1952).

Hobson, P. T., "Developments in Magnetic Recording," *Electronic Engineering* 19, 377–382 (December, 1947).

———, "Design Requirement for Magnetic Tape," *Sound Recording and Reproduction* 3, 224–231 (February, 1952).

Holmes, L. C., "Some Factors Influencing the Choice of a Medium for Magnetic Recording," *J. Acoust. Soc. Am.* 19, 395–403 (May, 1947).

——— and Clark, D. L., "Supersonic 'Bias' for Magnetic Recording," *Electronics* 18, 126–136 (July, 1945).

———, "Techniques for Improved Magnetic Recording," *Electrical Engineering* 68, 836–841 (October, 1949).

Howell, H. A., "Magnetic Sound Recording on Coated Paper Tape," *J. SMPE* 48, 36–49 (January, 1947).

Hust, L. B., "Combination Phonograph-Tape Recorder," *Radio and Television News* 46, 43–46, 102 ff. (November, 1951).

———, "Two-Channel Magnetic Recording," *Radio and Television News* 44, 45–47, 143–144 (November, 1950).

Irish, S. R., "Magnetic Recording of Sound," *Cornell Engineer* 5, 5–7, 26 ff. (November, 1939).

James, J. H., "Magnetic Playback-Recorder using Paper Discs," *Communications* 27, 32, 55–58 (April, 1947).

Javitz, A. E., "Appraisal of Design Trends in Magnetic Sound Recorders," *Electrical Manufacturing* 37, 107–111 ff. (June, 1946).

———, "Magnetic Recording Media as Components in Product Design," *Electrical Manufacturing* 41, 82–87, 139–141 (May, 1948).

———, "Magnetic Recording Systems in Product Design," *Electrical Manufacturing* 45, 74–81, 186 (February, 1950).

Johnston, H., "Design for Accessibility in Magnetic Tape Recorders," *Electrical Manufacturing* 50, 150–151 (October, 1952).

———, "Factors Affecting Spurious Printing in Magnetic Tape," *J. SMPE* 52, 619–628 (June, 1949).

Killian, L. G., "Data Recording on Magnetic Tape," *Electronic Industries* 2, 3–5, 31 (April, **1948**).

Klippel, K. L., and Dahl, E. A., "Railway Entertainment," *Electronics,* 118–121, (May, **1947**).

Kolb, O. K., "Magnetic Sound Film Developments in Great Britain," *J. SMPTE* 55, 496–508 (November, **1950**).

———, "Some Aspects of Magnetic Sound Recording," *J. Brit. Inst. Radio Engrs.* 12, 307–316 (May, **1952**).

Kornei, O., "Frequency Response of Magnetic Recording," *Electronics* 20, 24–28 (August, **1947**).

———, et al., "Investigations of New Magnetic Recording Media," *O.S.R.D.* Report 5325, *P.B.* 24881 (June, **1945**).

———, "Survey of Magnetic Recording," *Proceedings* of a Symposium on Large-Scale Digital Calculating Machinery, 223–237, Harvard University Press (**1948**).

Latham, W. S., "Limitations of Magnetic Tape," *Audio* 36, 19, 20, 68 ff. (September, **1952**).

Ledbetter, Robert P., "A Tape Editing and Duplicating Machine," *Audio* 36, 18, 20, 44 (December, **1951**).

Leevers, N., "Magnetic Recording in Film Production," *J. Brit. Inst. Radio Engrs.* 12, 421–427 (August, **1952**).

———, "Magnetic Recording in Kinematography," *Photographic J.* 91B, 56–59 (May-June, **1951**).

Lennert, Frank, "Equalization of Magnetic Tape Recorders for Audio and Instrumentation Applications," *Trans. Inst. Radio Engrs.* PGA Au-1, 20–25 (March-April, **1953**).

Lewin, George, "Special Techniques in Magnetic Recording for Motion Picture Production," *J. SMPTE* 56, 653–663 (June, **1951**).

———, "Synchronous 1/4-Inch Magnetic Tape for Motion Picture Production," *J. SMPTE* 56, 664–671 (June, **1951**).

Lindsay, H., "Precision Magnetic Tape Recorder for High-Fidelity Professional Use," *Electrical Manufacturing* 46, 134–139 (October, **1950**).

———, and Stolaroff, M., "Magnetic Tape Recorder of Broadcast Quality," *Audio* 32, 13–16 (October, **1948**).

Long, T. H., and McMullen, G. D., "B-H Curve Tracer for Magnetic Recording Wire," *Electrical Engineering* 65, 146–149 (March, **1946**).

Lorant, M., "A New Magnetic Tape Memory," *Electronic Engng.* 25, 97–98 (March, **1953**).

Lowden, R. W., "Recording on Tape," *Wireless World* 57, 283–284 (July, **1951**).

Lübeck, H., "The Bases of the Magnetophone System," *A.E.G. Mitteilungen* no. 9, 453–459 (in German) (September, **1938**).

Lucia, Raymond, "Tape Recorder Remote Control," *Audio* 35, 76–77 (November, **1951**).

Macy, A. C., "Tape Recording," *High Fidelity* 1, no. 2, 45–56 (Fall, **1951**).

Mallina, R. F., "A Mirror for the Voice," *Bell Labs. Record* 13, 200–202 (March, **1935**).

Malloy, T. J., "Magnetic Recorder for Recording Sound on Steel Wire," *Electronics* 11, 30–32 (January, **1938**).

Mankin, A. H., "Improving Response of Magnetic Playback Heads," *Electronics* 20, no. 7, 150–151 (July, **1953**).

————, "Interference Effects in Magnetic Recording Heads," *I.R.E. Trans.,* PGA 9, 16–21 (September-October, **1952**).

Marchant, R., "Duplicating Tape Recordings," *Electronics* 22, 72–76 (July, **1949**).

————, "Tape Characteristics for Audio Quality," *Tele-Tech* 8, 30–33, 56–57 (July, **1949**).

Marsh, W., "Tape Recorder Time Clock Control," *Communications* 29, 24, 34 (April, **1949**).

Masterson, E., "35 mm. Magnetic Recording System," *J. SMPE* 51, 481–488 (November, **1948**).

————, Putzrath, F. L., and Roys, H. E., "Magnetic Sound on 16-mm. Edge-Coated Film," *J. SMPTE* 57, 559–566 (December, **1951**).

McProud, C. G., "Universal Amplifier for Magnetic Tape Recorder," *Audio* 36, 17–19 (May, **1952**).

Menard, James Z., "High-Frequency Magnetophon Magnetic Sound Recorders," *Field Information Agency,* Technical Final Report 705, *P.B.* 12659, 44 pp. (**1946**).

————, "A New Recording Medium for Transcribed Message Services," *Bell System Technical Journal* 31, 530–540 (May, **1952**).

Meyer-Eppler, W., "Reversed Speech and Repetition Systems as Means of Phonetic Research," *J. Acoust. Soc. of Am.* 22, 804–806 (November, **1950**).

Miller, A. E., "Consumer Interviews," *Printer's Ink* 213, 122 ff. (October, 5, **1945**).

Miller, D. C., *The Science of Musical Sounds,* The Macmillan Company, New York (**1922**).

Miller, W. C., "Magnetic Recording for Motion Picture Studios," *J. SMPE* 48, 57–62 (January, **1947**).

Mittell, B. E. G., "The Development of the Magnetic Tape Recorder," *Proc. Inst. Elec. Engrs.* Part III 96, 305–306 (July, **1949**).

Molyneux, L., "Recording Low-Frequency Phenomena on Magnetic Tape," *Electronic Engng.* 24, 130–131 (March, **1952**).

Montani, A., "The Mechanism of the Supersonic Bias," *Electrical Engineering* 68, 511 (June, **1949**).

Montgomery, J. R., "Tape Transport Theory and Speed Control," *J. SMPTE* 57, 63–68 (July, **1951**).

Morris, Harold N., "Measuring Magnetic Tape Recorder Flutter," *Electronics* 26, no. 3, 230 ff. (March, **1953**).

Mueller, W. A., and Groves, G. R., "Magnetic Recording in the Motion Picture Studio," *J. SMPE* 52, 605–612 (June, **1949**).

Mukenhirn, O. William, "Recording Demagnetization in Magnetic Tape Recording," *IRE Proc.* 39, 891–896 (August, **1951**).

Murphy, B. F., and Smith, H. K., "Head Alignment with Visible Tracks," *Audio* 33, 12–13, 38–39 (January, **1949**).

Nagai, Kenso, et al., "Delay Apparatus using Magnetic Recording," *Nippon Electrical Communications Engineering*, no. 2, 143–149 (February, **1936**).

———, "Experimental Consideration upon ac Erasing," *Inst. of Elec. Engineers of Japan Journal*, no. 180 (March, **1938**).

———, "Magnetic Sound Recording Materials," *Japan Nickel Review* 8, 256–264 (October, **1940**).

———, Sasaki, and Endo, "Studies of Noise and Record Materials and New Erase Method," *Institute of Telephone and Telegraph Engineers Journal* no. 161 (August, **1936**).

Nasarischwily, A., "Neue Versuche Mit den Telegraphon," *Electrotechnische Zeitschrift* 42, 106–108 (in German) (September 22, **1921**).

O'Brien, R. S., "Adapting Paper Tape Recorders for Broadcasting," *Audio* 31, 10–14 (June, **1947**).

———, " 'Edispot,' Spotting Device for Magnetic Tape Editing," *Audio* 32, 11–13, 46 (July, **1948**).

O'Dea, D., "Magnetic Recording for Technician," *J. SMPE* 51, 468–480 (November, **1948**).

Olson, Harry F., *Musical Engineering*, McGraw-Hill Book Company, Inc., New York, 369 pp. (**1952**).

Olson, M. N., "Multiple Tape Recording," *F.M. and Television* 9, 30, 32 (March, **1949**).

Pauly, W. W., "Studio Tape Recorder," *F.M. and Television* 10, 25–26 (February, **1950**).

Perron, R. R., "Contour-Recording by Magnetic Tape," *Electrical Manufacturing* 47, 130–131 (June, **1951**).

Poulsen, Valdemar, "The Telegraphone," *Electrician* 46, 208–210 (November 30, **1900**).

Power, R. A., "German Magnetophon," *Wireless World* 52, 195–198 (June, **1946**).

Pugsley, D. W., "Wire Recording," *Electrical Engineering* 65, 316–321 (July, **1946**).

——, "Fundamentals of Magnetic Recording," *QST* 28, 10–12 (May, **1944**).

Pulling, M. J. L., "The Magnetophon Sound Recording and Reproducing System," *B.I.O.S.* Final Report 951, Item 7, 9, *P.B.* L60899, 113 pp. (**1946**).

Queen, I., "Tape Recording," *Radio-Electronics* 23, 38–40 (August, **1952**); 51–53 (September, **1952**); 52–54 (October, **1952**).

Ranger, R. H., "Magnetic Tape Recorder for Movies and Radio," *Electronics* 20, 99–103 (October, **1947**).

——, "Performance Features of New Magnetic Tape Recorder," *Tele-Tech* 7, 40–42, 64–65, 72 (October, **1948**).

——, "Sprocketless Synchronous Magnetic Tape," *J. SMPTE* 54, 328–336 (March, **1950**).

Ravalico, D. E., "Tape Recording Adaptor," *Radio Electronics* 23, 28 (April, **1952**).

Read, Oliver, "A New Wire Recorder," *J. Aud. Engng. Soc.* 1, 22–26 (January, **1953**).

——, *The Recording and Reproduction of Sound,* Howard W. Sams and Company, Indianapolis (**1952**).

Reed, Harold, "Top Tape Recording Performance," *Audio* 37, 26–27, 59 (June, **1953**).

Rettinger, Michael, "Azimuth Film Calibration," *Audio* 36, 15–16 (April, **1952**).

——, "AC Magnetic Erase Heads," *J. SMPTE* 56, 407–410 (April, **1951**).

——, "Magnetic Recording in Motion Pictures—Part I," *Audio* 34, 9–12, 32–35 (March, **1950**).

——, "Magnetic Recording in Motion Pictures—Part II," *Audio* 34, 18–20, 42–43 (April, **1950**).

——, "A Magnetic Record-Reproduce Head," *J. SMPTE* 55, 377–390 (October, **1950**).

Robin, H. L., "Magnetophone, Type K7," *Field Information Agency,* Technical Final Report 841, *Field Information Agency,* Technical Microfilm Reel 183, *P.B.* 60743, 504 pp. (January, **1947**).

Roe, D., "Magnetic Recording Technique," *Wireless World* 55, 362–364 (October, **1949**).

Roys, H. E., "Magnetic Recording," *International Projectionist* 22, 7–8 (January, **1947**).

Rust, N. M., "Telegraphone," *Marconi Review* no. 46, 1–11 (January-February, **1934**).

Ryder, Loren L., "Motion Picture Studio Use of Magnetic Recording," *J. SMPTE* 55, 605–612 (December, 1950).

—— and Denney, Bruce H., "Magnetic Sound Track Placement," *J. SMPTE* 58, 119–136 (February, 1952).

Sano, K., "Synchronisation Precise," *Photo-Service*, Gevaert Photo-Producten N.V., Antwerp, no. 17, 18–19 (in French) (mars-avril, 1950).

Scherb, M. V., "Cathode-ray Magnetization Curve Tracer," *Review of Scientific Instruments* 19, 411–419 (July, 1948). (correction 19, 674, October, 1948)

Schmidt, Edward, and Franck, Ernest W., "Manufacture of Magnetic Recording Materials," *J. SMPTE* 60, 453–462 (April, 1953).

Schrage, W. E., "Sound Recording on Magnetic Materials," *Radio Craft* 7, 537–562 (March, 1936).

Sear, A. W., "Wire Recorder Wow," *J. Acoust. Soc. Am.* 19, 172–178 (January, 1947).

Selby, M. C., "Investigation of Magnetic Tape Recorders," *Electronics* 17, 133 ff. (May, 1944).

Selsted, W. T., "Synchronous Recording on 1/4-Inch Magnetic Tape," *J. SMPTE* 55, 279–284 (September, 1950).

Shaper, H. B., "Frequency-Modulated Magnetic Tape Transient Recorder," *IRE Proc.* 33, 753–760 (November, 1945).

Singer, K., and Pettus, J. L., "Building Block Approach to Magnetic Recording Equipment Design," *J. SMPTE* 59, 319–334 (October, 1952).

—— and Rettinger, Michael, "Frequency Response Variations Caused by Magnetic Head Wear," *Audio* 37, 29, 46–48 (July, 1953).

—— and Ward, H. Connell, "A Technical Solution of Magnetic Recording Cost Reduction," *J. SMPTE* 58, 329–340 (April, 1952).

Smith, Caldwell, P., "A New Technique for Reducing Distortion in Sound Recording," *Audio* 34, 28 (April, 1950).

Speirs, B. H., "ABC Uses Magnetic Tape for Delayed Broadcasts," *Radio and Television News* 43, 41, 134 (April, 1950).

Spratt, H. G. M., "Magnetic Recording Tape, 1," *Wireless World* 41, 88–91 (March, 1951).

——, "Magnetic Recording Tape, 2," *Wireless World* 41, 149–151 (April, 1951).

Stevens, S. S., and Davis, Hallowell, *Hearing, Its Psychology and Physiology,* John Wiley and Sons, Inc., New York, 489 pp. (1948).

Stewart, W. E., "New Professional Tape Recorder," *Audio* 35, 21–23, 36–37 (April, 1951).

——, "RCA RT 3A," *Tele-Tech* 8, 40–41, 50–51 (April, 1949).

Stolaroff, Myron J., "Low-Cost Precision Magnetic Recorder for Professional Use," *Audio* 33, 17–18, 30–31 (August, 1949).

Tall, Joel, "The Art of Tape Recording," *Audio* 34, 13, 31–35 (May, **1950**); 34, 20–22, 43–45 (June, **1950**); 34, 22–23, 39–40 (July, **1950**); 34, 16–18, 29–31 (August, **1950**); 34, 15, 42–45 (September, **1950**).

———, "Using Hearing Characteristics in Tape Editing," *Audio* 36, 15–16, 50–51 (May, **1952**).

Tarry, P. A., "Magnetic Tape Recording," 4th ed., Audiograph Ltd., Birmingham, England, 70 pp. (November, **1951**).

Temple, M. D., et al., "Investigations of New Magnetic Recording Media," *O.S.R.D.* 3399, *P.B.* 33200, 129 pp. (February, **1944**).

Thompson, C. S., "An Analysis of Magnetic Recording," *Trans. Amer. Inst. Elect. Engrs.* 68, 407–417, no. 1 (**1949**).

———, "An Analysis of Magnetic Recording," *Electrical Engineering* 68, 793 (September, **1949**).

Tinkham, R. J., and Boyers, J. S., "Magnetic Sound Recorder of Advanced Design," *J. SMPE* 48, 29–35 (January, **1947**).

Toomin, H., and Wildfeuer, D., "Mechanism of Supersonic Frequencies as Applied to Magnetic Recording," *IRE Proc.* 32, 664–668 (November, **1944**).

Ulner, Martin, "A German Magnetic Sound Recording System in Motion Pictures," *J. SMPTE* 56, 411–423 (April, **1951**).

Vaile, R. B., "Recent Developments in Magnetic Recording of Sound," *National Electronics Conference Proc.* 2, 597–602 (**1946**).

del Valle, G. A., and Ferber, L. W., "Notes on Wear of Magnetic Heads," *J. SMPTE* 60, 501–506 (April, **1953**).

——— and Putzrath, F. L., "Optical-Magnetic Sound 16 mm. Projector," *J. SMPTE* 58, 277–290 (April, **1952**).

Vilbig, F., "An Apparatus for Speech Compression and Expansion and for Replaying Visible Speech Records," *J. Acoust. Soc. Am.* 22, 754–760 (November, **1950**).

Wallace, R. L., Jr., "Reproduction of Magnetically Recorded Systems," *Bell System Technical Journal* 30, 1145–1173 (October, **1951**).

Washburne, R. D., "Sound-on-Wire," *Radio Craft* (May, **1939**).

West, C. F., and DeTurk, J. E., "Digital Computer," *IRE Proc.* (December, **1948**).

Wetzel, W. W., "Review of the Present Status of Magnetic Recording Theory," *Audio* 31, 14–17 (November, **1947**); 31, 12–16, 37 (December, **1947**); 32, 26–30, 46–47 (January, **1948**).

———, Murphy, B. J., and Herr, R., "A New Explanation of the Action of ac Bias in Magnetic Recording," *Audio* 34, 49 (October, **1950**).

Wever, Ernest Glen, *Theory of Hearing,* John Wiley and Sons, Inc., New York, 484 pp. (**1949**).

White, D. L. J., and Stutz, W. H., "Compacting a Field-type Magnetic Film

Sound-Recorder," *Electrical Manufacturing* 49, 100–103, 256 ff. (January, **1952**).

Wiegand, D. E., "The Testing of Magnetic Recording Media" (Symposium on Magnetic Testing), *American Society for Testing Materials* 141–153 (**1948**).

———, "Testing of Magnetic Recording Media" (Preprint 30a for meeting of June, 1948), *American Society for Testing Materials,* 21–25 (June, **1948**).

Wiggin, Lyman J., "Magnetic Print-Through—Its Measurement and Reduction," *J. SMPTE* 58, no. 5, 410–414 (May, **1952**).

Wight, Vinton, "KFAB's Magnecorder Modifications," *Tele-Tech* 10, 37 (June, **1951**).

Wolf, S. K., "Synthetic Production and Control of Acoustic Phenomena by a Magnetic Recording System," *IRE Proc.* 29, 365–371 (July, **1941**).

Wood, M. C., "The Amplification and Recording of Foetal Heart Sounds," *Electronic Engng.* 25, 90–93 (March, **1953**).

Wooldridge, D. E., "Signal and Noise Levels in Magnetic Tape Recording," *Electrical Engineering* 65, 343–352 (June, **1946**).

Wortman, L. A., "Magnetic Tape Duplication," *Radio and Television News* 47, 40–41, 134 (April, **1952**).

Yarnes, D. C., "New Editing Machine for Professional Tape Recordings," *Tele-Tech* 10, 32–33, 58–59 (January, **1951**).

Zenner, R. E., "Magnetic Recording of Meter Data," *Audio* 34, 16–17, 33 (February, **1950**).

———, "Magnetic Recording with AC Bias," *Proc. IRE* 39, 141–146 (February, **1951**).

——— and Vaile, R. B., "Two-Channel Two-Way-Drive Magnetic Tape Recorder," *Audio* 33, 11–15 (April, **1948**).

Additional References

The names of authors of the following references were not given.

"Blattnerphone," *Wireless World* 34, 8–10 (January 5, **1934**).

"British Broadcasting Corporation Recording Service," *Electrician* 122, 303–304 (March 10, **1939**).

"Briton's First with Tape Sound Unit for Silent Home Movie Projectors," *American Cinematographer* 31, 204 (June, **1950**).

"Continuous Wire Record," *Scientific American* 175, 131 (September, **1946**).

"Crashes May Be Reduced," *Science News Letter* 57, 101–102 (February 18, **1950**).

"Der Telephonograph im Eisenbahnbetrieb," *Electrotechnische Zeitschrift* 41, 513 (in German) (July 1, **1920**).

"Discussion of Magnetic Recording," *J. SMPE* 48, 50–56, Research Council Basic Sound Comm. (January, **1947**).

"Electromagnetic Sound Recording," *Electrician* 103, 472 (October 18, **1929**).

"Engineers Note Sound Phenomenon," *Technical Data Digest* 15, 16–17 (July 1, **1950**).

"F.C.C. Order No. 14292, Docket No. 6787," *Federal Communications Committee,* Washington, D.C. (November 26, **1947**).

"F.C.C. Public Notice 60591," *Federal Communications Committee,* Washington, D.C. (March 28, **1951**).

"Ferrite Recording Heads," *Electronics* 26, 397–398 (March, **1953**).

"German Magnetic Tape Machine Brought to United States," *Science News Letter* 48, 399 (December 22, **1945**).

"H.F. Bias in Magnetic Recording," *Radio Electr. Weekly* 31, 13–14 (November 3, **1950**).

"High Frequency Magnetophon Magnetic Sound Recorders," *Field Information Agency Bulletin* 705 (**1947**).

"Hyflux Tape," *Engineering Bulletin* EBT 101 of the Indiana Steel Products Company, Chicago, Illinois (**1947**).

450

"Invasion Recorder," *General Electric Review* 47, 44 (July, **1944**).

"Inventory Taking Speeded by Wire Recorders," *Electrical World* 130, 116 (December 18, **1948**).

"It Pays to Listen," *Scientific American* 173, 18–20 (July, **1945**).

"Lorenz Steel Band Recorder," *Wireless Engineer* 13, 175–178 (April, **1936**).

"Magnetic Recording Heads" (Raytheon Manufacturing Company), *Electronics* 24, no. 2, 257 (February, **1951**).

"Magnetic Recorder-Projector" (Radio Corporation of America), *Audio* 35, 38 (September, **1951**).

"Magnetic Recording Rubber" (Brush Development Company), *Electrical Manufacturing* 49, 138, 140 (January, **1952**).

"Magnetic Recording Tape" (Durex Abrasives, Ltd.), *Electronic Engng.* 23, 73 (February, **1951**).

"Magnetic Sound Film Projector" (Radio Corporation of America), *Electronics* 24, no. 10, 144 (October, **1951**).

"Magnetic Sound Recorder and Reproducer, **1939–1946**, A. E. G., Berlin and Kiel," *P.B.* 95211, 756 pp. (in German and English).

"Magnetic Sound Track on Film" (Reeves Soundcraft Corporation), *Audio* 35, 28 (June, **1951**).

"Magnetic Tape and the CBC," *Radio News* 47, 38, 84 (June, **1952**).

"Magnetic Tape Is Memory for Computer," *Electronics* 23, 196, 198, 200 (May, **1950**).

"Magnetic Tape Memory for SEAC, A," *National Bureau of Standards Technical News Bulletin* 34, no. 9, 161–163 (November, **1951**).

"Magnetic Tape Recorder," *Engineer* 188, 198–199 (August 19, **1949**).

"Magnetic Tape Recorder for Dictation" (Permoflux Corporation), *Electrical Manufacturing* 46, 88 (December, **1950**).

"Magnetic Tape Recording," *Fortune* 43, 97 (January, **1951**).

"Magnetic Wire Recorder" (G.E. Models 50A and 51), *Technical Manual* 11-2548, *P.B.* 37072, 26 pp. (February, **1945**).

"The 'Magnetophon' of A. E. G.," 150 Hohenzollern Damm, Berlin, Grunewald, *B.I.O.S.* Report 207, H.M. Stationery Office and U.S. Department of Commerce, 4 pp. (**1946**).

"Magnetophon Recorders," *B.I.O.S.* extract, *Wireless World* 53, 128 (April, **1947**).

"Magnetophon Sound Recorder and Reproducer **1939–1946**, A. E. G. Berlin and Kiel," Office of Publication Board Report, *P.B.* 95210, 711 pp. (in German and English).

"The Magnetophon Sound Recording and Reproducing System," *B.I.O.S. Report* 951, H. M. Stationery Office and United States Department of Commerce 34 pp. (**1946**).

"Mass Production Tape Recording," *Audio* 33, 21, 47 (April, **1949**).

"Measuring Procedure for Magnetic Recording," *Audio* 33, 19, 41–45 (April, **1949**).

"Mechanism of Magnetic Recording," *Wireless World* 41, 47–50 (February, **1952**).

"Mirrophone," *Wireless World* 48, 42–43 (February, **1942**).

"New Magnetic Tape Records Data in Flying Rockets," *Science News Letter* 56, 217 (October 1, **1949**).

"New Professional Tape Recorder, A," *Tele-Tech* 8, 34–35 (March, **1949**).

"New Tape Recorder" (Ampex Electric Corporation), *IRE Proc.* 29, 18A (February, **1951**).

"Poulsen Telegraphone," *Scientific American* 83, 191 (September 22, **1900**).

"Recording Equipment" (Cook Research Laboratories, Chicago, Illinois), *Bulletin* R-8 (**1951**).

"Safety Messages," *Safety Engineering* 97, 31 ff. (April, **1949**).

"SEAC, The National Bureau of Standards Eastern Automatic Computer," *National Bureau of Standards Technical News Bulletin* 34, no. 9, 121–129 (September, **1950**).

"Standardization of Magnetic Recording" (British Broadcasting Corporation), *Electronic Engineering* 19, 396 (December, **1947**).

"Standards on Sound Recording and Reproducing: Methods of Measurement of Noise," *IRE Proc.* (New York) 41, 508–512 (April, **1953**).

"Sterophonic Sound," *Electronics* 21, 88–89 (August, **1948**).

"Storage of Magnetic Recording Tape," *Electronics* 26, no. 3, 270 (March, **1953**).

"Telegraphone," *Electrician* 51, 611–612 (July 31, **1903**).

"20-Kilocycle Recording Phase Direction Finder," *Blaupunktwerke,* Publication Board report *P.B.* 54174 (November, **1940**).

"Unique Uses—Wire Recorder Techniques," *Electronics* 22, 160 ff. (January, **1949**).

"Using the Tape Recorder" (New York City Board of Education), *Curriculum and Materials* 7, no. 1, 4–5 (September, **1952**).

"Video Recording," *P.B.* 37825, U.S. Navy Dept. Bureau of Aeronautics Specifications EP-224 (September, **1944**).

"Wire Recorders for Inventory," *American Business* 18, 12 ff. (October, **1948**).

"Wire Recording," *Electrician* 138, 935–936 (April 11, **1947**).

Pamphlets Available

Audio Record and *Fundamentals of Magnetic Recording,* both by C. J. LeBel, Audio Devices, Inc., 444 Madison Ave., New York 22, N.Y.

Elements of Single- and Dual-Track Magnetic Recording, Amplifier Corporation of America, 396 Broadway, New York, N.Y.

The Handling, Repair, and Storage of 16mm and 8mm Films, Sales Service Division, Eastman Kodak Company, 343 State Street, Rochester 4, N.Y.

The Ipsophone, Ipsophone Exploitation, Ltd., Zurich, Switzerland.

Magnetic Recording Bibliography, The John Crerar Library, 86 East Randolph Street, Chicago 1, Ill.

Modern Reservations Procedures by Means of the Intelex Automatic Reservations System, International Standard Trading Corporation, 67 Broad Street, New York, N.Y.

NARTB Recording and Reproducing Standards, National Association of Radio and Television Broadcasters, 1771 N Street, N.W., Washington 6, D.C. (For tape recording).

Sound Talk, Minnesota Mining and Manufacturing Company, 900 Fauquier Avenue, St. Paul 6, Minn.

Standards on Magnetic Recording, American Standards Association, Inc., 70 East 45 Street, New York 17, N.Y. (For film recording).

Index

455